Gustav Mahler

MEMORIES AND LETTERS

Gustav Mahler: Last photograph

GUSTAV
MAHLER

MEMORIES AND LETTERS

BY *Alma Mahler*

TRANSLATED BY *Basil Creighton*

UNIVERSITY OF WASHINGTON PRESS
SEATTLE AND LONDON

Gustav Mahler: Erinnerungen und Briefe
copyright © 1940 by Verlag Allert de Lange, Amsterdam
Gustav Mahler: Memories and Letters
copyright © 1946 by Alma Mahler Werfel
Library of Congress Catalog Card Number 46-1148
Original hardcover edition published by the Viking Press, 1946
First University of Washington Press edition, 1968,
published by arrangement with the Viking Press
Printed in the United States of America

PREFACE

I wrote this book many years ago, and my only reason for doing so was because no one knew Gustav Mahler as well as I and because I did not want the experiences we shared and the expressions of his thought to be crowded out of my own memory by the pressure and hurry of life.

It was not originally my intention to have the book published during my lifetime.

But now the whole of Europe has been rocked to its foundations and nothing stands where it did. Rodin's bust of Mahler, which I presented to the Vienna Opera House and which was unveiled by the last President of Austria, has now been removed from its pedestal. The wide street in Vienna named after Gustav Mahler has been renamed Meistersinger Street. The large sum of money subscribed throughout the world for a Gustav Mahler monument has been appropriated without ceremony for one of the usual welfare funds of annexed Austria. I therefore have no scruple in saying openly what I know from experience of persons who live their lives and play their parts in the Third Reich. The doors have been slammed. And not from one side only. All that I say of Richard Strauss is taken from the daily entries in my diary. It should not be forgotten that Richard Strauss, the greatest master of contemporary music in the first decade of this century, was Gustav Mahler's only rival.

Only those who were there at the time, and able to appreciate it, know what Mahler did for Vienna during the glorious years of his reign there. Today Germany is deprived of his music, and the memory of his life and compositions is carefully effaced. In other countries the great conductors, Willem Mengelberg, Bruno Walter, and Otto Klemperer exert themselves on his behalf, and the best of the young conductors follow their example. They keep the torch alight and hand it on, until the day when the doors of his own country are thrown open again and his work is joyfully welcomed there once more.

I myself live a wholly different life today, and for me these pages from past days are faded. But the work and personality of Gustav Mahler have not faded. And so I give to the world these recollections of years of pain and joy as a testimony to him.

The foregoing was written at Sanary-sur-mer, France, in the summer of 1939. Events of the turbulent years since then necessitated the postponement of an English version until now.

Alma Maria Mahler Werfel

Beverly Hills,
October 1945.

CONTENTS

ILLUSTRATIONS

Memories

FIRST MEETING
1901

ONE AFTERNOON in November 1901, as I was walking along
the Ring with some friends, I happened to meet the Zuckerkandls.
Zuckerkandl, besides being an eminent anatomist, was something
of a highbrow and had a great sense of humor.

"We've got Mahler coming in tonight—won't you come?"

I declined. I did not want to meet Mahler. In fact I had purposely
and with considerable difficulty avoided meeting him that summer, because of all the stories people told about him. I knew
him well by sight; he was a small, fidgety man with a fine head.
I was acquainted also with the scandals about him and every
young woman who aspired to sing in opera. I had been to the
concert that autumn at which he conducted his First Symphony,
a work I had thoroughly disliked and even angrily rejected. At
the same time, he was of importance to me as a conductor and I
was conscious of his mysterious and powerful fascination. But
this I now belied.

My "no" was scarcely uttered when Frau Zuckerkandl broke
in: "It wouldn't do in any case. I had to promise his sister, Justine,
that there wouldn't be anyone else. He can't bear strangers."

"Nonsense," Zuckerkandl shouted. "I insist."

But I was resolute.

A week later Berta Zuckerkandl wrote that Mahler had put
them off after all, but proposed coming the following Sunday,
which was always their day. She had asked Gustav Klimt and Max
Burckhard and several more, and urged me to come, as she did not

now feel bound by her promise to Justine. Klimt, the well-known painter, and Max Burckhard, the idol of my youth, director of the Burgtheater, poet, most liberal-minded of Austrians, and my fatherly counsellor—I should be among friends and I accepted. I went there feeling rather intimidated. Mahler had been in Paris, giving concerts with the Philharmonic orchestra, and there, at the Austrian Embassy, he had met Madame Sophie Clemenceau, sister-in-law of Georges Clemenceau and a sister of Berta Zuckerkandl. She was extremely cultured, and they had agreed to meet at the Zuckerkandls' when she was next in Vienna.

From the very first moment Mahler observed me closely, not simply because of my face, which might have been called beautiful in those days, but also because of my piquant air. He studied me long and searchingly through his spectacles. The last guest arrived and we went in to dinner. I sat between Klimt and Burckhard, and we three made a merry trio and laughed a great deal. Mahler, at the other end of the table, looked on and listened, covertly at first and then without disguise. At last he called out enviously: "Mayn't we be allowed to share the joke?" His unfortunate neighbor was ignored that evening.

Then a belated guest turned up. He came straight from a recital of Kubelik's and was so enthusiastic about his playing that it was impossible for him to keep silent. When he asked me whether I had heard Kubelik, I said that soloists' recitals didn't interest me. Mahler chimed in approvingly. "Nor me," he said loudly from the other end of the table.

After dinner the party broke up into groups and there was a discussion about the relativity of beauty. "Beauty!" Mahler said. "The head of Socrates is beautiful." I agreed and added that in my eyes Alexander von Zemlinsky, the musician, had beauty. He was almost the ugliest man I had ever seen—and yet the force of his intellect was felt in every glance of his eyes and in every one of his abrupt movements. Zemlinsky was a disciple of Brahms and almost all the musicians of his day and of the next generation too were recruited from among his pupils. Mahler shrugged his shoulders. That was going a bit too far, he thought.

I flared up and made a point of bringing the talk round to Zemlinsky. "Now that we are talking of him—why don't you do his Hofmannsthal Ballet, *Das Goldene Herz?* You promised him you would."

"Because I can't understand it," Mahler rapped out.

I had been instructed in the somewhat confused symbolism of the poem by Zemlinsky himself. "I'll tell you the whole story and explain what it means."

Mahler smiled: "I'm all eagerness."

"But first," I said, "you will have to explain for my benefit the full meaning of the *Bride of Korea*." (This ballet was a standing dish on the Vienna repertoire and incredibly confused and stupid.) Mahler laughed loudly, showing all his flashing white teeth. He went on to ask me about my musical studies and I told him I studied composition with Zemlinsky. He begged me to bring some of my work to the Opera for him to see.

We had long ago drawn apart from the rest, or else they had left us alone. There was that magic circle round us which quickly encloses those who have found each other. I promised him to come one day, when I had something good to show him. He smiled ironically, as though to say that he would have a long time to wait, and then invited me to the dress-rehearsal next morning of the *Tales of Hoffmann.* Madame Clemenceau and Frau Zuckerkandl came up at that moment and he invited them also. I hesitated at first: my composition for Zemlinsky was not done yet. Then my feelings carried me away and I accepted. There was just time before we parted for a quick question:

"Where do you live?"

"Hohe Warte——"

"I'll take you——"

But I did not want to go on foot. It was late and I was tired.

"Well, you'll be at the Opera? For certain?"

"Yes, indeed, as long as I can get my work done."

"Then that's a promise?"

It was over. I was not pleased with myself. I had the distinct feeling of having put myself in a false light. Owing to my wretched, inborn shyness I could never be my real self in company or when I met people for the first time. Either my obstinate silence was broken only by distracted replies, or, as tonight, I was as bold as brass and kept nothing back.

My stepfather, Karl Moll, talked to me at length about this new friendship, which did not altogether please either of us. Mahler by that time had acquired a way of talking as though he were addressing an assembled crowd. "Yes, but I tell you——" That was how he talked. He had wielded power so long, encountering only abject submission on every hand, that his isolation had become loneliness. I thought no more of my impressions, but I was certainly flattered by the exclusive attention he had paid me.

But it is time to say something of Mahler's family and upbringing.

His father was a man of strong and exuberant vitality, completely uninhibited. He married a girl of a good Jewish family named Frank who, being lame from birth, had no pretensions to a good match. The man she loved did not give her a thought and so she married Bernard Mahler without love and with utter resignation. The marriage was an unhappy one from the first day. There were children in plenty, twelve in all. Her martyrdom was complicated by a weak heart, which grew rapidly worse owing to the strain of childbearing and housework.

They began their married life in a small way at Kalischt, a village in Moravia. He had a distillery there, which his family called jokingly the manufactory. As soon as the Jews were granted the freedom to move from place to place, Bernard Mahler migrated to Iglau, the nearest town of any size, and there set up his business again. His pride and reserve cut him off from other people and he was left to himself. He possessed what might almost be called a library, and was goaded by the ambition to better himself. However, he was uncertain how this craving was to be satisfied, so he decided that his children should achieve what he had been denied.

His mother, Gustav Mahler's grandmother, was a woman of masculine energy. She was a hawker and from the age of eighteen went from house to house with a large basket on her back. In her old age she had the misfortune to transgress some law regulating hawkers and was given a heavy sentence. She did not for a moment think of putting up with it, but set off on the spot for Vienna and sought an audience of the Emperor, Franz Josef, who was so much impressed by her vigor and her eighty years that he granted her a

Mahler's birthplace, Kalischt (Bohemia)

pardon. Mahler certainly inherited his inflexibility in the pursuit of his aims from his grandmother.

His talent for music was shown at an early age. Once on a visit to the parents of his mother, who because of her superior refinement was jokingly called the "duchess," Gustav could not be found. After a long search he was at last discovered in the attic, strumming on an old piano. From that day on his father was convinced that he was destined to be a musician. He was at that time five years old.

Five of his brothers and sisters died at an early age of diphtheria. The sixth, a boy, died at twelve of hydrocardia after a long illness. This was the first harrowing experience of Gustav Mahler's childhood. He loved his brother Ernst and suffered with him all through his illness. For months he scarcely left his bedside and never tired of telling him stories. To all else he was blind. Indoors and out he lived in a dream; he dreamed his way through family life and childhood. He saw nothing of the unending tortures his mother had to endure from the brutality of his father, who ran after every servant, domineered over his delicate wife and flogged the children.

Every day his father exploded over the untidiness of Gustav's drawer—the one and only place where tidiness was demanded of him; and yet every day Gustav forgot all about it until the next explosion burst about his ears. It was quite beyond him to bear this one trifling command in mind. These scenes did not stop at words, but nothing could break in on his daydreams until the day when his father sent him to Prague to be placed with the celebrated music firm of Grünfeld to study music. Here he came into touch with the ugliness of life for the first time. His clothes and shoes were taken from him and worn by others while he had to go barefoot, and hungry also. All this he scarcely noticed. When he told me about it he added: "I took it as a matter of course." His worst experience was being the involuntary witness, when he was sitting in a dark room, of a brutal love scene between servant and son of the house, and he never forgot the shock of disgust it caused him. He jumped up to go to the girl's help, but she did not thank him for his pains. Instead he was soundly abused by both of them and sworn to secrecy.

This little episode left a deep mark on his mind. Just as one can be angry all day long with people who have annoyed one in a dream, so Gustav never forgave the young pianist who had given him this shock.

At last his father heard in a roundabout way of the neglect in which he was living. He found the boy in a pitiful condition and took him off to the inn at which he was staying to eat his fill for once, and then returned to this odd specimen of a *pension* to collect what was left of his son's wardrobe. Gustav meanwhile sat in the inn and never stirred until his father returned in a fury and took him to the station for the train to Iglau. Mahler's passivity as a child, his power of obstinate endurance, is illustrated by another episode which I have given elsewhere. His daughter in her childhood had the same faculty: she could sit and wait for hour after hour as though in a physical trance.

His mother patiently bore her lot and, as the years passed, her joy in Gustav's expanding life was her greatest and at last her only happiness. His father gave way to his temper whenever the mood took him. I have never heard Mahler say an affectionate word of his father, but his love for his mother had the intensity of a fixation, then and always. Often and often he has told me with bitter remorse how when playing the piano as a child he used suddenly to feel there was somebody there, and it was always his mother listening at the door, in the covered gallery. Then he used to stop playing and show his annoyance. His harshness to her in those days haunted him in later years.

In due course he arrived at the Vienna *conservatoire* to study with Julius Epstein and Robert Fuchs. He must have been an odd pupil. Fuchs himself told me: "Mahler always played truant and yet there was nothing he couldn't do." His fellow-students regarded him as a marvel and spoke of him as "another Schubert." He won the first prize for composition. His fellow-student and friend, Hans Rott, an extraordinarily talented musician, was unsuccessful. Mahler went home and told them proudly of the prize he had won. His mother wept tears of indignation and said: "All the same, Rott's work was better than yours." It was just like his mother.

Rott went out of his mind while he was quite a young man. He composed continually in the asylum. He used the sheets of music-paper he had written on for a very different purpose and said with a grin of delight: "That's all the works of man are worth."

Mahler's eldest sister, Leopoldine, was yoked to an unloved husband and died in early life of a tumor on the brain. In after years Mahler reproached himself, as though he were partly to blame for her unhappiness, because he was too young and ignorant of life to know what went on in his home.

Justine, his second sister, had an unusually vivid imagination. The practice of lying was systematically inculcated in her by her father's short-sighted harshness. It was long before she awoke from a nightmare of whippings. This little story—a legend, as it were, of her life—is thoroughly characteristic of her. While still a child, she stuck candles all round the edge of her cot. Then she lay down and lit the candles and firmly believed that she was dead.

As for Gustav's brothers, Otto, the elder, a very talented musician, but lacking in seriousness and perseverance, was by far his favorite. Mahler acted as his tutor and got him through his schoolwork by hook or crook. In later years he found him jobs as choirmaster in small German towns, but all to no purpose. Otto grumbled and complained. He thought himself as good as his brother and envied him his greater success. Again and again he threw up the livelihood provided for him, and finally shot himself. He left a note saying that life no longer pleased him, so he was handing back his ticket. He was a fanatical disciple of Dostoevski and philosophized about his approaching death in the manner of the great Russian with an old friend of Mahler's, a woman, who however did nothing to prevent his suicide. People of his kind, who know too much, often cut a very sorry figure in life.

The second brother, Alois, was sickly from birth. All the children, Gustav included, were handicapped by their mother's heart disease. The boy was rather a fool than a freak. He was crammed full of senseless absurdities. One day he hired an old horse and had riding-breeches made with one leg blue, the other red. He rode up and down the streets of Iglau as a German mercenary, to the joy of all beholders but to the bitter shame of his family. "You wait," he said. "I'll ride past the castle in Vienna like this, and the Crown Prince will ask: 'Who's that fine young fellow on horseback?' He'll summon me to his presence and I'll get some wonderful post." Once he accompanied Justine to Bozen, where Gustav sent her for a cure. During the table d'hôte, which in those days was served at long tables, she suddenly heard him loudly boasting of the year he had served as a volunteer in a smart cavalry regiment. A man at the table, an officer on the active list who was in civilian dress, asked him about some of his fellow-officers, of whom of course Alois knew nothing whatever, but about whom he lied volubly. The officer was astonished and Justine beside herself. In another moment her brother would be held up to public disgrace. There was a reprieve in the nick of time, when the company rose from the table. She left Bozen then and there.

Alois later called himself Hans, because it sounded less Jewish. When he wanted to look smart, he wore a top hat, a flowered waistcoat and white spats. He ran into debt, forged notes and finally had to flee to America.

These anecdotes—Justine's death fantasy; the half-witted ambition of Alois, who talked of going to Vienna in medieval garb to win broad acres; the sinister suicide of Otto, the Wandering Jew —all betray features which one may call Gustav Mahlerish. They are the sheet-lightning which portends the real thing, the chaotic elements which precede creation.

Mahler passed in rapid strides from Hall, Laibach, Cassel and Leipzig to Budapest, where he directed the opera. His parents, to his great satisfaction, lived to see all this. Then his father died suddenly and in the same year, after a lingering illness, his mother followed. Justine nursed her until her death and Mahler loved her at his beloved mother's dying behest. He sent for her to join him at Budapest and, although quite inexperienced, she kept house for him there. He was so much concerned by her weakness after the fatigue of nursing their mother that he carried her in his arms every day up the four flights of stairs to his flat.

His engagement at the Royal Opera House came to an abrupt end. There was a quarrel with the manager of the Theatre Royal, the one-armed piano virtuoso, Count Vichy, and next morning Mahler found his office door at the Opera House bolted and barred against him. He lodged a formal protest; nevertheless his engagement was terminated, but with the payment of an exceptionally large sum as indemnity. Meanwhile he had accepted an offer from Pollini to go to Hamburg.

There were now five of his brothers and sisters depending on him for their education and financial support. The business had been sold, badly of course, since none of them understood anything about it. The meager inheritance was shared. Mahler gave up his share to his sisters and demanded the same sacrifice of his brothers. They obeyed, but Otto was indignant and Alois furious. Mahler now had difficult times to face—drudgery and worries without end.

He took a large flat for the family in Vienna, and Justine, the eldest, was put in charge. It was too much for a scatter-brained girl of twenty. She could be of little help. Her task was to run the household while the rest were to set to work learning something. They learned nothing. Mahler had to keep on sending money and very often, as he once wrote in a letter, could not afford to have his own shoes soled. Letters flew to and fro, bearing demands for money from the one side and exhortations to economy from the other. Then Otto came to his tragic end. It was a terrible blow to Mahler. He broke up the household in Vienna and took his two sisters to live with him in Hamburg. Alois, meanwhile, had obtained a job.

Mahler fell in love in Hamburg with a singer, M. He confided in Justine, who clung to him jealously, and therefore did all she could to inject his feelings with suspicion. He suddenly felt the throttling coils and decided to break loose.

It was a wholly self-seeking love on the part of the singer. She insisted on his accompanying her songs for hours, when he came back worn out from rehearsals. At first he enjoyed it. She was talented and he was in love with her. But soon there were rifts; the enforced rehearsals became a torture to him, and his feeling for her died down just as hers for him reached its zenith. Often she lay in wait for him at night after the performance at the Opera and wept and fell on her knees, behaving like a madwoman. He found these scenes so unpleasant that the last spark of affection for her was extinguished.

He decided to leave Hamburg and to get a foothold in Vienna. He went there for an interview and found on his arrival that M., behind his back and helped by the intrigues of her teacher, Rosa Papier, had signed a contract to sing in Vienna herself. He asked her to come and see him and mercilessly told her that all was over between them; that it was solely because of her that he had left Hamburg; that it was never again to be *Du* between them, and that he forbade her ever to cross his threshold again.

Once during the winter she succeeded in enticing him back to her on the plea that she was ill. Secretly she asked a Benedictine monk called Father Ottmar to be present, and begged him, before Mahler arrived, to marry her then and there to her lover, who, she said, would be willing. The Father replied that he could do nothing of the sort in the circumstances and she stormed at him up to the very moment of Mahler's arrival. She hoped by staging this opera scene to induce him to take the step in spite of his shyness of the marriage tie. Father Ottmar told me all this many years later.

And so he bade farewell to Hamburg and, in spite of all the intrigues set on foot against him, particularly by Cosima Wagner, who could not tolerate a Jew as director of the Opera in Vienna, he secured his engagement, first as conductor of the orchestra and heir-presumptive of Wilhelm Jahn and, before many weeks had gone by, as director. He was thirty-six. The sufferings of his earlier years as a conductor are an ever-recurring theme in his letters to his parents.

He often said to me: "You are lucky. You were born with a silver spoon in your mouth. You can go your flowery way—no grim past, no family round your neck—but I have had to stagger on all my life with clods of earth weighing down my feet."

Justine met the distinguished violinist, Rosé, first violin at the Royal Opera, as soon as she arrived in Vienna. They fell in love and embarked on a love affair which they kept a secret for fear of Mahler's strict morals. Many of the dissensions which dogged Mahler to the end as director of the Opera were due to this intimacy of his sister's with the leader of the orchestra.

Justine was in a terrible dilemma. She loved the violinist, but she loved her brother quite as much, and it seemed impossible to her to be parted from him. A friend of hers, who although she was old and ugly was in love with Mahler and hoped for the return of her passion, bargained to keep her secret if Justine would put her in the way of being frequently alone with him. If this service were refused her, she threatened a betrayal. And so, all through the summer which preceded the inevitable catastrophe, whenever

Gustav Mahler
1900

Mahler was ready for the usual walk with his sister, Frau B. confronted him, in the full hope of the reversion of his love. When he asked impatiently what had happened to Justine, he was put off with one excuse after another for her absence and became more and more annoyed. So it went on until, as had to happen, they all betrayed each other.

Mahler was extremely puritanical. Up to now he had been in a sense married to Justine. He regarded himself as bound to her by vows of fidelity and deliberately eluded all temptations. And there were many. Not only at the Opera, but everywhere he went he caused a flutter. He was not in the ordinary sense good-looking, but he had a great fascination. He exacted without mercy the same self-denial of Justine, who was much too temperamental and too young to tread the stony path.

Often and often in these years he had inklings of Justine's feelings for Rosé, but whenever he taxed her with them he was given delusive answers: it was friendship, comradeship and all those other things which since the beginning of the world have been called into play to veil love affairs from profane eyes. The fear he inspired was such that there was no possibility of confiding in him honestly.

When he discovered that his trust had been met only with deceit he was so disconcerted that he refused to speak to Justine for weeks; and when at last it came to painful scenes and explanations he insisted that she should either break with Rosé or marry him. At the same time he told her that he now regarded himself as entirely free. So far he had rejected the thought of any other tie for her sake, but now if he met a woman he liked he would not keep out of her way but take his share of happiness like another. His love of her, great as it had been, was now gone forever. He trusted people blindly, but once his eyes had been opened his distrust knew no bounds.

In the early spring of 1901 Mahler had a severe hemorrhage which was only stopped by an immediate operation the same night. Two more very painful operations followed and then he was sent off to Abbazia, where he slowly recovered. For months afterwards he walked with two canes. I saw him conduct twice on the very day of this disaster. I did not know him then. In the afternoon, the

Philharmonic concert; in the evening, a performance of the *Meistersinger*. He looked like Lucifer: a face as white as chalk, eyes like burning coals. I felt sorry for him and said to the people I was with: "It's more than he can stand." That night he had the hemorrhage. It was impossible to work two such miracles on the same day without breaking, considering the intensity of his interpretation.

The moment they heard of his illness the Philharmonic Orchestra, relentless enemies of Mahler's, chose Josef Hellmesberger, a conductor of mediocre gifts, to take his place without even first making sure of his resignation.

Mahler's domineering manner, the way he stamped his feet at rehearsals when his patience gave out, the stabs of his baton aimed at some miscreant who did not play or blow quite cleanly, or came in a moment late—all this embittered the orchestra, whose hearts were in any case hardened against him by the growing anti-semitism of those days. When one violinist remarked to another: "I don't understand why you find Mahler so infuriating—Hans Richter pitches into us far worse," the reply was: "Yes, but he's one of ourselves. We can take it from him." This attitude of the Philharmonic was one of the many causes of his later being driven from Vienna.

All this took place before my acquaintance with Mahler began. On the day after meeting him for the first time at the Zuckerkandls', on the 10th of November, I called for Madame Clemenceau and Frau Zuckerkandl early in the morning. Mahler was impatiently awaiting us at the Opera. He helped me out of my coat and impolitely omitted to do the same for the other two. Keeping my coat over his arm he ushered us with an embarrassed air into his office. My two companions began a conversation, apparently unaware of the tensely emotional atmosphere of the room. I went to the piano and turned the pages of the music I found there. I was not in a state to join in the commonplaces of conversation. Mahler stole glances at me, but I was in a malicious mood and would not help him out. I was in all the glory of untrammeled youth and not to be imposed upon by fame or position. The one thing that might have humbled me, his inner significance, was at that time almost hidden from me. And yet I was puzzled by a sense of awe in the face of his outstanding genius and it threatened to cloud my untroubled serenity. "Fräulein Schindler," he called out to me, "how did you sleep?"

"Perfectly. Why not?"

"I didn't sleep a wink the whole night."

I made some silly reply, which, thank God, I have forgotten.

This dress-rehearsal of the *Tales of Hoffmann* was the first at which I was present in close proximity with him. I have never known a greater producer. The rehearsal went without a hitch. The orchestra was intoxicating. The small audience was keyed up and scarcely seemed to breathe. The performance was only broken off once and this was when Gutheil-Schoder came on as Julietta. Mahler ordered her off in a fury. Her dress was slit up each side to the waist and had to be stitched up instantly on account of the gross indecency. As soon as the poor lady had vanished he continued to rail for some time over the heads of the orchestra at Schoder's shamelessness in coming on the stage in such a state of undress. If he had dreamed that ten years later whole rows of more or less naked women would crowd the stages of the "straightest" theaters (to mention only *Franziska,* or *The Legend of Joseph* at the Opera), he would have lost his faith in the drama. To him, it was sacred. Too sacred almost. Prince Liechtenstein, Lord High Steward, remarked once at a rehearsal: "It doesn't do you any good to shift the scenes yourself." It was not only a metaphor.

I was still without a suspicion and never imagined I had made so deep an impression. I was overawed, and yet my work for Zemlinsky still came first.

By the next morning's post I received some verses of great beauty. My mother gave a sharp look at my anonymous letter. She took it out of my hand and asked whom it could be from. I said it could only be from Mahler. She replied that I need not imagine that a man like Mahler would write verses to a simple girl and laughed at me. Somebody, she said, must have been playing a joke on me.

But my instinct told me the poem could only be from him. I walked along the streets in a dream, not yet loving him, but unable to think of anything else. I did not answer him. A fortnight later my mother and I went to the Opera. It was *Orpheus and Eurydice.* Almost at once I discovered Mahler in the director's box. There was nothing wonderful in that. Every opera fan knew Mahler's box.

What was a wonder, however, was that he had discovered me at once too. After that a full-dress flirtation began—a thing nobody would have believed possible of such a man, who, if anything, carried seriousness too far.

In the intermission we went into the foyer and there stood Mahler as though conjured up from the floor. He hurriedly requested to be introduced to my mother, who was not present on the evening of our first meeting. Soon we were surrounded by inquisitive onlookers, and so Mahler proposed our retreating to his private room, where, since the occasion of the dress-rehearsal, I felt myself at home. I sat down, as before, at the piano and left my mother and Mahler to themselves. A mutual sympathy drew them together immediately and forever.

"You live on the Hohe Warte? That is my favorite walk."

"Then you must come and see us one day——"

"I certainly shall. But when? Soon?"

"That is for you to say."

He got up to consult his large engagement book and suggested the following Saturday. I was asked whether I was at liberty that day. I had a lesson in counterpoint with Robert Gound, but I promised to put it off.

As we left I said I should like to be engaged as conductor of the orchestra at the Opera and he promised in all seriousness to let me try my hand: it would give him at least great pleasure. I replied that that was not enough: his verdict would not, I thought, be impartial. To which he replied, "No verdict is ever impartial."

We parted in high spirits, feeling that something great and beautiful had come into our lives.

We had a rendezvous with Moll and Max Burckhard in a restaurant after the performance. My mother told them guilelessly of our encounter with Mahler, but it would have been better to say nothing. Moll was furious.

"You mean to tell me you took an innocent girl, your own daughter, into the private room of a roué like him?"

Mahler, ascetic though he was, had a lurid reputation. In fact, he was a child and women were his dread. It was only because I was a stupid, inexperienced girl that I took him off his guard.

Max Burckhard knew life too well to be taken in. He saw the whole truth more clearly than even Mahler or I.

"He was head over ears in love—the other night."

"I didn't notice it," I replied.

"Now, what are you going to do about it if he proposes?"

"Accept," I said calmly.

I did not know then that Mahler and Burckhard had left the Zuckerkandls' together and that on their way home Mahler had tried to put Burckhard through a regular catechism about me. Mahler told me all about it years later. Burckhard had declined to give any information about me whatever. What he actually said was: "Those who are acquainted with Fräulein Schindler know what she is. Those who are not, have no right to ask."

But now, as we sat there after *Orpheus,* his concern for me was for the first time seriously aroused. He bent all his mind and knowledge of life to the task of curing me of what he clearly saw to be a rising fever.

"It would be a positive sin," he said in his ironical way. "A fine girl like you—and such a pedigree too. Don't spoil it all by marrying an elderly degenerate. Think of your children—it'd be a sin! Besides, fire and water, that's all right. But fire and fire, that's all wrong. It would be for you to give way, not him. And you're too good for that."

He practically forbade the match. But whether he forbade it or not, I longed for Saturday and for Mahler to come. Later on, I confess, I often recalled what he had said, waking, as I did, from years of silence, searching in vain for any prospect of my own, finding to my horror that my life was forfeit.

On Thursday afternoon, just as I was working out figured basses under Robert Gound's eye (I had changed his day to Thursday), the servant burst into the room. "Gustav Mahler is here!" He was a celebrity even in the servants' hall. And that was the end of counterpoint forever and a day.

We had just moved into a new house and my books were still waiting to be installed. Some lay flat, some stood on end, some were on the shelves, some in heaps all round the room. Mahler walked to and fro, inspecting them. My taste appeared to please him, except for a complete edition of Nietzsche, at which his eyebrows went up in horror. He demanded abruptly that it should be cast then and there into the fire. I refused and said that if his abhorrence had any justification it would be easy enough to convince me; and it would be more to his glory if Nietzsche stayed where he was and I refrained from reading him than if I consigned him to the flames and yet yearned for him ever after. He was put out, but not for long. He proposed that we should go for a walk. We met my mother in the hall, and in that unruffled way which was her peculiar charm she invited him to stay to dinner.

"There are *paprika-hendeln* and—Burckhard. Do stay."

"I'm not very fond of either. But I'll stay all the same."

And then we walked over the crunching snow, side by side—so near and yet apart—down to Döbling, and there he wanted to telephone to his flat to say that he would be out that evening. Every other minute his shoe-laces came undone and he selected the highest point of vantage to put his foot upon and tie them up. His childlike helplessness went to my heart. In Döbling we went to the post office, but he did not know his own number; and so he had to ring up the Opera. His message gave no explanation of his absence, a thing unexampled in all the nine years Justine and he had lived together. Then we climbed the hill again in silence.

Suddenly he burst out: "It's not so simple to marry a person like me. I am free and must be free. I cannot be bound, or tied to one spot. My job at the Opera is simply from one day to the next."

A feeling of suffocation came over me. He laid down the law without thinking of consulting my feelings. After a moment's silence I said:

"Of course. Don't forget that I am the child of artists and have always lived among artists and, also, I'm one myself. What you say seems to me obvious."

I can still see the sparkle on the snow as we passed each lamp-post. I can recall how we both, without a word, drew attention to its fairy-tale beauty. We did not speak another word all the way home. He seemed cheerful and reassured. We went by tacit agreement straight up to my room. There he kissed me and went on to talk of a speedy marriage, as though it went without saying. Those few words on the way up seemed to him to have settled everything. Then why wait?

And I—I was silent—silent. He had simply made up his own mind about it. We went down to join the rest, both of us in a strange sort of enchantment. Burckhard and M., an architect, an old admirer of mine, were already there. The elemental undercurrent of that evening drove poor M. from our house forever. Mahler, in the company of the others, now revealed all his charm, all the resources of his mind. We argued about Schiller, whom he loved and I at that time did not. He knew him almost by heart and there was such a fascination in the way he rose up in his defense that I, after having let him kiss me without really wishing it, and speed on the wedding before I had even thought of it myself, knew now that in both he was right and that I could no longer live without him. I felt that he alone could give my life meaning and that he was far and away above any man I had ever known.

One of our early discussions was about Jesus Christ. Although I was brought up as a Catholic, the influence of Schopenhauer and Nietzsche had made a free-thinker of me. Mahler contested my point of view with fervor. It was paradoxical that a Jew should hotly defend Christ against a Christian.

Many years later I experienced the very same thing a second time. Mahler was a disciple of Dostoevski's and was always saying: "How can one be happy while a single being on earth still suffers?" I have noticed that it is egocentrics mostly who talk like this, and even downright egoists. Exalted pity for the "poor and humble" is often expressed, but seldom leads in given cases to any tangible result. Mahler did not always live up to his convictions, but that he always wished to is certain.

It was about that time that I met Ludwig Karpath, the music-critic, at a party. He and Adalbert von Goldschmidt (a somewhat muddle-headed person of great originality) were my neighbors at table. We talked of Mahler. Goldschmidt said: "He—that little Hop-o'-My-Thumb. He's not a man. And his music is not music."

I was soon to learn why he was so enraged against Mahler. He had submitted his opera *Gaea* and it had been refused.

Karpath became very earnest in Mahler's defense, more especially as a composer. "Surely I ought to know. I made him in Vienna," he said.

Neither of the two knew that I was even acquainted with Mahler, let alone secretly engaged to him. Next day I told him about this occasion. He wanted to know all about it and all we had talked about, and I innocently repeated what Karpath had said. I knew little of him at that time except that he was the nephew of the celebrated composer, Karl Goldmark. Mahler was obviously annoyed and I felt I had said too much.

A day or two later Karpath happened to be seeing Mahler at the Opera. Mahler leaned back in his chair at his writing-table and his manner was very much *de haut en bas.* Their talk proceeded very haltingly and at last Karpath prepared to take his leave. Mahler left his chair and went close up to him.

"Before you go I really must thank you for having made me in Vienna."

Karpath was utterly taken aback.

"Did Fräulein Schindler tell you that?"

Mahler replied that he did not know me. But a few days later our engagement was in the newspapers. Mahler had no sense of humor in such matters and after this experience and some others of the kind I learned to hold my tongue. He was very touchy.

Ludwig Karpath was not far off the truth. He had great influence as a journalist and critic, and had in fact exerted it to the utmost to get Mahler's works performed in Vienna. Perhaps Mahler was all the more angry just because there was some truth in it. After this occurrence Karpath was for years an unpleasant enemy of Mahler's.

Early in our secret engagement Mahler once conducted *The Magic Flute* for me alone. He sent me his official pass. His sister did not know what to think when the pass, which was always at her disposal, was not to be had that day. But Mahler said nothing and she dared not ask. At the end of each act he stood for a long while at the conductor's desk, chatting casually to Rosé, the first violin, so that we could see one another better. I gave him my impressions in a letter, as he had asked me to do.

Productions of Mozart's operas, not only in Vienna, were very drab and down-at-heel before Mahler's day. Mahler went so far as to alter the libretto of *Figaro* to suit Beaumarchais' comedy. He used motifs of Mozart's for the recitatives he had to write in. He did all this to make the work more living. It was he who gave the signal to the whole world for the Mozart renaissance.

The younger generation grew up to take Mozart as a matter of course. To me he was unfamiliar, and also I was too young in those days to appreciate his genius. Mahler had first to teach singers to sing in the Mozart style, hitherto beyond their power. Later Roller came to his help as stage-manager.

Shortly after this Mahler went to Berlin and Dresden. He wrote often to me and put us both on the rack. Then he sent for Justine to join him at Dresden and put her on the rack as well by firing off questions such as: "Should a middle-aged man marry a young girl?" "Has he the right to do so?" "Can autumn chain spring to its side?"

Justine, feeling herself narrowly observed, was filled with foreboding and could only reply: "Oh, yes—oh, no."

In one of his last letters he said I might speak to my mother on his behalf, because he wanted to be accepted by her as a son as soon as he got back. However, just before his return to Vienna our first serious quarrel occurred. I happened to say that I could not write any more that day as I had some work to finish, meaning composition, which up to now had taken the first place in my life. The idea that anything in the world could be of more importance than writing to him filled him with indignation, and he wrote me a long letter, ending up by forbidding me ever to compose any more. It was a terrible blow. I spent the night in tears. Early in the morning I went sobbing to my mother, and she was so horrified by his unreasonable demand that, deeply as she loved him, she urged me to break with him. Her unqualified support brought me to my senses. I recovered my calm and confidence and finally wrote him a letter, promising what he wished—and I kept my promise.

His man was to come for my answer before he would see me again; for, as he had told me in his letter, he would not know where he was until he had had it. In my agitation I went out to meet his messenger. I gave him my letter, but he had brought one for me, and in it Mahler, clearly uneasy about the effect of his earlier letter, was less exacting in his demands. He came that afternoon, happy and confident, and so charming that for the moment there was not a cloud in the sky.

But there was. I buried my dream and perhaps it was for the best. It has been my privilege to give my creative gifts another life in minds greater than my own. And yet the iron had entered my soul and the wound has never healed.

It was at about this time that my stepfather, Moll, guileless man, came to me and said: "Alma, my dear, I've a sort of idea Mahler takes an interest in you, you know. I think we ought to have a talk about it."

I was sitting on the piano-stool and I whipped round and stared him in the face. Could it be possible he had observed no more than this? But he went on, unperturbed.

"It isn't exactly what I should have wished for you. He's not young. To my certain knowledge, he's in debt. He's not strong. And then, it's all up with his job at the Opera." (This was common talk in Vienna for ten years before he went; by the time he did go these rumors had all died down.) "He's certainly no beauty. Composes, too, and they say it's no go."

At that I burst out laughing and he went out shaking his head, no wiser than when he came in.

Mahler now came to see me every day and stayed until late at night. He often had to walk the whole way from the Hohe Warte to the Rennweg, as the busses had stopped running. But that did not worry him. He sang and whistled on his way.

Mahler kept our secret from Justine out of fear of her jealousy. One day they went for a walk after lunch. When they reached the Ringstrasse, he greeted a man whom she recognized as the painter, Moll; they had both met him on the same occasion not long before. "What a charming man he is," she said. "Yes," he replied without thinking, "but you ought to know her mother!"

The murder was out. Justine's riddle was solved. She had felt sure that only a woman could account for his being out night after night, but, closely as she watched him, she had failed to discover who it was. After this she was initiated by degrees and soon he brought her up to the Hohe Warte to see us. Before this I had paid her a visit at his request. It was not a great success.

By degrees Mahler got to know all our friends and he particularly took to the painter, Kolo Moser, and Theobald Pollak. As he and Pollak were walking home together after spending the evening with us, he remarked that the first time he met me he had felt as if he had been suddenly taken out of a stuffy room into the fresh air. Kolo Moser, too, said to me once: "As soon as Mahler came into the room you suddenly went as still as the sea when oil is poured on it."

He brought me his Fourth Symphony one day. I did not, at that time, care for it. I said frankly: "I feel Haydn has done that better." He laughed and said I would live to think differently about it. The same day we played it as a duet. I missed a sixteenth note. He laughed and said: "I make you a present of that sixteenth. So I would if it had been an eighth, or a quarter. Yes, or the whole —myself!" When we joined my mother, he said to her: "Mamma, after playing the piano with her, I ask you once again for your daughter's hand."

After our engagement was made public a delegation from the Vienna Philharmonic orchestra waited on me with the request that I would set Mahler free from the dangerous influence of the first violin. I was then twenty and incapable of carrying out such a mission. Rosé was on friendly terms with the members of the orchestra and with Mahler too; and there is no doubt that, sometimes purposely, sometimes unconsciously, he did influence Mahler's decisions, which were not always just, and that the members of the orchestra always knew the source of them; but there is no doubt, either, that Mahler not only listened to him but pumped him very often too. In after years I was able to avert many an injustice, but it was too late: Mahler's relations with the Philharmonic and theirs with him were ruined by then.

Christmas came, the first we had spent together. Sacred to me from my childhood, it meant nothing to him, and he took my suspense and excitement as an affectation. His "friends" were already making mischief. He was full of suspicion and scented danger on every hand; and so a period of martyrdom set in for me. Everything in me which had so far charmed him became suddenly suspect. My style of hairdressing, my clothes, my frank way of speaking, everything, in fact, was interpreted as being directed against him; I was altogether too worldly for him. Wrought upon by envious tongues and by his so-called friends, he lived a life of torment and inflicted torments a thousand times worse on me.

Our lovely beginning had turned to gloom and misery. His friends could never be friends of mine. Since his early youth he had had them clamped to his feet like irons, and I could never regard them with anything but dislike. There was an old barrister, dull and obtrusive; an old librarian, dull and obtrusive, and there was Siegfried Lipiner and his set. Brahms said of him once: "That lying hound of a Pole interests me." The description could not be bettered; but while Brahms might find his society an amusing distraction, I was quite incapable in those days of putting up with cads of this sort. These friends formed a group round the "celebrity" and the director of the Opera, whose box they treated as their own; and they had no intention of budging an inch for any claims of mine.

Lipiner was introduced to me at Mahler's flat. He patronized me, called me "my dear girl," and put me through my paces; he expected me to agree with him that Guido Reni, who meant nothing to me, was a great painter, and I refused to. I was reprimanded for reading the *Symposium*—it was far above my head. I had never before encountered such aridity in any human being— if he were a human being.

Then came the full-dress review. There were present Lipiner, whom our first meeting had made my avowed enemy; his first wife; his second wife; his current mistress (Mahler's one-time friend, M.); his first wife's husband (Lipiner's bosom friend); Rosé, Justine's friend; my mother; Moll and Kolo Moser. I shall never forget the grandiose and festive air which so completely belied the hollowness of that occasion. No one spoke, but angry hostile eyes followed every movement I made. Then M. said: "What is your opinion of Gustav's music?" I replied in a temper: "I know very little of it, but what I do know I don't like."

Mahler laughed out loud. The others let their heads hang lower than before. My mother blushed for my bad manners. The atmosphere became unendurable. Then Mahler took me by the arm and we went into Justine's little room. "It was frightful in there," he said. "We'll do better on our own for a bit." So there we were —together again, happy and free of care. But in the next room my downfall was decreed.

Siegfried Lipiner was undoubtedly a very clever man—an all-round scholar without a single idea of his own. Even in conversation he always brought quotations to his aid in order to make anything clear; he never had anything of his own to say. He may have had originality in his youth; if so, that spring had prematurely dried up. Nietzsche had hopes of him; Wagner too. But his surviving work is eclectic in matter and turgid in manner. He was an ill-natured, harsh-tempered brute—his eyes much too close together and surmounted by an enormous bald skull. He had a stammer; he was a bogus Goethe in his writing and a haggling Oriental in his talk. Mahler was always overcome by his stupendous knowledge. The only thing of his which might survive is his translation of Mickiewicz's *Totenfeier*.

JANUARY 1902

*F*ROM that evening onwards his friends launched a regular campaign against me, which ended only with Mahler's retirement from the Opera in Vienna, although during the latter years their smoldering hatred emitted only an occasional spark. Mahler, however, was from the first so firmly attached to me that all their plots miscarried. All they achieved was his final severance from themselves. In those days he conducted a great deal. One morning, owing to the indiscretion of someone we had taken into our confidence, the newspapers all came out with headlines proclaiming our "betrothal." We went to the opera the same evening. Mahler was conducting. I was in such a state of agitation and agony of mind that I heard nothing and saw nothing. I don't know why it was, but I was ashamed in those days to be seen in the street. I felt that everybody stared at me. As soon as Mahler appeared there was such a prolonged outburst of clapping that he had to bow his acknowledgments again and again. It was the congratulation of the public on his engagement.

At the end of January there was the première of Richard Strauss's *Feuersnot* and Pauline Strauss was in our box for the occasion. She raged the whole time. Nobody, she said, could possibly like that shoddy work. We were only pretending to; we knew as well as she did that there wasn't an original note in it. It was all pilfered from Wagner and many others, including even Schillings (Maxi, as she called him) whom, she said, she liked a great deal better than she did her husband. She stopped at nothing; and we could only look foolish, not daring even to agree with her, since her moods were so unaccountable that she might easily turn round and, with a great clamor, resent our saying what she had just said herself. After the performance, which Mahler had not been conducting, because he disliked the work so much, we were all to meet in the Restaurant Hartmann. But there was a delay, for Strauss joined us in our box in great elation over the number of times he had been called before the curtain.

"Well, Pauksl, what do you say to that for a success?"

He might better have held his tongue. She sprang at him like a wildcat.

"You thief—get out of my sight. I'm not going with you. You disgust me too much."

Mahler, unable to stand any more of it, pushed them into his large studio and we went into the room next door to await the end of the controversy. A confused clamor was audible and Mahler, who found it all very unpleasant, knocked on the door and called out that we couldn't wait any longer and were going ahead to the restaurant. The door flew open and Strauss reeled in with Pauline at his heels. "You can go," she shouted, "I'm going back to the hotel and I shall spend the night alone."

"But mayn't I even take you?" Strauss begged.

"Ten paces in the rear, not otherwise." She set off, with Strauss following at a respectable distance.

We preceded him to the restaurant without a word being spoken. He soon joined us, obviously worn out, and sat down next to me.

"My wife's a bit rough now and then," these were his very words, "but it's what I need, you know."

Even in my eyes, Strauss lost all his glamor that night. During the whole of supper he thought of nothing but money. He plagued Mahler without mercy to reckon the royalty on a great, or a less great, success, and the whole time he had a pencil in his hand or behind his ear, where he put it only half in joke, for his behavior was exactly that of a commercial traveler. Franz Schalk, the conductor, said to me in a whisper: "And the sad part of it is, he's not putting on. It's the real man."

Strauss calculated his profits to the last penny, whether he was gambling in the money-market or exploiting opera; he was a barefaced materialist and the more so the longer he lived.

Meanwhile preparations for our wedding were going forward, and for that of Rosé and Justine as well. Mahler went to the Sem-

mering for a few days after the première of *Feuersnot*. He always
went up there once or twice during the winter for the sake of the
altitude.

When he was in Dresden just before our secret engagement, a
panic seized him while he lay sleepless In bed. "Suppose I am too
old," he thought. After that, this thought never left him and he was
an altered man when he returned to Vienna. He was nerve-ridden
and ill.

He had lived the life of an ascetic and was completely at a loss.
The strain of apprehension and self-torture was terrible; sometimes he longed for death, sometimes for life at its fiercest.

We were sad and had no one to guide us.

"Oh," he said, "if only you had had a love affair or were a widow,
it would be all right."

These outbursts were painful to me. Up to now my virginity had
always seemed a glory. It never occurred to me that all good, even
this too, is relative and that he was only blurting out what many
think who secretly wish for "an experienced woman." That I
certainly was not; and so we tormented ourselves not from love
so much as fear of love. At last the only natural solution occurred.
The consequences soon followed and I suffered bitterly. In every
convention there is a core of truth, as we soon had to recognize.

The rehearsals for the first performance in Vienna of the Fourth
Symphony and *Das klagende Lied* came on. It was the first time I
had ever heard any work—let alone a work of his—rehearsed day
by day from the first reading-rehearsal onwards. A work which was
new and strange to me, very strange at the outset, became by degrees so familiar that I soon knew its every beauty and how each
instrument came in. After that I shared the experience with
Mahler of hearing each of his works from the sounding of the first
note up to the last time he conducted it. They were the most unforgettable and exalted hours of my life.

Mahler was in a state of nervous exasperation just at this time
and so prejudiced, into the bargain, against the Philharmonic
orchestra owing to the persistent agitating on the part of some of
its members that these rehearsals threw me into paroxysms of
fright. He raged, he stamped; he picked on victims for special
castigation and shouted at the orchestra as a whole until they

played unwillingly, and some even made a show of leaving in the middle of the rehearsal. It took us all our time to calm him down in the brief pauses, and even so these rehearsals were a martyrdom for players and audience. A young musician asked my leave to look over my score. I was very glad to share it with a musician; and I could sympathize with his enjoyment of the passages which came through best. It was Gustav Brecher, the since celebrated conductor.

The performance took place on the 12th of January, 1902. It was in the afternoon and I was not feeling well. I was stared at as Mahler's fiancée and I found it hard to bear. I was more conscious of the blood singing in my ears than I was of the music.

The Fourth came to an end; I looked round the hall and caught sight of an old friend, the President of the Society of the Friends of Music, in the Director's box. He smiled and bowed to me and I was glad to see a face I knew. The friends of Mahler, however, had their eyes glued to me and before the intermission was over they reported me to him for flirting outrageously throughout the whole performance.

Das klagende Lied began and ended without giving me any real pleasure. I was too much ruffled by all I saw and felt. M. was lying on the sofa in the artists' room simulating a fainting attack. I was ignored by the "friends" and Mahler treated me as a criminal. I was beside myself. I knew nothing of the clouds which had gathered about my head in my absence. His friends had been dinning it into him that whereas M. sacrificed herself for him (she had sung the chief part in the *Klagende Lied*) and gave her last breath for him, I sat and flirted all through the concert. Mahler was in consternation over this. He begged M. to spare herself and thanked her again and again. To me he was exceedingly chilly. The plot had worked.

This was their last assault. We walked back by ourselves, the baying of the hounds died away, and we had it out as we walked. By the time we reached his flat we were blissfully happy. Justine saw that we could never now be separated.

After the sensational disclosure of Mahler's engagement in the press, M. invaded his private room at the opera and made a scene, at the end of which she once again had a fainting fit. This scene showed that up to the last moment she had not given up hope. But

Mahler had taken the measure of her theatrical faintings. He asked her to come outside with him and in the street she could not avoid controlling herself. She recovered her composure and begged him to restore the *Du* of earlier days. He said he could not make up his mind without consulting me, and so she put her request in another way by begging for friendly relations with an apparent desire to include me. He was trapped, and so promised to bring me to see her in a day or two.

I refused at first; for even though Mahler, by his own confession, had never been on intimate terms with her, they had at least been on affectionate ones, and her sudden interest in me could not be genuine. However, we arrived at Hietzing, where she was living in a dreary hotel. Disregarding the common politeness due to a visitor, she sat me down in a corner with the barest of apologies and gave me a book to look at. She then took Mahler into the next room, whence I soon heard raised voices. I glanced occasionally at the piano score of *Tristan and Isolde,* with Stratz's horrible illustrations.

We were in a very bad humor on the way home and started to argue about these illustrations, which Mahler liked and I did not. As it really had nothing to do with Stratz, but everything to do with those deep influences with which Lipiner strove to set Mahler against me, I fought like a lion; and being the daughter and step-daughter of painters I knew something of pictorial art, although at the moment it was the last thing on earth I cared about.

These people in their blindness had badly miscalculated. They thought my unpracticed youth was an instrument ready to their hand. Their plan was to degrade me in his eyes, to show me up in my raw immaturity; and so to wound his pride. But they had not reckoned with my fierce spirit of independence or my sensitive pride. In any case, as Mahler hated nothing more than argument and thrashing things out, he simply kept more and more out of the way of his trusty old friends. They achieved exactly the opposite of their designs.

MARRIAGE AND
LIFE TOGETHER

*W*E WERE married on March 9, 1902, and on the 10th, the day after we had left for our honeymoon, Justine and Arnold Rosé followed suit.

Mahler went to the church on foot in galoshes, as it was raining hard; my mother, Justine and I drove. There was no one in the Karlskirche except ourselves and the witnesses, Moll and Rosé. It was early in the day. When it came to kneeling down, Mahler misjudged the hassock and found himself on the stone flags; he was so small that he had to stand up again and make a fresh start. We all smiled, including the priest. There were six of us at the wedding-breakfast, a rather silent occasion, and our guests took their departure immediately afterwards, leaving us alone to pack and drive to the station. As the wedding had been publicly announced to take place in the evening, a crowd of inquisitive people must have come to the church in vain.

Once in the train for St. Petersburg we breathed again. Mahler's clouded spirits cleared as though by magic; and I too, alone at last with my husband, was no longer oppressed by the need to conceal my condition. He had been invited to conduct three concerts in St. Petersburg and so we had decided to make this trip our honeymoon. Unfortunately, Mahler caught a severe feverish chill on the journey, induced in this case by the overheated compartment of a Russian train. He suffered all his life from these infections and his fatal illness was partly due to one of them. I was aghast as I saw him rushing up and down the corridor—his face as white as a sheet, incapable of uttering a syllable. He jumped out at every station and walked about the platform, without hat, coat or gloves though it was twenty-two degrees below zero. The Russians, who kept out the cold with huge fur caps and gloves, were greatly amused.

I sat in our compartment, waiting anxiously for his martyrdom to end, as I was often to do during these onsets of his.

He arrived in St. Petersburg with a temperature and a cough, so hoarse that he could hardly speak, and afflicted further by chilblains; and I soon caught his cold. But in spite of all, those three weeks were unforgettably beautiful. He could only whisper at the rehearsals, but he was so perfectly understood that the result in every case was a magnificent performance. In this strange, far-away world, I heard the *"Liebestod."* As I was still unwell and might be unable to sit it out, I was allowed to stand behind the orchestra, and so could see his face, which had a divinely beautiful expression. His exaltation when he was conducting was always intense and the sight of his face on these occasions, uplifted and open-mouthed, was so inexpressibly moving that I felt a thrill of utter conviction: I knew once and for all that it was my mission in life to move every stone from his path and to live for him alone.

He conducted works of Haydn and Schubert, the "Funeral March" from *Götterdämmerung* (it was encored) and the *Eroica*. At the end of the *Eroica*—I was at this time sitting among the audience in the hall—I heard two people say in French: "Mahler's tempi are not at all what we are accustomed to, but it's beautiful, and new, like that." The other replied: "Of course, and why not?" Imagine such a criticism among us in Vienna, where everyone has a leasehold on his own Beethoven and his own tempi.

Mahler had a cousin there, called Frank, who was high up in the public service. He showed us all the wonderful sights and street scenes of St. Petersburg; the Hermitage, the palaces—all of it so strangely foreign and impressive. The Neva was frozen over and tram-lines were laid down across it. Toward evening it was a lively, crowded scene: elegance and fashion turned out to skate with an ease and gaiety which were fascinating to watch.

There was another side to the picture: now and then a member of the orchestra was missing and when Mahler asked the reason he was told it was not impossible that he had been sent to Siberia.

The devoutness of the people, which an effort has since been made to stamp out, was very touching. We were always driven about in a small, low sleigh, with three horses harnessed abreast, not knowing at first that no Russians ever drove in an open troika at this time of the year. When we did know it, we persisted all the same because we enjoyed it so much. One evening, as we were passing the Kazan church in a bitter wind and driving snow, the coachman got down from the box and threw himself on his knees in the snow to pray. He did not give us a thought. When we were frozen to the very marrow and he had turned into a snowman, he quietly got up and drove on again without a word.

We saw a good deal of high society, as it is called. I often asked Mahler to go alone if I did not feel well enough; but in the concert-hall I could not avoid these introductions, and I found the arch-dukes I spoke to easier and more amiable in manner than our nobility at home. Conversation was in French. But as for what was actually said, we felt there was no difference: it meant just as little to us.

Among our acquaintances was a beautiful old lady of hysterical tendencies, who, years later when Mahler was in Russia by himself, summoned him and told him that she felt her death to be near, and would he enlighten her about the other world, since he had said so much about it in his Second Symphony. He was not quite so well informed as she supposed and he was made to feel very distinctly, when he took his leave, that she was displeased with him. He gave me a description of this scene in a letter.

What surprised us more than anything was that scarcely any one was acquainted with Dostoevski, people only sniffed when Mahler mentioned his name.

We saw nothing of the theater except a good production of *Eugene Onegin*. It was Advent and all the theaters were closed. This was a charity performance and permitted for that reason. The production was on a very high artistic level.

Our charming flat awaited us in Vienna, and the life we lived for six eventful and—up to the final shock—happy years began. The flat now consisted of three larger rooms and three smaller rooms. It was smaller before our marriage.

Mahler had suffered from a great affliction there; an officer occupied the small room next his bedroom and had such a hatred of him that he gave orders to his servant always to turn on the gramophone during his working hours. Having unearthed his plot, we bribed the man and after this he put on a record only when his master came in sight.

I had to take over the domestic finances in a state of virtual bankruptcy. There were debts upon debts; for although Mahler had been paid a big indemnity in Budapest and had earned large salaries ever since, his brothers and sisters, with Justine at their head, squandered his money to such a tune that in Hamburg he was borrowing from his friends even at the beginning of nearly every month, because he was completely cleaned out. Justine showed me a letter of his in which he wrote: "Do, for heaven's sake, be more careful. I have been waiting for months to get a pair of shoes soled and never have the money." And this was the principal conductor of the Hamburg Municipal Theater. He said to me when we married: "Justine, unfortunately, did not understand housekeeping. I resigned myself long ago to being perpetually in debt. But now, see what you can do."

I found that he owed 50,000 crowns gold. Besides this, he had the building of his house at Maiernigg to pay for; and first of all I had to pay his three sisters their share of the patrimony. I had been brought up in such a modest way that the strict economies of our early married life were no hardship. On the contrary, I took pride in getting him out of debt. But to him these five long years of parsimony were very trying. Once when I took Justine to task for her wild extravagance, she replied: "Well, if the worst had come to the worst, *I would have gone begging with him from door to door.*"

In May 1902, the Secession got up a private festival in honor of Max Klinger. The Secession painters self-sacrificingly painted frescoes, all of which were lost except those of Gustav Klimt; and these were peeled from the walls at extravagant cost. The subjects of all of them were allegories referring to Beethoven, and Max Klinger's monument to Beethoven was to be exhibited for the first time in the center of the gallery.

Next, Moll approached Mahler with the request to conduct at the opening and he kindly agreed. He orchestrated the chorus of the Ninth Symphony for wind instruments only, and rehearsed it with the winds from the Opera orchestra. He conducted the chorus on the day and with the new instrumentation it rang out as starkly as granite. Klinger, who was a very shy man, came in just as the first note clanged out above his head. He was so moved that tears ran slowly down his cheeks.

We saw a lot of him at that time. His personality was not impressive and it seems likely that he was overestimated in those days. He was entirely dominated by Assenjeff, a red-headed Russian woman, who had him completely under her thumb. She was hysterical, and on one occasion suddenly burst into tears at table, because she had once had a jaguar she loved and it had died. Klinger tried to control her by glances of despair, but it was no use. Some scene or other broke out at every moment, and we felt sorry for him.

He never said anything very much to the point, and so his company was no particular joy to us and we dispensed with it by degrees. He was a great drinker and his days and nights were invariably spent over the bottle, for which we had neither time nor inclination. He was the owner of a champagne factory and it cannot have done him much good.

The next première, *Butterfly,* was not one of Mahler's productions. Puccini attended the final rehearsals, but took no part in them. Mahler and he had not a particle in common. During the dress-rehearsal the *maestro* never took his eyes off the Royal Box, in which, as he took pains to find out, were two archduchesses. He requested Mahler to have him presented to them; and Mahler reluctantly did so. He was no courtier, although on given occasions very strict in his observance of form. Puccini, in spite of his genius, was utterly enamored of the outward show.

Mahler's attitude to the aristocracy was peculiar. He resisted the Emperor's orders but stood to attention if an archduke or the managing director passed by. Once we fled across the Michaelerplatz to escape Princess Pauline Metternich, celebrated as a ghost of the Second Empire, who had caught sight of him from her carriage and was in pursuit. She overtook us at the bottom of the Kohlmarkt. I retreated into the entrance of a house and Mahler went up to the carriage-door, where she kept him talking for some time. She was always trying to enlist his influence on somebody's behalf or to get hints of future operatic events from the fountain-head. When at last he joined me, he spat on all sides. "Horrible woman—those scarlet lips." The worst he could think of in the intervals of spitting was not bad enough. When he lost his temper over bad taste of this sort he never refrained from relieving his feelings on the spot. It was his nature to react with violence against any annoyance.

The first public performance of the Third Symphony took place in Crefeld in June 1902. I was in the middle of my pregnancy and we traveled to Cologne in a heat-wave. Mahler did his utmost to make the time pass by playing jokes on me. I was always asking impatiently when we should arrive and he kept me in such a state of suspense by inventing one answer after another that when at last we arrived I utterly refused to believe it.

Tentative Titles for Movements of the Third Symphony

THE HAPPY LIFE

A SUMMER NIGHT'S DREAM

(Not after Shakespeare. Critics and Shakespeare scholars please note.)

1. What the forest tells me.
2. What the twilight tells me.
3. What love tells me.
4. What the twilight tells me.
5. What the cuckoo tells me.
6. What the child tells me.

A SUMMER NIGHT'S DREAM

1. Summer marches in
   (Fanfare and lively march) (Introduction)
   (Wind only with concerted double-basses).
2. What the forest tells me (1. Movement).
3. What love tells me (Adagio).
4. What the twilight tells me (Scherzo) (Strings only).
5. What the flowers in the meadow tell me (Minuet).
6. What the cuckoo tells me (Scherzo).
7. What the child tells me.

The rehearsals at Gürzenich were unique. Mahler came to me at the end of each movement and we discussed it in every detail.

After the first movement, which had never been played before, he came up to me laughing, calling out from a distance: "And he saw that it was good!"

I made notes in my score of the passages which did not seem to me to come through. A small boy, sitting behind me, looked with lively interest over my shoulder; so I held my score up for him to see. A short time ago the pianist, Edwin Fischer, thanked me for my kindness on that occasion to a child whom I did not know.

We stayed at the Dom hotel. We always drank Moselle or Rhine wine at dinner there (a thing we seldom did, as Mahler drank little). After lunch, for which, owing to the long rehearsals, we were always late, we went for a drive through the flat country. We became completely one during those wonderful days together. For hour after hour as we were driven along we discussed the first hearing of this stupendous work—the entry of the oboe, for example, in this passage, or the dynamic effect of the strings in that. Often he fell asleep with his head on my shoulder.

When the rehearsals were over we moved on to Crefeld to stay with some wealthy silk manufacturers, who were undisguisedly put out by our arrival. We were assigned a bridal chamber where we scarcely dared to move for fear of toppling some ghastly knickknack from its ghastly stand. Ancient myrtle-wreaths moldered beneath domes of glass.

They regarded Mahler as a great director of opera, who to please himself had composed a monstrous symphony and now to pain everybody else was having it performed. Any donkey felt himself entitled to pass judgment on him. All the beauty of the days of the rehearsals was blotted out. A mob of musicians and critics surged about us wherever we went: there was no escape. We felt that the liberty to come and go as we pleased was taken from us and cursed the place for having no hotels. We were obliged to accept hospitality which was not spontaneously offered but extorted from our hosts by a committee. It was the first time and the last we ever accepted an invitation of this kind.

There was one cheerful little episode. The house was tall and narrow and we were on the second floor. We emerged from our room, ready to go out. Mahler stopped a moment at the top of the stairs to polish his spectacles and then, stepping out in his impulsive way without looking where he was going, he kicked against a large pail of water which was on the edge of the top step. It went bouncing in a cascade to the bottom, where, as we had every right not to expect, our hostess happened to be standing. She held up her hands in consternation. "Well, Herr Mahler, the Graces assuredly did not preside at your cradle!"

And now for an example of the retentiveness of the human memory: at the Mahler festival at Amsterdam in 1920 a lady came up to me with a message from Frau X. of Crefeld, who wished me to know that she treasured in her memory the "unforgettable" days Mahler had once spent in her house. *Così fan tutte!* They all "remember" today; but at the time these people were for the most part extremely discouraging and quick to take offense.

On top of all the rest, our unconventional appearance caused an unwelcome sensation. I was wearing a so-called reform dress (designed by Kolo Moser) and was well advanced in my pregnancy. Mahler always went about bare-headed, with his hat in his hand and his head poked forward; his gait too was peculiar, unrhythmical, urgent and stumbling. Whatever his suits cost he always looked badly dressed. In short, the school-children followed us about, at first in twos and threes and then in a crowd. On one occasion, one of them advanced and shouted amid the tumult: "You've lost your hat, sir!" A roar greeted the announcement. It was quite true. He had left his hat behind in a teashop. It was the last straw. Back we had to go to recover it. We were hunted through the streets again as we made for the refuge of a wretched little hotel. The Rosés were expecting us upstairs and helped us to pour water on the heads of our persecutors and put them to flight.

The performance was awaited with breathless suspense, for the rehearsals had done something to reveal the greatness and significance of the work. A tremendous ovation broke out at the end of the first movement. Richard Strauss came close to the stage, applauding emphatically as though to set his seal on its success. The enthusiasm rose higher with each movement and at the end the whole audience got up from their seats in a frenzy and surged to the front in a body. Strauss had become more and more subdued and at the end was not to be seen.

I was sitting among the audience by myself, as I did not wish to be with my relations. I was in an indescribable state of excitement; I cried and laughed softly to myself and suddenly felt the stirrings of my first child. The hearing of this work finally convinced me of Mahler's greatness, and that night I dedicated to him my love and devotion with tears of joy. I saw what hitherto I had only surmised.

Strauss gave a further and final proof of his coolness before the night was over. We had supper after the concert at a small inn. Strauss, as he passed our table, gave us all his hand in a lordly way and went on, without noticing Mahler's extreme agitation or addressing a single word to him. Mahler took this very much to heart. For some time he could not speak. His spirits sank and the public acclamation now seemed of no account.

I owe my lasting friendship with Hans Pfitzner to those days at Crefeld. Mahler and I were in our large bedroom, where in an alcove, curtained off with black curtains, there was an enormous double bed. A visitor was announced and Mahler, after a glance at the card, asked me to retire for a few minutes within the recess, as he wished to speak to the man alone.

Next I heard a thin, high voice interceding urgently with Mahler; and what I heard affected me deeply. It was painful and degrading—an artist (and that he was one I could hear in his very first words), pleading for the production of his work: *Die Rose vom Liebesgarten*. And Mahler refused, coldly, calmly, tersely. He must have forgotten his own youth.

"No singers—libretto too bad—whole symbolism incomprehensible, too long, far too long."

And at intervals the pleading voice broke in. One trial—last hope—Mahler, the only musician who could understand him—Otherwise, despair. The two voices rose higher as the door was reached. I could not hold myself in any longer. I jumped up, pulled the curtains apart, ran to Pfitzner and squeezed his hand to show how deeply I sympathized. I shall never forget the look he gave me. Then he went out. Mahler was not angry. To my astonishment, he was not angry.

We went straight from there to Maiernigg, where we lived a life of utter peace and concentration. Mahler wore his oldest clothes there and was almost unrecognizable. He got angry if any one spoke to him on his long walks. He had the sketches for his

Fifth Symphony with him, two movements completed and the rest in their earliest stages. I tried playing the piano very softly, but when I asked whether he had heard me he said he had, although his studio was far away in the woods. And so I changed my occupation; I copied all he had ready of the Fifth straight away, so that my manuscript was ready only a few days behind him. He got more and more into the way of not writing out the instrumental parts—only the first bars; and I learned at this time to read his score and to hear it as I wrote and was more and more of real help to him.

In the intervals of work we walked a great deal. Too much. He counted too much and too proudly on my youth, and as we were both as thoughtless as children my stock of health was squandered in the common cause. I had to climb over fences and creep through hedges. My mother paid us a visit at this time. She was horrified when he dragged us up a hill which was almost perpendicular.

The house at Maiernigg had been built for Mahler, in a somewhat philistine style, by a neighbor at Wörthersee. Its position was as enchanting as its interior was frightful. Mahler once caught me standing on a chair tearing down the fretwork ornamentation from the tops of the cupboards. He understood and gave his approval. There were two large verandas, one open and one shut in. The open one gave access to the sitting-room and my bedroom, the closed one to the dining-room and spare bedroom.

High above, the balcony of Mahler's bedroom had a magnificent view over the lake. He had a large studio-bedroom with an enormous writing table, and next door a small dressing-room. There was a very large spare bedroom next to the sitting-room, very close therefore to my bedroom, but by the second year this had been turned into a nursery.

During the early years of our married life I felt very uncertain of myself in my relations with my husband. After I had conquered him by my audacity before I knew what I was about, all my self-assurance was undermined by the psychological effects of becoming pregnant before being married. From the moment of his spiritual triumph, too, he looked down on me and did not recover his love for me until I had broken his tyranny. Sometimes he played the part of a schoolmaster, relentlessly strict and unjust. He soured my enjoyment of life and made it an abomination. That is, he tried to. Money—rubbish! Clothes—rubbish! Beauty—rubbish! Traveling—rubbish! Only the spirit was to count. I know today that he was afraid of my youth and beauty. He wanted to make them safe for himself by simply taking from me any atom of life in which he himself played no part. I was a young thing he had desired and whose education he now took in hand.

Frau M., envious as ever, settled down promptly in our immediate neighborhood. In the evenings she paid us visits uninvited, accompanied by a mangy dog she had bought from a loafer out of pure kindness of heart, as she carefully pointed out, and from other no less elevated motives. Nevertheless, Mahler had a horror of the beast. His love for animals was theoretical only. He escorted her home for the first few times, and this was the object of her maneuvers, but finally her maneuvering annoyed him. He sent the servant home with her and at once her regular visits ceased.

She came one day just at the outbreak of a terrific thunderstorm and dragged Mahler out on to the terrace for closer contact with the fury of the elements. I was afraid, in the condition I was in, of being hit by the branches of trees which came hurtling through the air. But I had never been afraid of thunder. On the contrary, I loved its grandiose effects. The Wagner-interpreter let her hair fall about her face and played Valkyrie and Ortrud in the same breath. She called to me to come and when I made a sign of refusal she turned in scorn to Mahler: "She's a coward."

On another of her descents I was alone in the house and she began to play Ortrud in good earnest for my benefit. She was vulgar as well as voluble about Mahler and about his sister, giving intimate details, which, if I had not known his whole life from his own lips, would have suffocated me. But I knew more than she. I knew that he had really loved her for a time in Hamburg and that she during that time had been a torment to him; that she had later done her utmost to keep him at any cost, but he was finished with her and "disgusted" (his own word) and wanted to be left in peace. I also knew from his own lips why he had fled from Hamburg.

He had been baptized before he left Hamburg. He was afraid lest otherwise he might find it difficult as a Jew to get his engagement in Vienna. His account of his recalcitrance and doubts during his instruction in the Catholic faith, of the embarrassing questions he put to his catechist and the sudden surging up of Old Testament pride was delightful. Then he arrived in Vienna, where the fullest powers were guaranteed him and where he hoped to carry out at last all his far-reaching plans for stage and orchestra.

And now, on that afternoon at Maiernigg, M. poured out all her fury and tried to enlist me, of all people, in her war against him. This showed me that she could never have been a great tactician; or she would not have confided in me, her natural enemy, who could only be waiting for her to show her hand. I did not hesitate to report our conversation to Mahler the same evening. He wanted to forbid her the house at once and forever; but I deprecated a scandal and suggested making a musical occasion of it when next she came. This we did. We played and sang the whole of the last act of *Siegfried* together. Her voice that afternoon was truer and her singing more beautiful than they had ever been on the operatic stage and as our concert carried right down to the lake, there was a crowd of boats in front of our house by the time we had finished, and an outburst of enthusiastic applause. This was the last of our meetings.

Mahler's daily program during the next six summers at Maiernigg never varied. He got up at six or half-past and rang for the cook to prepare his breakfast instantly and take it up the steep and slippery path to his hut, which was in the woods nearly two hundred feet higher up than the villa. The cook was not allowed to take the usual path, because he could not bear the sight of her, or indeed of anyone whatever, before setting to work; and so, to the peril of the crockery, she had to scramble up by a slippery, steeper one. His breakfast consisted of coffee (freshly roasted and ground), bread and butter and a different jam every day. She put the milk on a spirit-stove, matches beside it, and then beat a hasty retreat by the way she had come in case she might meet Mahler climbing up. He was not long about it; he was very quick in all he did. First he lit his spirit-stove, and nearly always burned his fingers, not so much from clumsiness as from a dreamy absence of mind. Then he settled down comfortably at the table and bench in front of the hut. It was simply a large stone building with three windows and a door. I was always afraid it was unhealthy for him, because it was surrounded by trees and had no drainage; but he was so fond of this retreat that I could do nothing about it.

He had a piano there and a complete Goethe and Kant on his shelves; for music, only Bach. At midday he came noiselessly down to the villa and went up to his room to dress. Up in the woods he delighted in wearing the oldest rags. After that he went down to the boathouse, where we had two beautiful boats. On each side of it there was a bathing-hut with a platform of planks in front. The first thing he did was to swim far out and give a whistle, and this was the signal for me to come down and join him. Once I had both little children with me in the bathing-hut. Mahler went off with one under each arm and then forgot all about them. I was just in time to catch one of them as she was falling into the water.

I usually sat down on the boathouse steps. When he came out of the water we talked and he lay sun-bathing, until he was baked brown; then he jumped into the water again. As I watched this procedure I always felt a terrible anxiety about his heart. I was ignorant in those days, but I knew at least that it could not be good for him. But nothing I could say could induce him to give it up, and he persisted in heating himself up and cooling himself down, often four or five times running. After this he felt invigorated and we went home for lunch, making a tour of the garden on the way. He loved the garden and knew every tree and plant in it. The soup had to be on the table the moment we got in, and the food had to be simple, even frugal, but perfectly cooked, and without tempting the appetite or causing any sensation of heaviness. In fact he lived all his life on an invalid's diet. Burckhard's opinion was that it was enough to ruin a man's stomach for good and all.

We sat and talked for half an hour afterwards. Then up and out, however hot or however wet it might be. Sometimes our walk was on our own side of the lake; sometimes we crossed to the other side by the steamer and then set off on our walk—or run, rather. I see now that his restless energy after meals was his way of escape from the pressure of a full stomach on an overworked heart. It was purely instinctive. He could not bear lying down after meals, but he never knew the real reason.

Our expeditions were fairly long. We walked for three or four hours, or else we rowed over the dazzling water, which reflected the glare of the sun. Sometimes I was too exhausted to go on. We invented a hypnotic cure for my collapse: he used to put his arm round me and say: "I love you." Instantly I was filled with fresh energy and on we tore.

Often and often he stood still, the sun beating down on his bare head, and taking out a small notebook ruled for music, wrote and reflected and wrote again, sometimes beating time in the air. This lasted very often for an hour or longer, while I sat on the grass or a tree-trunk without venturing to look at him. If his inspiration pleased him he smiled back at me. He knew that nothing in the world was a greater joy to me. Then we went on or turned for home if, as often happened, he was eager to get back to his studio with all speed.

His remarkable egocentricity was often betrayed in amusing little incidents. Sometimes he liked to break off work for a day or two in order to go back to it with his mind refreshed. On one such occasion we went to Misurina. My mother was with us and we had three rooms next door to each other. My mother was in my room and we were whispering cautiously, as our habit was, for Mahler's ears detected the slightest sound and the slightest sound disturbed him. Suddenly my door flew open and was banged shut and there stood Mahler in a fury. "Do you hear that? Someone banging a door again along the passage. I shall make a complaint." For a moment we looked duly horrified and then burst out laughing.

"But, Gustav, you've just done the same thing yourself."

He saw the absurdity.

One of his favorite quotations was from *The World as Will and Imagination:* "How often have the inspirations of genius been brought to naught by the crack of a whip!"

His life during the summer months was stripped of all dross, almost inhuman in its purity. No thoughts of fame or worldly glory entered his head. We lived on peacefully from day to day undisturbed in mind, except for an occasional letter from the Opera which was sure to bring trouble.

In the autumn he played me the completed Fifth Symphony. It was the first time he had ever played a new work to me and we climbed arm in arm up to his hut with all solemnity for the occasion. When he had done, I told him of all that won my instant love in this magnificent work, but also that I was not sure about the Choral at the end. I said it was hymnal and boring. He disageed.

"Yes, but Bruckner——" he protested.

"He, yes; but not you," I said, and on the way down through the woods I tried to make clear to him the radical difference between his nature and Bruckner's. I could not feel he was at his best in working up a church choral.

I was touching here on a rift in his being which often went so deep as to bring him into serious conflict with himself. He was attracted by Catholic mysticism, an attraction which was encouraged by those friends of his youth who changed their names and were baptized. His love of Catholic mysticism was, however, entirely his own.

Soon after this our holidays came to an end and we returned to Vienna. The Fifth was completed and he worked at the fair copy all through the winter, in this, too, following an invariable practice, for his winter program was as strict as his summer one. Up at seven, breakfast, work. At nine, to the Opera. Punctually at one, lunch. His servant telephoned from the Opera as soon as he left, and as soon as Mahler rang the bell on the ground floor, the soup had to be on the table on the fourth. The door had to be open to avoid the slightest delay. He stormed through all the rooms, bursting open unwanted doors like a gale of wind, washed his hands, and then we sat down to lunch. Afterwards, a brief pause just as at Maiernigg; and then either a race four times round the Belvedere or the complete circuit of the Ringstrasse. Punctually at five, tea. After this he went every day to the Opera and stayed there during part of the performance. I picked him up there nearly every day and we hastened home to dinner. If he was still busy in his office, I sometimes looked in at whatever opera was on, but never stayed on after he was free. That is why there are many operas I have seen a part of but never seen to the end. Now and then he told me the end, adding every time that I hadn't missed anything, in which, in the case of many operas, he was perfectly right. They were often more interesting as torsos. After dinner we sat together on one sofa and talked, or I read aloud.

This first winter, of course, I had the birth of my first child to think of. It took place on the 3rd of November. Owing, as the doctor said, to the fatigues I had undergone during my pregnancy, the child had become misplaced. Mahler was not told of this, for fear of agitating him; but he read it in the faces of the doctor, the nurse and my mother, and raced through the streets as though frantic. When a friend of his, Guido Adler, asked how I was, he shouted at him: "Idiot, I forbid you to ask me." I could hear him raging up and down in the next room, waiting in a frenzy of anxiety for the end of this frightful delivery. When at last it was over, he cried out: "How can people take the responsibility of such suffering and keep on begetting children!" He was crying hard when he came to my bedside. When I told him subsequently that it had been a posterior presentation he laughed uncontrollably. "That's my child," he said. "Showing the world straight off the part it deserves." He loved this child beyond measure from the first day. She was christened Maria after his mother, but the happiness of keeping her was denied him and us, and although I recovered, my recovery was very slow. We saw her in all her beauty only to lose her; within a few months she fell ill and lay for long unconscious, between life and death. She was given hot and cold frictions. Mahler carried her about in his arms and was convinced that his voice alone recalled her to life.

In October he had studied and rehearsed an entrancing little opera of Mozart's, *Zaïde*. It was not given often and then vanished altogether from the repertoire. He had to pay dearly for dropping it. It had been adapted by a critic, who drew the royalty; and when it vanished so quickly from the repertoire, he protested and said that Mahler ought to go on giving it, which the box-office receipts made it impossible to do. The man was Mahler's bitter enemy ever afterwards and harried him in the press at every opportunity.

The critics in general were inexcusably unjust to him. At first they all turned to him in the hope that he would listen to their advice, but as soon as they saw that he had an unbending will of his own, they first withdrew in silence and later became more and more aggressive. During his last years in Vienna he was surrounded by a mob of enemies. We opened the evening paper with dread. "Another incident at the Opera Royal"—in large type, and all because some young lady had a complaint and some reporter lent a willing ear. Or if Mahler made a short journey to conduct one of his Symphonies he at once was accused in the press of neglecting his duties at the Opera. It was intolerable.

In December 1902, Mahler put on Tchaikovsky's *Pique Dame*. We enjoyed this enormously. He took me to many of the rehearsals and was always playing bits of it to me. For weeks we lived with no other music in our ears. Our life was very quiet. The only people we ever saw were my parents, the Rosés, the Zuckerkandls, the art historian, Strzygowsky, Burckhard, Gustav Klimt, and Pollak, who idolized Mahler.

Strauss too came to Vienna at about this time with his wife and gave some concerts. He was still the much debated, eccentric composer and she an unbridled, ambitious wife. She sent word to me at once, asking me to come and see her. I went and found her in bed. There was a concert that evening, at which she was to sing, but she did not rise from her bed. Then the door burst open and Strauss came in with a little case in his hand. "I've got your ring and now you'll get up, Pauksl, won't you?" And Pauksl got up at once and the concert came off, a dear one for Strauss; for it was a large diamond ring. She asked me at the end of this little scene to bring her some books to read: "Something light, you know, thrillers." On this occasion Strauss conducted to a completely empty hall. We sat in the front row and while he conducted he kept up a conversation in a loud voice with Mahler about the idiotic public, which deserved only trash, and so forth. He rejoiced in his own audacity and we found him charming.

Next, they came to see us when several friends of ours were there. As his wife was put out by any kind of serious conversation Strauss got up and said: "Come along, Mahler—let's go into your room for a bit." From this moment she began to rage. "Yes, you can laugh—but it's no joke bein' the wife of a misunderstood genius. I tell you, it's frightful! We never have a penny and I never see him to speak to. Soon as he's done workin', out he goes to play skat and I'm always alone." She burst into tears and laid her head on the table. We felt most uncomfortable. To soothe her was not easy. I got up quietly, and brought Mahler and Strauss back into the room. Her face cleared at once. Strauss asked her what was the matter. "Nothing," she replied. "Good," he said, turning to Mahler. "Then we can continue our conversation." They stayed in the room with us after that and began discussing Mommsen's *History of Rome.* Mahler loved it. Strauss thought it unsound. They argued the question at length. Pauline sat in a corner and beckoned me to her. "I say, which is the best hairdresser in Vienna?" I could hardly reply.

Next they discussed Beethoven. Strauss preferred early Beethoven to late, to which Mahler replied that a genius such as he could only get better as he grew older. Strauss maintained the contrary: inspiration often failed him in his later years. The spontaneity of youth was worth all the rest. Mozart, for example—

"And blouses—where do you go for them?"

I got up and left her to herself. I was not going to miss another word of that evening's talk. Mahler and Strauss enjoyed talking to one another, perhaps because they were never of one mind.

"The mistake you make, for example, in your production of opera is in preferring the player who can't sing to the singer who can't play. You have a fellow like Demuth, a woman like Kurz— and enthuse about Mildenburg, or Schoder." And Strauss shuddered over these foes of *bel canto,* these barbarians of the voice and called them "singing players."

He said too: "I travel about conducting until I've collected enough money—" (and he was not overparticular where or what he conducted, or where and with whom he ate and associated)— "and when I've collected enough I settle myself down in peace to compose."

Mahler observed to me afterwards: "But by that time he's gone near to losing his soul."

We all took Mahler's side about operatic singing, because we had been educated by him, and he by Wagner, to appreciate the German school of singing. In those days we scorned *bel canto.* And yet, during his last years, Mahler fell more and more under the charm of Italian voices in New York, whereas Strauss was seduced into composing title-roles for German singers—Mildenburg as Clytaemnestra, Schoder as Elektra, and so on. His taste had come round to what Mahler's turned from in his last years.

Here are some observations of Mahler's on conducting:

The tempo is right if it allows every note its value.

If a phrase can no longer be grasped because the notes run into one another, the tempo is too fast.

The extreme limit of distinctness is the right tempo for a presto. Beyond that, it has no effect.

He said that if an adagio seemed to be lost on the audience, he slowed the tempo down instead of quickening it, as was commonly done.

The following anecdote is amusing and also sheds light on his attitude toward Wagner. He met Goldmark one day on his way to the Opera.

"Well, Master, won't you come along to the Opera?"

"No, I never listen to Wagner. I'm afraid of getting too like him."

"But," said Mahler, "you eat beef without becoming an ox."

SPLENDID ISOLATION
1903

I GIVE this title to the following years because it was a favorite phrase of Mahler's to describe our completely solitary way of life.

There was a dock at Unterach on the Attersee, and there, before the arrival of every steamer, all the good people of Unterach gathered, to see and to be seen—which was quite as important—and to be well up on whatever was going on.

"We don't go and stand on the dock, and that's unforgivable," Mahler used to love saying.

We were always a center of interest and therefore always enveloped in a cloud of gossip, of which, thank heaven, we were mostly unaware. We lived as though under a *cloche* in our "splendid isolation."

After the première of *Euryanthe*—it was in the middle of January 1903—we all, my parents, the Rosés, Roller and a young musician, went out to supper as our custom was on such occasions, to let off steam, as Mahler called it. "I must let off steam after a production, hear what people think and talk about it until I calm down."

It happened that Mahler went ahead with the others and I followed on with Roller and the young musician. We spoke with indignation as we walked along about the wretched libretto, and the musician said that it was entirely the fault of the libretto if that divine music refused to come to life. We all arrived at the same moment at the Restaurant Hartmann. Mahler turned round in the doorway and called out to us: "Don't you agree that the libretto of *Euryanthe* is really not at all bad? When you think of it, all the characters in *Lohengrin* are foreshadowed—Elsa is Euryanthe, Lohengrin is Adolar, Ortrud is Eglantine, etc. In spite of all her feminine nonsense, Wilhelmina von Chezy was a talented playwright."

The musician replied without a moment's hesitation: "Exactly what I was just saying." Mahler's power of suggestion was irresistible.

In the course of studying *Euryanthe* afresh, Mahler had revised the whole libretto, making great alterations both in the wording and the sense. He was always very much amused by the childishness of the librettists of these early operas. When, for example, an ensemble was called for, all the characters were brought together by chance in a wild ravine. "Our jolly rustics all united once again," he said with a chuckle. So, with *Euryanthe,* he endeavoured to steer clear of its absurdities, but he did not altogether succeed. In any case the opera could not hold its own in its renovated dress. The young man was right.

His defense of the libretto was due to his passionate engrossment in his work. All through the rehearsals he was determined to find excuses for it. He identified himself so completely with any work he studied that even though it impressed him only moderately before and after, he loved it without reserve and fought its battles with fury at the time.

We paid my mother fairly frequent visits up at the Hohe Warte, where painting was the chief interest. Mahler got to know there the friends of my childhood, and among others Alfred Roller. They fell at once into a discussion of the technique of the stage and Roller remarked that he had never missed a production of *Tristan*. But he could only listen to the music—never look at the stage, because the stage-setting as it was managed up to now destroyed the whole illusion. Mahler asked him what he would do about it himself and Roller replied by unfolding schemes of such magnificence that Mahler gave him an appointment at the Opera next day. "That's the man for me—I'll engage him," he said to me on our way home.

Sure enough, Roller was commissioned the very next day to design new scenery for *Tristan,* and shortly afterwards he was appointed permanent stage-manager. It was taking a colossal risk, as Roller had never in his life before been behind the scenes; and there were indeed the most absurd ructions during rehearsal. M., who was accustomed to her old time-honored properties, burst into tears. "I don't care if I have to tear up the footlights," she screamed. "I won't stand it."

Mahler sent Roller to pacify her and in a very brief space all went smoothly; for M. had fallen in love with him. Mahler and I were now to learn that the tales he told of her were no exaggeration. We were all three about to have supper together in Mahler's large studio during one of the evening performances. A servant came to the door in ill-concealed mirth with a message from M. Would Herr Roller please go to her immediately, as only he could put on her bracelets. Mahler was extremely angry. He sent back word that Roller was not able to come just then, as he was engaged in an important discussion with the director. After a few minutes the man came back, this time grinning broadly, with the message that she would not sing again, unless Herr Roller came immediately. We thought better of it, and he went.

The production was wonderful. The great yellow awnings made an illusion of such sunlight as is seen only in the desert or on the sea. But Mahler was tired. The hemorrhage, a year before he got to know me, had sapped his vitality. After the second act he lay on the sofa; his face was white, he could hardly pull himself together to conduct the third act. "If only someone would take it off my hands," he said.

One day in January he told me he had had a very remarkable opera sent him. "It doesn't inspire great confidence in the piano score, but the full score is brilliant and dramatic. Couldn't be otherwise. It was the hit of this year's opera season in Paris."

It was Charpentier's *Louise*.

Rehearsals began at once. A double cast, as there always was with any production of Mahler's. Schrödter, Foerster-Lauterer, Slezak, Schoder. Charpentier preferred Madame Foerster's simple, homely appeal. He said of Madame Schoder: *"Oh non, ce n'est pas ma Louise!"* From the first she was too sophisticated for him. Demuth was the father in both casts.

One morning during rehearsals Mahler and I were walking along the Ring to the Opera House. There was a man in front of us in a flapping black cape, which made him look like a gigantic bird. It was Charpentier. Mahler pointed him out to me and we had a good look at him as we followed on behind. He looked like a perambulating windmill and was an odd sight altogether.

He had come to Vienna for the première at Mahler's invitation and was present at the final rehearsals. He thought the scenery quite impossible. In a sense, he was the first of the Surréalistes and his observations on stage-management were as incomprehensible to the management as to Mahler. All Mahler could do was to postpone the première and leave the field to Charpentier. The whole setting was too "grand" for him. The seducer now had to wear a red electric bulb beneath his dress-coat, so that when he opened it his heart was revealed. The ballerina, when she danced on Montmartre, had to come on in a short ballet-skirt, followed all the time by a pink spotlight. All realism was very properly eliminated as being out of date. Mahler learned a great deal from these rehearsals; above all, lightness and a sense of humor, as he himself afterwards confessed. But he too was wonderful. He was not touchy about it. "I was wrong," he said from the first. "After all, the author must know best."

We saw a lot of Charpentier. Indeed, he made love to me, but was so clumsy over it that both Mahler and I found it merely comic. Besides, it was not love-making in the accepted sense. *Louise* was his only love. We put our box at his disposal, as we did for all musicians from abroad. He made use of it daily and took with him a girl he had picked up. Rosé warned me against making a public appearance in such company. I should not have died of it.

But I had better let my diary tell of these days.

28 March, 1903.
Exciting days for us. The première of *Louise* is over.
A work of genius.
Charpentier a complete bohemian.
Have made great friends with him.

His manners are not all they might be. Spits under the table, bites his nails, draws your attention by a pressure of his knee or a nudge of his elbow. Trod on my foot last night in our box to call attention to the beauty of *Tristan*. But as it comes of his associating mostly with people of quite another sort I don't take it amiss. He's wonderful.

He called Mahler and me his two children. It did him so much good to talk to people who honestly said what they meant.

His method of composition is original. First of all he sees a picture, then he hears the music and lastly the words. You can feel it. After the first rehearsal I said to Mahler: "Charpentier is a painter, as much a painter as a musician." He's intoxicated by his success. He talks of his music as of a mistress. He sang some of *Louise* to us as he first wrote it—with great dramatic talent.

To me: "You are very fortunate to have so great a man for a husband."

To Mahler about me: "She's a *gamin, la clarté, le printemps*— we artists need that."

My room is a flower-garden. A bouquet, beautifully beribboned, and inscribed: *"À Madame Mahler, gracieuse muse de Vienne, la muse de Montmartre reconnaissante."*

His account of his life: Member of an orchestra, great poverty. Began composing *Louise,* and got into such a fever of work that he couldn't go out to eat or earn money. Wrote on because he couldn't be parted from his composition. Nobody would give him credit, he hadn't a sou, he had lost his job in the orchestra by this time—only an old milkman brought him his daily litre of milk. Then he submitted his score by the hand of the milkman—and became a celebrity overnight. The première caused a sensation in Paris. He sat in the author's box, the milkman in smock and blue apron by his side. He's a socialist and wants to convert me. Has founded a workers' school of music. It's called "Mimi Pinson." The students of this *conservatoire* sent him a long telegram after the première here.

He told us he had composed a whole new opera. It was very lovely, but when he played it through again he woke up to find it was by Wagner. So he destroyed it. He bears the mark of genius on his forehead. He who has eyes may see it.

Paris: November 1926. I have tried to see Charpentier again. I discovered his address with great difficulty. Everybody said: "Oh, he's dead long ago." But the Austrian Embassy found out for me where he lived. I drove there. It was in the outskirts. I climbed steep stairs. A girl came running down. "Does M. Charpentier live here?" I asked. She said yes. "Is he at home?"—"*Oh, non, Madame*—" So I went downstairs again. I would have liked to see him once again. Although he is said to be worse than dead. I was told terrible stories. Probably only because he lives as he chooses, in a manner incomprehensible to conventional persons. Who knows?*

In the middle of June Mahler conducted his Second Symphony in the Cathedral at Basel. He went ahead of me, as always, because I could not be parted so long from my child. This time he came from Amsterdam where he had conducted the Third. Our contralto, Kittel, sang the contralto solo there, and now in Basel she sang the *Urlicht*. Mahler made a life-long friend in Amsterdam, Willem Mengelberg, and so arrived at Basel beaming with joy.

No one who was there will ever forget the rehearsals, the dress-rehearsal or the performance in the Cathedral. The building, the galaxy of lighted candles, the lofty roof, and the music all combined to make an unforgettable impression. Oscar Nedbal knelt down outside and kissed Mahler's hand, and no one found it surprising. (Nedbal was a brilliant musician and has written some delightful music.)

We met Hans Pfitzner also, and Mahler immediately asked him to a meal with us. The friendship between him and me grew apace. He asked me if he might send me his string quartet. Our friendship, and my respect for him, have gone on growing ever since.

Summer had come, and with it we resumed our life at Maiernigg and its unvarying and peaceful routine. Mahler soon began working. This time it was the first sketches for the Sixth Symphony. He played a great deal with our child, carrying her about and holding her up to dance and sing. So young and unencumbered he was in those days.

The hot walks through woods and scrub came round again, and utter tranquillity.

* Now—1939—I have seen Charpentier again. He is just the same. All he told me was full of courage and high spirits. He has kept as young as his own *Louise,* which is as lovely as on its natal day.

One day a letter announced the arrival of Hans Pfitzner's string quartet in manuscript, and the manuscript followed. He asked me in his letter, with a touching nonchalance, to take good care of it, as it was the original and he had no copy. When the manuscript came, I took it up to Mahler in his hut. He came down two hours later.

"It is the work of a master," he said with emphasis, delighted to give his approval.

In the autumn Mahler as usual went back to Vienna before I did, and being left to myself I took out the piano score of *Die Rose vom Liebesgarten*. I grew more and more enthusiastic and told Mahler so in every letter I wrote; and when I got back to Vienna soon afterwards the opera was always on my music rest. And since the piano in any room of ours was always open and Mahler automatically played whatever he found there, he came to share my enthusiasm for *Die Rose vom Liebesgarten* so fully that he decided to produce it, in spite of all his previous objections. It was the one and only time during all the six years I lived with him while he was Director of the Vienna Opera that I purposely and openly influenced him; and I certainly had no cause to regret it.

Two movements of the Sixth were finished in the summer and the scheme of the others had taken final shape in his head.

I used to play a lot of Wagner, and this gave Mahler the idea of a charming surprise. He had composed for me the only love-song he ever wrote—*"Liebst Du um Schönheit"*—and he slipped it in between the title-page and the first page of *Die Walküre*. Then he waited day after day for me to find it; but I never happened to open the volume, and his patience gave out. "I think I'll take a look at *Die Walküre* today," he said abruptly. He opened it and the song fell out. I was overwhelmed with joy and we played it that day twenty times at least.

He and I were jealous of each other, at first I of him more than he of me. I was jealous of his past, which in my innocence I used to think very objectionable. He was jealous of my future, and that I can now understand.

SPLENDID ISOLATION
1904

AT THE beginning of this year the Secession held an exhibition of the work of Hodler and Amiet.

Ferdinand Hodler was like a tree, uncouth and gigantic. There was not a woman he did not deem his prey, without prelude or postscript. He even laid hands on B.Z., who gave him a resounding box on the ear. He came to a performance of *Tristan*—it was the first time he had ever heard this work—and sat in my box, showing every sign of discomfort. In the middle of the third act he got up to go. "That kissing-match in the second act was all very well, but they can get on with their dying without me—I'm off."

Once when he came to see us, he asked to see my child and I brought her in my arms. "Hold it—don't move," he shouted. "I shall have to paint you like that!" More acclamations followed. But Mahler did not like it when I excited admiration of this kind. It put him in a bad humor and he did his utmost to see that it did not happen.

The first performance of Hugo Wolf's *Corregidor* took place on the 12th of February. Mahler rehearsed and conducted it himself, and Roller was responsible for the setting. Wolf had recently died after spending years in an asylum; the production was a debt of honor owed to his memory by the Opera and by Mahler. This was the keynote of the occasion, an evening at half-mast. It was not a great success, for a series of songs, however beautiful, does not make an opera. The box of the authoress of the libretto, Rosa

Mayreder, Hugo Wolf's friend for many years, was wreathed in flowers. Mahler went and spoke to her after the first act. But it all came too late.

Mahler himself told me the story of his friendship with Wolf and how it ended. Their friendship went back to their early life, when, with another man called Krzyzanowsky, they shared a room for a few months. They were very poor and, as all three were musicians, extremely sensitive to noise; so when any one of the three had any work on hand, the other two had to tramp the streets. Once Mahler composed a movement of a quartet for a competition while the other two spent the night on a bench in the Ringstrasse.

Mahler gave lessons; Wolf did not, or only a very few. When their money ran out, one of them gave a pupil notice. The plan was for one of them to ring the bell, say he was suddenly obliged to go away and request payment for the lessons already given. The ready money provided meals for all three for a day or two. On the other hand, a pupil was lost forever.

Mahler did not come of a poor home, merely from one of soul-destroying narrowness; and while he was a student at the *conservatoire,* where his friendship with Wolf began, his parents often sent him parcels of food, which the others very quickly disposed of. In one of these parcels there was once a green overcoat as a Christmas present; but, as his father had sent it to him to grow into, it trailed at his heels and caused such a sensation in the street that he became aware at last that something must be wrong. As soon as his two friends explained what was the matter, nothing would induce him to wear the coat again, and the long and lank Krzyzanowsky became the fortunate possessor.

When he was eighteen Mahler got an engagement at Bad-Hall. Wolf would not accept any job and said arrogantly that he was going to wait until he was made "God of the Southern Hemisphere"; and he went hungry until his death.

The three friends made their first acquaintance with *Götterdämmerung* together, and in their passionate excitement they bawled the Gunther-Brunhilde-Hagen trio to such effect that their landlady came up in a fury and gave them notice on the spot. She would not leave the room until they had packed up their scanty belongings, and then she locked the door angrily behind them.

One day, as they were talking, Wolf got the idea of writing a fairy-tale opera. This was long before Humperdinck and undoubtedly an original inspiration. They considered many themes and finally hit on *Rübezahl*. Mahler was young and impulsive and he began on the libretto that very night and finished it next day. In all innocence he took it to Wolf for him to see. But Wolf also had made a start and was so put out by Mahler's having stolen a march on him that he threw up the whole idea and never forgave him. Outwardly they remained on friendly terms for some time longer, but they avoided each other's society. Many years later they met on the way to the *Festspielhaus* at Bayreuth and passed by with a curt: "Hello."

Soon after Mahler had been made director of the Vienna Opera, Wolf was announced; and there he stood, lean as a skeleton, with burning eyes, and imperiously demanded the instant production of *Corregidor*. Mahler, knowing the work and its defects, made the usual evasions: no singer suited to it, etc. Wolf grew obstreperous and Mahler did not like the look of him. He had a special bell within reach for such occasions. He pressed it and his man came in with the prearranged message: "The *Intendant* wishes to see you at once, sir."

Wolf found himself alone. He rushed downstairs and along the Ring. His mind gave way; he thought he was the director and on his way home. When he arrived at Mahler's flat, 2 Auenbruggergasse, he rang the bell; and when the servant opened the door, he shouted at her to let him pass—he was the director. She slammed the door in his face in terror. Shortly afterwards he was shut up in a lunatic asylum.

I saw Wolf myself in my father's house when I was a child. He came into the room and stared at the ceiling. "Oh—so you've just moved in, have you?" The unadorned ceiling must have annoyed him. My father had stripped off all the mouldings, because he hated that sort of ornamentation. Wolf then sat down at the cottage piano and began to improvise wildly. When Papa shyly asked what it was he was playing, Wolf without stopping shouted: *Aïda—Aïda,* and hammered away madly. I was standing behind the piano, sliding one finger to and fro over the surface. "What's she doing there? Is she a lightning-conductor, or what?" I was sent out of the room. I have never forgotten that weird apparition.

Mahler was dissatisfied with the reception of *Corregidor,* and on the 10th of March he gave it a second time in its earliest version. It was a labor of love, and had only a very short run in Vienna.

I was expecting my second child in June and this caused a disturbance in our habits, one of which was to race every day after lunch three times round the Belvedere or the Ring. But now I often had to stay at home, and Mahler came back from his "runs," as he called them, in a surprisingly short time.

Verdi's *Falstaff* was given in German for the first time on the 3rd of May; but I could not be at Mahler's side during the rehearsals as he liked me to be.

On the other hand, our life was now much more sociable. Max Burckhard tried to bring us in touch with his friends. It was not easy. Mahler seldom felt happy when he went out anywhere and, his gloom being infectious, everyone felt as if "there was a corpse under the table." I am sure there was always a sigh of relief when we left. But one day Burckhard invited us to meet Gerhart Hauptmann, his friend; Margarethe Marschalk, whom he married soon after; and Josef Kainz. Mahler reluctantly consented to go. That evening was unforgettable.

It was the first of many talks Hauptmann and Mahler had together and I remember it very clearly. There was a great argument between Hauptmann and Kainz during dinner about the end of *Die Versunkene Glocke,* which Hauptmann had altered. In the first version Rautendelein went back into the well as cheerfully as she had emerged from it. Now he made her go back sadly, which certainly is not in keeping with her elfish nature. Kainz called it a concession to the public. Hauptmann had given him a copy of the earlier version, and Kainz said with a laugh that if he outlived him he would have it printed at his own expense. Hauptmann said he did not mind what liberties were taken in the future, as long as the edition already printed survived. Kainz has since died, and what has become of the version he spoke of?

It was late when we left, and the long walk home from Frankgasse, where Burckhard lived, to Auenbruggergasse near the Rennweg, where we lived, was made longer still because Mahler and Hauptmann were so engrossed that they stopped and talked at every lamp-post for a quarter of an hour at a time. Margarethe

Marschalk, a lovely creature in those days, and I sat down on a seat and waited patiently until we could get a word in edgeways to remind them of our existence. At four in the morning I could walk no farther and we took a cab from the Michaelerplatz.

Next day we paid the Hauptmanns a visit at the Hotel Sacher. Margarethe was wearing a shirt and black satin trousers, and her short black curls hung down to her shoulders; I could tell at once that she and Rautendelein were one and the same. She and I were to go out together and Mahler to stay with Hauptmann. Hauptmann took me aside as we were starting. "Do keep an eye on Gretchen," he said. "Don't let her enter a shop. She hasn't a notion of the value of money, and simply spends all she's got. Once, in Berlin, I gave her a thousand mark note to keep for me until we got to Italy, but when I asked her for it she hadn't the faintest recollection I'd ever given it to her. It put me in great difficulty because I'd been absolutely counting on it. So I made a search. And do you know where I found it? At the bottom of her trunk, screwed up in a ball. What do you say to that?"

I gave my promise, but it was not easy to keep it. She wanted everything she set eyes on in a manner entirely elfish. She pitched into me, too, for living in such a poor style: I ought to see to it that I had an easier life of it. She had eight servants, she told me, and never did a thing for herself. Hard words have been said since of her extravagance, but my impression was that Hauptmann liked her for it. He encouraged in her the qualities he had given to Rautendelein and which, like another Pygmalion, he wished to bring to life and enjoy in her.

Their stay in Vienna this time was short, but there was a longer one to come, which was to mean even more to us.

In the spring, just before the birth of my second child, I went to Abbazia with my little Maria and a scatterbrained maid, who literally expected me to wait upon her, which in my condition was absurd. I have often experienced the same thing with servants.

Mahler soon followed me. He took a sleeper, as he always did, whereas I traveled in an ordinary compartment. I went to meet him at Mattuglie. He told me he had been persecuted the whole morning by two small boys, who spied on him through the curtains of his sleeper. Later on there was a coming and going along the corridor and he recognized them as the sons of the Archduke Otto. One of these two boys was later the Emperor Karl. I was standing close to Mahler as they got out. The Archduchess Maria Josepha took the children up to him and told them not to forget having seen him. After greeting him very graciously she rejoined her attendants, who were looking on in surprise. She was very fond of Mahler, because he pensioned off the dancer, Schleinzer, Archduke Otto's extremely tactless mistress. When Schleinzer asked him why, he replied: "I can't do with an archduchess in my company."

Mahler brought his work with him even to Abbazia. I never knew him to have a real holiday. We were given the privilege of having our meals served in our own rooms, which as they were in an annex called Tusculum at the far end of the garden must have been somewhat troublesome.

I enjoyed the "splendid isolation," as he called it, as much as he did. Once or twice, to please our landlady, we joined the company in the dining-room, where as usual Mahler's presence caused an embarrassed silence, broken on this occasion only by the comedian, Treumann, who was unabashed and asked Mahler some foolish questions. He did not take them amiss; on the contrary, he was glad to have the solemn pall lifted.

We returned to Vienna a day sooner than we had intended. Mahler could never stay long anywhere. There was no rest for him. He was driven on without respite, either by his own work or his duties at the Opera.

On the 14th of June, 1904, we went for a drive in the Prater, as we had every afternoon for the last few weeks. On our return we found the Rosés in the hall, on the point of going to the Burg-theater. They had come in the hope of persuading us to join them. It was *Der arme Heinrich*. Mahler was all the more glad to go when he saw how eager I was, and so we all four drove straight on to the theater.

It was like wine to me. Kainz played Heinrich. I was shattered, which was not surprising in my condition. When I got home, Hauptmann's musical verse was still in my ears and I took the play to bed with me and read it through. The verse sounded on through my dreams and I suddenly woke, as though God had touched me with a finger. My hour had come—and still I heard Hauptmann. I did not want to wake anyone. I opened the window.

It was the 15th of June; all nature bloomed; leaves rustled, birds sang. I had no fear. It was five o'clock by now, and the pangs were severe. I went to Mahler. He put on his clothes and hurried out in alarm to fetch the midwife, and then did all he could think of to mitigate my pain. But the best he could think of was to read Kant aloud. I sat at his writing table and writhed in agony. The monotonous drone of his voice drove me crazy; I could not understand a word he read, and at last I could bear it no longer. But I know now he was right: mental concentration is the one means of overcoming pain. Only—the book, in the circumstances, was a bad choice; it was too difficult to understand.

The birth, at midday, in the middle of the week (Wednesday), in the middle of the month, in the middle of the year, might have been an allegory. From the first moment the child was a great joy to us and was nicknamed Guckerl, from her wide-open, blue eyes.

I was fast asleep later in the day and awoke with a violent start. An enormous stag beetle hovered in the air an inch or two from my face. Mahler was holding it by a single leg, beaming with delight, in spite of his horror of beasts of all kinds. "You're so fond of animals," he exclaimed exultingly. "I caught this fellow for you."

Once I had a sudden longing for a little piece of cheese. Such a thing never crossed our threshold, so Mahler ran out at once to the largest dealer in cheeses he knew of and bought an enormous wedge of strong Schwarzenberg cheese. I never knew till then that so large a piece could be seen at one time. As he would never carry anything in his hand he hung it on a button of his overcoat and promptly forgot all about it. He hurried along and the dangling cheese spread a pungent aroma abroad. They were repairing a gas-main in the Walfischgasse and, as there seemed to him to be a suffocating smell of gas, he turned aside into the Ring; but still there was the noxious smell of gas, and the faster he went the stronger it grew. At last he burst into my room. Even there the smell pursued him. We burst out laughing, and he was annoyed at first when we tried to persuade him that he himself was the origin of it all. Then he laughed too.

Mahler was extremely susceptible to suggestion. If I had a pain anywhere, he immediately had it too. He was also as credulous as a child in such matters and never had the slightest idea what did him good. He believed in any cure, whoever recommended it, and no medicine came amiss to him. When we moved from Auenbruggergasse, our large dining-table at its full extent could scarcely accommodate all the medicaments he had collected, and our friends were able to lay in a stock to last them for years.

His sister once recommended unleavened bread, and it was sent to him every three or four days to the Tyrol. I, of course, had to eat it too and it lay like lead on my stomach. I endured in silence. But one day I had spasms and could think of no cause but this bread. Mahler was overjoyed. He jumped up and cried out: "You can't bear it either? Thank God for that! It's given me hell for the last week. We won't eat any more of it." We stopped it at once.

It was often like that.

There was an entertaining episode at a dentist's: Mahler had toothache, but was not sure which tooth ached. I had found it for him, and I was sitting in the waiting-room, which was full of people. Suddenly the door flew open and Mahler called out: "Alma dear, which tooth is it actually that's aching?" He was astonished when everyone laughed.

We saw more of him at home now than ever before. He could scarcely bear to be parted from the children, and for each he had a special form of entertainment—stories, jokes or funny faces. He loved telling the elder one Brentano's fairy tale—"Gockel, Hinkel and Gackeleia."

Zemlinsky paid us a visit in the summer (I had been playing with him a little in the winter). He revered Mahler as a god and Mahler got to like him more and more. Roller, of whom he had always been very fond, came also, and so we were quite lively. Mahler became more human and expansive. He finished the Sixth Symphony and added three more to the two *Kindertotenlieder*. I found this incomprehensible. I could understand setting such frightful words to music if one had no children, or had lost those one had. Moreover, Friedrich Rückert did not write these harrowing elegies solely out of his imagination: they were dictated by the cruellest loss of his whole life. What I could not understand was bewailing the deaths of children who were in the best of health and spirits hardly an hour after having kissed and fondled them. I exclaimed at the time: "For heaven's sake, don't tempt Providence!"

The summer was beautiful, serene and happy. Before the holidays came to an end he played me the completed Sixth Symphony. First I had to get everything done in the house, so as to have all my time free. Once more we walked arm-in-arm up to his hut in the woods, where nothing could disturb us. These occasions were always conducted with much ceremony.

After he had drafted the first movement he came down from the woods to tell me he had tried to express me in a theme. "Whether I've succeeded, I don't know; but you'll have to put up with it."

This is the great soaring theme of the first movement of the Sixth Symphony. In the third movement he represented the unrhythmic games of the two little children, tottering in zigzags over the sand. Ominously, the childish voices became more and more tragic, and at the end died out in a whimper. In the last movement he described himself and his downfall or, as he later said, that of his hero: "It is the hero, on whose head fall three blows of fate, the last of which fells him as a tree is felled." Those were his words.

Not one of his works came so directly from his inmost heart as this. We both wept that day. The music and what it foretold touched us so deeply. The Sixth is the most completely personal of his works, and a prophetic one also. In the *Kindertotenlieder,* as also in the Sixth, he anticipated his own life in music. On him too fell three blows of fate, and the last felled him. But at the time he was serene; he was conscious of the greatness of his work. He was a tree in full leaf and flower.

One more word about his playing the work through to me: he always said he would never play an unfinished work, and he never did. It would, he said, be an immodesty. An artist could no more show unfinished work than a mother her child still in the womb.

I remarked to him once during a walk: "All I love in a man is his achievement. The greater his achievement the more I have to love him."

"That's a real danger. You mean if anyone came along who could do more than I——"

"I'd have to love him," I said.

He smiled: "Well, I won't worry for the time being. I don't know anybody who can do more than I can."

All the same, each of us was jealous of the other, though we belied it. He often used to say: "If you were suddenly disfigured by some illness, smallpox, for example, then at last, when you were pleasing in the sight of nobody else—then at last I could show how I loved you."

The load of debt I had taken over was heavy. Before we married, Mahler had entrusted its speedy liquidation to me with the words: "In the name of God and my *Euryanthe*, I pray you may soon be done with it." The apportionment of his income for this and all other purposes was my undivided responsibility. Mahler bought all his clothes from the best tailor, his shoes in large numbers from the best English shoemaker, whereas I wore the same dress for five or six years on end. I was unable to accept an invitation to lunch with Baron Albert Rothschild, because I had no hat to put on. It did not occur to either of us that I might buy one. Mahler went alone.

And so it was that the rigid economy, the cares of the household, which had to be run in exact conformity with his wishes, the children and the daily round all combined to wear down our love for each other; and yet his love, which in these mid-years of marriage seemed not only crowded back by inhibitions and petty worries but already buried, awaited its resurrection.

Roller was now commissioned to design a new stage-setting for *Fidelio*. Besides his wonderful scenery, there was a radical revision of the libretto and the groupings of the singers. The great Leonora overture now introduced the last act; and the effect was almost unbearably beautiful. As the music led the way from the somber prison, through darkness to light, the curtain rose and the Bastille towered up in a flood of brilliant sunshine. It was a stroke of dramatic genius on Mahler's part, which has been followed ever since.

For the quartet, *"Mir ist so wunderbar,"* Mahler made the players, who up to this moment had been in vigorous movement, suddenly form a tableau, and a ray of sunshine fell on the group through the window. The orchestra, the singers and every detail were studied and rehearsed to a pitch he had never reached in the production of any other opera. This was in October 1904, and its influence still lives on.

Although I was nursing my youngest child, I did not want to miss the final rehearsals; and so I sat unobserved in a box and ran out to the telephone every half-hour to make sure the children were well. I was continually harassed by anxious forebodings, not without good cause, as the future was to show—to my bitter sorrow. I was to learn that anxious care and all else are of no avail, if God has so decided. At the end of September Mahler asked me to wean the little one as soon as I could. I did it, but with a heavy heart, and only for the sake of the first hearing of the Fifth Symphony in Cologne, which I was unwilling to miss at any cost.

We were to travel together to Cologne for the rehearsals; but nature will not be trifled with. I fell ill through the sudden drying up of my milk, and our hope that I might be able to follow later was disappointed. And so I lay in bed with a temperature while the Fifth was given its first hearing; the Fifth, which had been my first full participation in his life and work, the whole score of which I had copied, and—more than that—whole lines of which he had left out, because he knew that he could trust blindly to me.

Early in the year there had been a reading-rehearsal with the Philharmonic, to which I listened unseen from the gallery. I had heard each theme in my head while copying the score, but now I could not hear them at all. Mahler had overscored the percussion instruments and kettle-drums so madly and persistently that little beyond the rhythm was recognizable. I hurried home sobbing aloud. He followed. For a long time I refused to speak. At last I said between my sobs: "You've written it for percussion and nothing else." He laughed, and then produced the score. He crossed out all the kettle-drums in red chalk and half the percussion instruments too. He had felt the same thing himself, but my passionate protest turned the scale. The completely altered score is still in my possession.

Mahler, then, set off alone for the first performance in public of a work I knew and loved so well. It took place on the 25th of October at Gürzenich in Cologne, and appears to have been very well performed and a great success. Mahler wrote me a detailed account. He had to go on to Amsterdam, where he stayed with Mengelberg and felt increasingly at home. He conducted the Second and the Fourth. It was the first performance of the Fourth in Amsterdam and Mengelberg put it twice in the same program: Fourth Symphony. Intermission. Fourth Symphony. Mahler conducted the first time, Mengelberg the second, with Mahler sitting comfortably in the stalls to hear his own work played to him. Mengelberg, he said when he came home, had grasped his meaning so perfectly that it was just as if he had been conducting himself.

He arrived in Vienna from Amsterdam early in the morning, and his warm bath was ready for him. As usual, I was waiting to look after him; and he told me all his experiences. Then he had breakfast and went to the Opera. At that time he was conducting there about twice a week. He made his own studies for almost entire productions, or took an active part if the rehearsals were under another conductor. His industry was unflagging. For a long time he alone conducted those operas in which he had trained the players, meanwhile working indefatigably at fresh interpretations of known works as well as the first production of new ones. His early mornings only were given up to writing the fair copy of his scores.

In December his Third Symphony was given a great reception in Vienna and the concert was repeated. Afterwards he entertained the orchestra at the *Goldene Birne* in Mariahilf—a sacred rite which he never failed to perform—and spent an hour with them. He loved these occasions and the people he worked with, each of whom he valued and esteemed. If only his orchestra had known it, how happily they might have worked together.

Christmas came and the New Year. There were parties and also a dinner party at a wealthy friend's. Mahler arrived in the middle, took an apple from the center of the table, while the other guests stared so hard they forgot to eat; after smelling it exhaustively he laid it down beside his plate and hurriedly swallowed what was put before him. Then he jumped up before the last course and vanished into the smoking-room, with his host and his host's daughter at his heels. In vain he protested that he wished to be alone: they kept him company by turns until the dinner was at an end and the whole company trooped in.

All stood in awe of him and he was the center of interest. But he did not help to make such evenings as this a success. There was a singer present who had persuaded his host that such a chance of singing before Mahler was not to be missed. But the moment the first notes of the accompaniment were heard and the singer had taken his stance, Mahler abruptly got up and left the room; after waiting, for decency's sake, until the song was over, he brusquely took leave of the company and hurried me off.

This dinner party and one other at the house of some moderately cultivated persons of noble birth were the only so-called social occasions we took part in during the whole of our married life in Vienna. We reckoned afterwards that the cost of clothes and cab-hire would have paid for a holiday. When we talked it over and discovered that each of us was making a sacrifice to the supposed pleasure of the other, we naturally decided to forego all such parties in the future.

Mahler lived the life of a Stoic—a small flat, no luxuries of any sort. His one aim was to be unconscious of the body, so as to concentrate entirely on his work. Besides this, I myself had come to a strange pass. I was shy when I was a girl, but in Mahler's company the affliction got to such a pitch that I could scarcely make a rational reply when spoken to; I felt I was nothing but his shadow. His celebrity was such that the moment we were seen in the street people stood stock-still and loudly exclaimed: "Look—there's Mahler with his wife." They laughed, nudged each other and turned round to stare and made me feel so uncomfortable that I could hardly walk on. But Mahler saw nothing. His utter unconcern was sometimes ludicrous.

Once, for example, we were waiting for an electric train in the Prater. Mahler's presence was a sensation. Every eye was on him. Just as the train came in sight, it suddenly occurred to him to retire to a nearby comfort station. An abashed smile passed from face to face and every eye was now fixed on me, who at such moments longed for the earth to open and swallow me up.

In a restaurant, too, it was his invariable habit to draw the waiter's attention to the dish somebody else was enjoying. If necessary, he stood up to point out the man whose luck he envied and desired to share, asking the waiter in a loud voice: "Waiter, what's that gentleman eating over there?"

Another episode has its appropriate place here, although I was not myself present. Mahler told me the story, which belongs to the days when he directed the Opera in Budapest. He and Justine went for a walk and arrived at a fashionable café, where the tables were disposed on two terraces one above the other. Mahler felt a sudden urge to wash his hands. Characteristically, he got up and marched up to the balustrade with the carafe of water from the table and without a thought emptied it over his hands. An outcry arose from below, chairs were pushed back, dresses shaken out, and then, after a look upward, there was the exclamation: "Oh—it's only Mahler!" Calm was restored after he had politely begged pardon; and he and Justine resumed their talk. Soon he felt the need to wash his hands once more. He took another carafe and carefully going to the other end of the terrace again poured water over his hands. To his great surprise the very same feminine outcry arose and looking down he saw the very same company as before, whom he had besprinkled for the second time. Fearing that this might occur, they had removed themselves to the farthest possible distance.

I found this extraordinary ingenuousness and total unconcern ever more of an embarrassment. The upshot, in any case, was that I suffered more and more from a torturing sense of inferiority. Often I had to affect a cheerful air with tears ready to burst from my eyes. And I must not let him see. I could have found in my music a complete cure for this state of things, but he had forbidden it when we were engaged—and now I dragged my hundred songs with me wherever I went—like a coffin into which I dared not even look.

One day he came home unexpectedly and found me in tears. He asked me the reason. Then he put his hand on my head: "Dreams that never flowered." I could not restrain myself any longer but broke into anguished sobs.

We came to an agreement while we lived in Vienna that, if I had heard any unpleasant news in the morning, I was to talk cheerfully during lunch, for fear of upsetting his digestion, and say nothing of my ill-tidings until he had been refreshed and invigorated by his brief siesta. How well I understand him today. Time has brought me the afflictions he suffered from years ago, and I have had no one to ward them off. I thank God I did as he wished in those days out of mere obedience to his will.

Another agreement between us, which I understood as little,

was that what he said one day was not to hold good the next. It was therefore out of the question for me to say: "But, Gustav, you said the very opposite yesterday" (as he very often did), because he reserved for himself the privilege of inconsequence. This characteristic of his was often a great shock to me. I could never be sure of what he thought and felt.

SPLENDID ISOLATION
1905

*I*n the winter a new production of *Rheingold* was rehearsed. There was one row after another between Roller and the Rhine maidens, who rebelled at singing in baskets on long poles. Roller took disciplinary action, but his strictness, his harshness, indeed, made bad blood in the company. His settings were beautiful but awkward even for the other singers. And Mahler was defenseless against him; he began to domineer and Mahler's power dwindled.

DIARY

January 26. Concert yesterday: Zemlinsky—Schönberg. My surmise was correct. Zemlinsky, in spite of many charming little inspirations and imposing knowledge, has not the strength of Schönberg, who for all his wrong-headedness is a very original fellow. The audience kept leaving in droves and slamming the doors behind them while the music was being played. There were whistles and cat-calls as well. But for us two his talent was beyond question.

When I was twenty Zemlinsky taught me in composition, and through him I came to know his pupil, Schönberg. He used to say when I confessed my lack of sympathy with Schönberg: "You wait. The world will talk of him before long." In those days I could not work up any belief in him. But Zemlinsky, who was at first Schönberg's teacher, later became his pupil. Nobody who entered the charmed circle of Schönberg's spirit could resist his intellectual pre-eminence or the force of his logic.

In those days we used to go to Frau Conrat's, a friend of Brahms, every Sunday evening. After Mahler's First Symphony we all arrived late, because we had been arguing passionately all the way about the music we had just heard. It had filled us with anger.

I met him again later. I was acquainted with Mahler by then, although nobody knew it. I asked Schönberg whether he was going to hear the performance of the Fourth Symphony. He answered me by one of those paradoxes he was so fond of: "How can Mahler do anything with the Fourth when he has already failed to do anything with the First?" This was true "Schönberg." Yet he was to be Mahler's greatest and most convinced follower. Zemlinsky brought him to see us later on, and a strange sort of friendship evolved between the three of them. Zemlinsky, from an exaggeration of pride, was dry in manner with Mahler. "I know," he said. "Everybody wants something from him and flatters him for that reason. He shall never say that of me."

I told Mahler this and he sent word by me that he was not to be so disingenuous but should take heart and be friendly.

Schönberg, on the other hand, was inspired by a youthful rebelliousness against his elder, whom at the same time he revered. They used to come in in the evening. After one of our devastatingly simple meals, all three went to the piano and talked shop—at first in all amity. Then Schönberg let fall a word in youthful arrogance and Mahler corrected him with a shade of condescension—and the room was in an uproar. Schönberg delighted in paradox of the most violent description. At least we thought so then; today I should listen with different ears. Mahler replied professorially. Schönberg leapt to his feet and vanished with a curt good night. Zemlinsky followed, shaking his head.

As soon as the door had shut behind them, Mahler said: "Take good care you never invite that conceited puppy to the house again." On the stairs Schönberg spluttered: "I shall never again cross that threshold." But after a week or two Mahler said: "By the way, what's become of those two?" I did not, of course, say:

"But you told me not to ask them again," but lost no time in send-ing them an invitation; and they, who had only been waiting for it, lost no time in coming. Nevertheless, it was a considerable time before there was much solace to be had from their intercourse together.

Mahler once said when he came home: "I've been stealing for you today." He took a sheet of paper folded in four from his pocketbook. It was the inner title-page of *Tannhäuser*. At the bottom in the right-hand corner were the words: "I conducted from this score on the ——. Richard Wagner." Mahler had been conducting *Tannhäuser* that evening, and it had pained him, as it often had before, to think of this sacred page being turned over and thumbed by any conductor who happened to come along; and so it occurred to him to abstract it. I was wild with joy. Mahler said he had rescued it, for the various conductors paid so little heed to it that their thumb-marks had almost obliterated the words. We smoothed it out and had it framed; and I hung it up in our music-room in perfect innocence. Not long after, Rosé saw it there: "What, *you've* got it? The whole opera's been looking everywhere for it. No, my children, that won't do." He took it away, frame and all. And that was the last we ever saw or heard of it.

I should very much like to know where it is now.

All foreigners of distinction had free use of our box, and there were often so many that there was scarcely room for me. Mahler came home from the Opera one day and said: "Richard Dehmel's in Vienna. I don't care for him, but I know he interests you. Shall I bring him along?" And so he came with his wife to see us. We had a good many people, the same company as usual. There were Roller, Klimt, Moser, my mother and Moll. Soon a fierce argu-ment broke out about Wagner. Mahler and all of us took up the cudgels for Wagner. Mahler loved him unreservedly. Dehmel was hard-set in his up-to-date, jejune antipathy, and the argument was threatening to take an unpleasant turn, when Dehmel said abruptly: " . . . and, anyway, Wagner reminds me of a poppy, and I can't stand poppies."

Silence fell, and the party broke up in gloom. And the odd thing is that such painful incidents live on, unforgotten and unforgiven, in the memories of all their victims.

There was another strange evening. Theodor Streicher, the composer, a neighbor of ours on the other side of the lake at Maiernigg, paid us a visit in the summer, which we returned. He did not appear to have any ulterior motive and little else passed between us. But he turned up again in the winter and out of his mouth came the words: "I should like very much to play you some compositions of mine."

"To what words?" Mahler asked.

"*Des Knaben Wunderhorn*," he replied.

Mahler grunted.

The evening came. There were Streicher, his wife in an old-fashioned silk court dress, Schönberg, Zemlinsky and Klaus Pringsheim (Thomas Mann's brother-in-law). At dinner we talked of anything but Streicher's compositions. Afterwards I made a sign to Mahler to ask him to play, but he only laughed and shrugged his shoulders. Conversation limped on. Streicher exchanged surprised glances with his wife. Again I gave Mahler a reminder and at last when it was nearly midnight I succeeded in decoying him into the hall; and there, projecting far from the pocket of Streicher's overcoat we saw the menacing roll of paper. Mahler went back into the room with a smile, and Streicher, released at last from his suspense, fell first on him and then on the piano.

He played a song, then a second, and a third. Mahler said not a word, but he bit the inside of his cheek, a sure sign that he was bored. Schönberg and Zemlinsky, finding the situation more and more painful, got up and stood like heraldic birds in support of Streicher, whose nervousness increased. In the kindness of their hearts they set about discovering little beauties. Streicher, who was so ill-advised as to read the words of each song aloud and then to expound them, was now encouraged to draw attention to happy inspirations and "remarkable" modulations; he panted and perspired and committed the one unforgivable sin a man can commit in such a predicament: he played on. Mahler took not the slightest notice; he lay prostrate on the sofa. Pringsheim leaned on the end of the piano. I stood behind the performer. We did not dare look at one another in case we should burst into uncontrollable laughter. Frau Streicher fixed her eyes on each of us in turn. It was a painful ordeal. At last the Streichers took their leave with marked coolness, and we could give rein to our merriment. That was Mahler all over; he never could say even one solitary word he did not mean.

January 28. Public rehearsal for the concert of Mahler's songs. Keen interest on the part of the audience. It was the first time people accepted Mahler's songs. Before, there was much hostility and criticism in the press, and among the audiences also.

After much debating, for and against, the rehearsals of Hans Pfitzner's *Rose vom Liebesgarten* began at the end of March. Meanwhile Pfitzner had paid me the great compliment of dedicating his string quartet to me. Many letters had passed between us and we had become friends in spite of the distance which separated us. Now he came to Vienna for the first rehearsals. He was frightfully nervous; kept a stern eye on the slightest unpunctuality on the part of any member of the company and was so self-centered that no one could hope for indulgence. I was the only person who could always calm him down.

March 21. Yesterday Pfitzner asked me to play some old songs of mine. He said they were good and that he was very glad to find I had a real talent for composition and a sound feeling for melody. "I wish we could work together for a time. It's such a pity about you." What a melancholy joy coursed through my veins! A moment's bliss.

March 22. Happy times with Hauptmann. He and Gustav together—it's a joy to listen to them. Last night was rather spoiled by Pfitzner's being there. He's somehow limited. He said that the deepest and truest thing in Wagner was his Germanness. Hauptmann and Gustav both replied that the greater an artist was, the farther he left nationality behind. Pfitzner writhed like a worm and left in mortification soon after. Since then he has altered. This was after a performance of *Fidelio*. Pfitzner and I had stayed at home and spent the time playing first his songs and then mine. We were to meet Mahler and Hauptmann in Meissl Schadn's restaurant. In the ardor of playing we forgot the time and were late, but no one took it amiss. Pfitzner played each of his songs about ten times, or as often as I needed in order to enjoy it thoroughly.

Today there was another argument between Mahler and Pfitzner about "*das ewig Weibliche zieht uns hinan.*" Anything less refreshing than this discussion it would be hard to imagine. Each purposely misunderstood the other and at the end each felt insulted. Besides, Mahler is jealous.

To get the better of his jealousy he constantly asked Pfitzner in and then left us alone. We spent hours making music together and talking, but Mahler was always there for me whether he was in the room or not. However, it was uncomfortable when the three of us were together, as he and Pfitzner were not made of the same clay; I was the only link between them and their brief moments of mutual understanding soon gave out. And so, in any case, it was a more peaceable and satisfactory arrangement.

DIARY

Lovely spring day. Rehearsals at the Opera—*The Rose*. Mahler had a brief rehearsal of his songs for orchestra (with Weidemann) coming on afterwards, and he asked Pfitzner, who naturally was present at the rehearsal of *The Rose*, to stay for this Weidemann rehearsal; but Pfitzner, once his own rehearsal was over, was in no mood to stay any longer to please Mahler; so he said something about urgent business and hurried off. Hurried off to me. On the way he stopped only to buy me a red rose, which without a word he laid upon the piano. This did not prevent his being in a very bad temper. It was the first of May and he had met a procession of workingmen in the Ring. Furious at the sight of proletarian faces, he darted down a side street and scarcely felt safe from pursuit in my room.

Mahler soon followed. He was both amused and vexed when he saw Pfitzner's flight in its true colors. But he was too happy to care: he too had met the procession in the Ring and had even accompanied it for some distance. They had all looked at him in so brotherly a way—they *were* his brothers—and they were the future!

That was enough to start the battle. It raged for hours, with ill-nature on both sides and me in the middle.

Pfitzner often complained to me that he could not make any contact whatever with Mahler's music. He didn't think it *was* music. Mahler was aware of his opinion, but all the same he worked himself nearly to death over the rehearsals of *Die Rose vom Liebesgarten*, conducted it magnificently and was so taken with it that he exclaimed at the end of the first act on the night of the première: "Since *Die Walküre*, Act One, there has been nothing written to touch it!" He was delighted by the eminent skill and success of the other man.

Hauptmann, who had been in Vienna that winter for the first night of his *Rose Berndt* at the Burgtheater, had a tender affection for Mahler which was not altogether returned. But I had an instinctive feeling that his society was, or would be, a blessing to Mahler, and so I telephoned every morning to arrange a meeting that day. Every day Mahler was confronted by the *fait accompli* and every day was better than the last. There were always only the four of us. On one occasion they talked about Christ. Hauptmann wrote "The Fool in Christ" very soon afterwards. Mahler talked in a fine exaltation and Hauptmann listened in silence. When Mahler went out of the room (we were dining at the Hotel Erzherzog Karl), Hauptmann said: "Your husband expresses clearly what I confusedly feel. I have never got so much from anyone as I have from him." Mahler grew more and more fond of Hauptmann; yet he was easily made impatient by his slowness of mind and labored expression.

I was right: these two genii of darkness and light were bound to harmonize and give out a beautiful note.

There was a very painful incident that winter. We were in Hauptmann's box for the first night of *Rose Berndt*. At the end of the first act the door opened and a friend of ours came in: "It's a boring play, don't you think, and pretty bad." He got kicks and pinches in plenty, but nothing could make him see that Hauptmann was there. Mahler jumped up and pushed him through the door. We never knew whether Hauptmann heard or not. We loved the play and the playwright.

We celebrated the première of *Die Rose vom Liebesgarten* in April by giving a party after the performance. Max Reinhardt, a Berlin banker (a friend of Pfitzner's), Cossmann from Munich, Roller, the Zuckerkandls, my family, the Rosés and Pfitzner were there. Mahler, to whom Pfitzner's circle was somewhat unsympathetic, began to feel bored. He got up during supper (as he often did) and went into the music-room to read a book. Nobody took offense at this except the fat banker, who was so much upset that he said he would never enter the house again. Mahler hated long sittings at table. Whoever might be present, he frequently got up and went into the next room to smoke or read, and came back again after a time. All the same, he was eager to know what we were talking about and always shouted through the wall to ask. All our friends knew of this habit of his, and did not mind in the least.

Although our menu was simple, it was extremely costly. Everything was of the best quality even though there was no luxury. This must have seemed to many very odd, but we preferred it.

One evening Zemlinsky and Schönberg came to dinner again. As usual there was only a dark beer (Spatenbräu, of which Mahler was very fond). At first, all went merrily, but then Schönberg's brow clouded and a discussion on musical matters, which did not seem likely to arouse violent antagonism, ended in a regular orgy of paradox on his part. At last Mahler lost patience with him. "Oh, do turn the tap off. That's enough of your small beer." To which Schönberg replied: "Well, really, it is not my fault if we don't get wine to drink."

We saw more and more of these two. At their suggestion, Mahler was elected honorary president of a composers' club which had recently been started. On the 29th of February, he let them have the *Wunderhorn* songs and the *Humoresques* and, at a later concert of theirs, he conducted Strauss's *Domestica*. These were their best attended concerts, but the club faded out, as all such enterprises do in Vienna, and probably everywhere else, unless they have the backing of "Society."

I meant to go to Maiernigg in May, but Mahler asked me to go to Strassburg with him. I left the children with a heavy heart. The two concerts were on the 21st and 22nd of May. Mahler conducted his Fifth and Beethoven's Ninth. Richard Strauss was there too.

ALSATIAN MUSICAL FESTIVAL

21 May, 1905		Strassburg
Fifth Symphony	*(Conductor, Mahler)*	Mahler
Rhapsody	*(Frau Kraus-Osborne)*	Brahms
Violin Concerto	*(Henri Marteau)*	Mozart
Sinfonia Domestica		Strauss
	(Conductor, Strauss)	

CONCERT II

22 May

(Mahler conducting the whole concert.)

Coriolan	Beethoven
Concerto in G Major	Beethoven
An die ferne Geliebte	Beethoven
Ninth Symphony	Beethoven

The end of the Rhapsody in the first concert had to be given again in response to the demand, and Strauss, who had only appeared in time for the final rehearsal, began to feel anxious about the performance of his own work. He foamed at the mouth and became violently angry. The *Domestica* was wretchedly performed: no entry was right.

We had arrived a week before Strauss. Mahler as usual had many rehearsals and his performances were magnificent. After the Fifth he and I were sitting on a balcony to enjoy the evening air. It was outside the round artists' room and we were hidden from view. Suddenly we heard Strauss come into the room in a fury. "What a circus—she ought to be singing at the Venezia in Vienna, the cow, not at a serious concert. 'Repeat the end—repeat the end,' " he shouted over and over again. "Tiring out my oboes until they can't blow another note. But of course—an old pundit like Brahms! If I had no more shame than to end on a C major triad, I should have equal success!" He raged on like this while we sat there not knowing what to do. At last the intermission brought Kraus, Frau Osborne's husband, on the scene; he had been told of Strauss's insulting remarks and said that, failing an apology to his wife in writing, for which purpose he drew up a document to be signed by us as witnesses, he would call him out. It all threatened to become very unpleasant. Mahler tried in vain to pacify Kraus. He merely shouted out: "My wife does not sing at Wanamaker's."* The intermission ended and events took their course. Strauss went fuming downstairs and ascended the podium. Mahler and I had to leave our refuge and listen to the infernal racket. Just before it ended we slunk out of the hall in a daze and back to the balcony, where as the end came we heard a scraping of chairs as the audience got up to go. And yet Strauss's vogue was such in those days that even for this chaotic performance he got something like applause, mingled with hisses; but these were to be heard too after the faultless performance of Mahler's Fifth.

Strauss joined us—fuming, followed by one or two members of the committee, who after expressing regrets, although it was not their fault that Strauss had had too few rehearsals, stood there in dismay while Strauss raved up and down like a tiger, cursing all music festivals and all committees. In spite of all this, an attempt was made to invite Strauss, Mahler and me to the banquet, an invitation he cut short by a curt refusal on behalf of all three of us. The gentlemen of the committee retired trembling, and Mahler dragged Strauss into the open air. We walked back to our hotel together and his temper made a rapid recovery. Mahler took the opportunity of telling him that it was his own fault for conducting his work without having rehearsed it. We went on to describe his exhibition of temper, to which he replied: "I must write and tell my wife that. She doesn't believe I've got a temper at all. But you must tell her too—give her a good scare." He agreed now to attend the banquet with Mahler so as to remove the bad impression he had made by his loss of temper. I stayed in the hotel; I always kept out of the way of these functions. After half an hour Mahler came back laughing. They had been received, he said, first with great astonishment and then with great cordiality. Strauss thereupon treated the committee to an explosive oration. Mahler was forgotten and was able to make his escape unobserved.

We were much alone. The Society of German Musicians made a point of avoiding Mahler. Schillings gave him only a timid greeting, Rösch looked the other way. Anti-Semitism was in the ascendant and Mahler was made to feel it. There was no mistaking

* Strauss had conducted concerts at Wanamaker's, a department store in New York.

it; we saw without envy how they made up parties at neighboring tables and left us out. We were very glad of our enforced quarantine. We went for walks in the country and over the old entrenchments. They were all overgrown and green, and breathed the spirit of peace, not war.

Friends of ours arrived from Paris—General Picquart, Painlevé, the great mathematician, afterwards French premier, Paul and Sophie Clemenceau and Baron Lallemand—the so-called quartet of the Dreyfus affair. They arrived at noon. Picquart went straight to the concert-hall before even going to his hotel, and there he sat with his hand over his eyes, patiently waiting for the time to pass. The reason was that he had been retired owing to the Dreyfus affair, but as he might at any moment be put back on the active list, he did not like to risk crossing the German frontier without official leave; so to avoid tedious formalities he had come incognito.

Picquart impressed everybody at the first glance as a man of fine character and nobility of feeling. His intervention in the Dreyfus affair was a great deal more courageous than Zola's, who challenged the world, heroically enough, with his *J'accuse!* But Picquart knew as a soldier that he lost all by standing firm in his indictment—his honor, his profession, his livelihood and perhaps his life.

The performance of Beethoven's Ninth Symphony on this occasion was the most perfect I have ever heard. The audience was wrought up to such a pitch that it looked from my seat in the gallery as though Mahler was in danger of his life; he seemed to vanish, as a wedge-shaped mass of frenzied men and women surged toward him. Picquart, Clemenceau and I ran down into the street and round the building in pursuit of him. We could see him running, his hat in his hand, at the tip of a monstrous tidal wave. He groaned with relief as soon as he saw us. Clemenceau hailed a comfortable old landau and, before the Bacchic maniacs could reach us and take the horses out of the shafts, we had escaped. We had a meal in an obscure little pothouse, where nobody recognized us.

Picquart, the Clemenceaus and Painlevé drove out next morning to Sesenheim, and followed up every trace left by Goethe there. They formed probably the most cultured circle in Europe. Picquart was scarcely human. He was a seraphic being with eyes like a mountain spring—they were so blue and clear. He spoke little and wisely. No one could meet him without feeling his strength of character and his genius. As soon as I looked into his eyes the first time, I knew that Dreyfus had been condemned unjustly, although until that moment the disgusting outcry in the press in his favor had made me think the very opposite. Picquart spoke fluent German, knew the whole of literature, knew Mahler's music—from playing it four-handed with Lallemand. He was a man in whom one saw the fullest development of the human spirit and not only the very pattern of a soldier.

Strauss, in spite of all, was cheerful and communicative. He had finished *Salome,* and asked Mahler whether he might play it through to him from the manuscript score. There is a story behind this. When he told Mahler he was going to make an opera of Wilde's *Salome,* Mahler was violently opposed. He had a thousand reasons; there was first of all the moral objection, but also, neither last nor least, that the production might be barred in Catholic countries. Strauss was unconvinced, but somewhat irritated all the same, though not for long. I told Mahler afterwards I was surprised that he should have tried to dissuade him. It was as if he had advised a man against marrying the woman he loved.

And now the composition of the opera was finished, and there was a note of triumph in his proposal. He had discovered a piano shop and the three of us made our way to the showroom, where there were pianos by the dozen. It had huge plate-glass windows on every side and passers-by loitered and stood still to peer in at what was going on.

Strauss played and sang to perfection. Mahler was charmed. We came to the dance—it was missing. "Haven't got it done yet," Strauss said and played on to the end, leaving this yawning gap. "Isn't it rather risky," Mahler remarked, "simply leaving out the dance, and then writing it in later when you're not in the same mood?" Strauss laughed his light-hearted laugh: "I'll fix that all right." But he did not. The dance is the one weak spot in the score —just botched-up commonplace. Mahler was completely won over. A man may dare all if he has the genius to make the incredible credible.

The new production and setting of *Don Juan* was an event which the musical world awaited with eager suspense. Roller's new setting, with the flanking towers, which remained throughout the whole performance but made a succession of different scenes owing to the effective use of lighting, broke new ground in its day, though it has been put in the shade since. It was the first time "symbolism"* was employed on the stage, if not rediscovered. Roller at that time went a good way in symbolism without having much insight into its future developments. For the finale of *Don Juan* he had black velvet rolled out over the whole stage, to give the impression of Don Juan's being devoured by darkness. It was a good idea, but it did not come off. The old theatrical fire and brimstone was more effective.

In the summer of 1905 Mahler wrote the Seventh Symphony in one burst. The "blueprints," as he called them, belong to midsummer of 1904. As he wrote the serenade he was beset by Eichendorffish visions—murmuring springs and German romanticism. Apart from this, the symphony has no program.

In between came the songs with orchestra and other songs.

---

* Literally, "allusion stage."

SPLENDID ISOLATION
1906

MAHLER's life in the winter months was very different from the life he lived during the short holiday at Maiernigg, but just as strictly regulated. He got up at seven, shaved and rang his bell. The parlor-maid brought his breakfast and the newspapers. The first was rapidly disposed of and the second merely glanced at. Then he sat down at once at his writing table, which no one was allowed to touch, and revised or orchestrated the summer's work. The sheets lay ready to his hand and he worked on them whenever he had a moment to spare. Shortly before nine he came into my room; then after paying the children a visit he hurried off to be in time to open his correspondence at the Opera before his subordinates arrived.

After lunch the newspapers came into their own. They fell sheet by sheet from the sofa to the floor, which was soon littered knee-deep.

This winter Mahler put the finishing touches to his Seventh Symphony in the mornings and made a fair copy of the score; and on the 29th of January *Seraglio* was produced, again with Roller's towers, which, however, were made better use of this time. It was an excellent performance. Immediately after it, Mahler took a few days' holiday, which we spent at the Semmering. There was deep snow and we went driving in sleighs, drank grog and indefatigably sang the last quartet from *Seraglio*. I still remember a talk we had about Mozart during a sleigh-ride. Mahler talked a great deal about "Constanzerl," whose speedy re-marriage he could not forgive, and about Mozart's wretched life. He loved him as a human being more than anyone who ever lived.

The Marriage of Figaro was given on the 30th of March, with Mahler's alterations. It was one of his finest productions and, with *Don Juan, Fidelio* and *Tristan*, one of the sacred few he kept under his own hand and eye.

Mahler went to Breslau this winter where he conducted his Third Symphony in response to the invitation of Albert Neisser, president of the Music Society. He was very fond of Albert Neisser and his wife, who welcomed all persons of distinction to their cultured house. While he was away D'Albert came to Vienna with his umpteenth wife and played and sang me his *Flauto Solo* in the hope that Mahler might perform it—as he did. D'Albert played, sang and mimed his small opus enchantingly.

In May Mahler and I went to Graz for the first performance in Austria of *Salome*. It was our only chance of hearing it, as Mahler had not succeeded in getting the censor to pass it for Vienna. His proposal to rechristen it *Jochanaan in Baalschem* was not found acceptable either; his persistence went so far as almost to make a cabinet question of it. We found Strauss awaiting us at the Elephant Hotel, and he at once proposed an expedition by motorcar that afternoon to see the Gollinger Waterfall. We set off immediately after lunch. It had been raining and we skidded on the wet road, but Strauss thought nothing of that. We arrived at a little inn and after refreshment walked on to the waterfall, with which we were so delighted that we could not tear ourselves away. At last hunger drove us back to the bare wooden table at the inn, but here again it was so delightful that Strauss refused to budge. "Bother it all, they can't start without me. Let 'em wait," he said savagely. Dusk was falling. It began to get chilly. Mahler jumped up. "Right. If you won't go, then I will—and conduct in your place."

That settled it. Strauss reluctantly got to his feet. Mahler urged the chauffeur to hurry up. Strauss told him to take his time. It seemed as if the wrong one of the two had stage fright, but perhaps Strauss was not so unmoved as he wished us to believe. He may have been hiding his tremors under a show of frivolity.

The performance was a great success, and there was no disturbance on the part of the Christian-Socialists, as it had been feared there might be. Strauss joined us for breakfast next morning and started pitching into Mahler for taking everything too seriously. "That old cow-shed of an Opera, for example. You ought to go easy on it. No one'll thank you for it if you racket yourself to bits. A pigsty that won't even perform *Salome*. Not worth it, I tell you."

There was a lot in what he said; I had always been of the same opinion, for however important his work for the Opera might be, it was nothing in comparison with even a single note of his own compositions. The one was ephemeral, the other eternal.

Mahler used to say: "Strauss and I tunnel from opposite sides of the mountain. One day we shall meet."

On the journey back to Vienna we were standing in the corridor, as we usually did. The country was green after much rain. We were discussing success and its illusions. An old gentleman was standing close to us and obviously listening to every word we said. It was Peter Rosegger. Mahler denied that there was any truth behind any success whatever. Had we not just come from the première of *Salome?* Tumults of applause—and yet we were convinced that not one in a hundred really understood the music. We ourselves, even during the performance, had grave doubts about the whole theme and subject-matter, about the music for the dance, which we did not like, and about a great deal else, in spite of so much that showed the hand of a master—and yet the public without hesitation gave a verdict of success. Whose was the verdict and on what authority? Rosegger said the voice of the people was the voice of God, to which we replied by asking whether he meant the people here and now or the people as posterity. He was a charming old gentleman, at peace with himself and all the world, a complete contrast to Mahler, to whom peace was unknown. He felt himself superior, but Mahler felt no inferiority.

One evening he and my mother and I drove from Klagenfurt to Krumpendorf, where we were met by our servant who had rowed over in the boat. It .was a night of brilliant moonlight. Mahler sat facing me, his overcoat buttoned up to his chin. His long white face, his long bronze-like forehead had a phosphorescent sheen. He looked frightful. He looked like death masquerading as a monk. I told him so, vainly hoping to exorcise my ghostly pang of dread. He laughed and told us that he once went to a fancy-dress ball in Hamburg as a monk, and nobody liked to accost him: he looked too much like the real thing. Savonarola must have looked as he did that night.

Mahler had a reading-rehearsal of his Sixth Symphony with the Philharmonic in the spring. The notes of the big drum in the last movement were not loud enough for him; so he had an enormous chest made and stretched with hide. It was to be beaten with clubs. He had this engine brought in before the rehearsal. The members of the orchestra crowded round the monster on the lighted stage—the rest of the house was in darkness. There was the breathless silence of suspense. The drummer raised his arm and smote: the answer was a dull, subdued boom. Once more—with all his strength: the result was the same. Mahler lost patience. Seizing the bludgeon from the man's hand he whirled it aloft and brought it down with a mighty whack. The answering boom was no louder than before. Everyone laughed. And now they brought out the old, big drum again—and the true thunder came. Nevertheless, Mahler had this chest despatched at great cost to Essen, where it was again tried out, and finally rejected as unfit for service.

There was another similar episode. Mahler was once plaguing the orchestra so unmercifully over the three opening notes of Beethoven's Fifth Symphony that some jumped up to go and some sat in stubborn fury, resolved not to play another note. Mahler seeing this shouted out: "Gentlemen, keep your fury for the performance, then *at last* we shall have the opening played as it should be."

The music festival of the United German Music Society was held this year at Essen in June. The first performance of Mahler's Sixth was on the program.

Mahler went there alone. I now had two children and was not strong enough to accompany him, as I should have liked to do. He wrote to me in great excitement over the work and the rehearsals and also over a new friend he had made. This was Ossip Gabrilowitsch, to whom he seemed to grow more and more attached. I arrived for the final rehearsals. The only person there of whom Mahler took much account was Strauss; the rest were more or less insignificant. Oscar Fried followed Mahler like his shadow.

None of his works moved him so deeply at its first hearing as this. We came to the last rehearsals, to the dress-rehearsal—to the last movement with its three great blows of fate. When it was over, Mahler walked up and down in the artists' room, sobbing, wringing his hands, unable to control himself. Fried, Gabrilo-witsch, Buths, and I stood transfixed, not daring to look at one another. Suddenly Strauss came noisily in, noticing nothing. "Mahler, I say, you've got to conduct some dead march or other tomorrow before the Sixth—their mayor here has died. That's the custom— But what's the matter? What's up with you? But ——" and out he went as noisily as he had come in, quite un-moved, leaving us petrified.

On the day of the concert Mahler was so afraid that his agitation might get the better of him that out of shame and anxiety he did not conduct the Symphony well. He hesitated to bring out the dark omen behind this terrible last movement.

Mengelberg came only in time for the performance. We looked in for a moment at the supper party after the concert for the sake of appearances. Mahler was in such a state that I dared not let him go alone; but his gloom vanished when he got there. He introduced Mengelberg to me; he seemed to me like Loge. I was planted ceremoniously next to Strauss at supper. "Why ever does Mahler smother his effect in the last movement?" he said. "He gets his fortissimo and then damps it down. Can't under-stand that at all." He never did understand. He spoke simply as the showman. Anyone who understands the Symphony at all understands why the first blow is the strongest, the second weaker and the third—the deathblow—the weakest of all. Perhaps the momentary effect might be greater in the inverse order. But that is not the point.

We met Strauss in the street the day we arrived at Essen. Mahler had just had a great success in Vienna with his Second Symphony, which had been repeated. Strauss came up to Mahler, bawling out: "Hullo, you celebrity of Vienna, how do you feel now?" We were so upset we walked on without a word. After this we saw him often in the distance, but kept out of his way.

It was a habit of his to boost quite mediocre talent, which

redounded to the credit of his heart without raising up any formidable rival. For example, there was a musician called Hermann Bischoff, whose one and the same symphony Strauss had performed annually at this festival of the Music Society and of whom he said darkly: "You wait. This year it'll come off." But it never did. A work does not become a work of art merely from being taken out and put away again.

He now became very scathing about Mahler as a composer; he was all right as a producer of operas.

But Pfitzner too was incapable of appreciating Mahler.

The Jewish question touched Mahler very nearly. He had often suffered bitterly from it, particularly when Cosima Wagner, whom he greatly esteemed, tried to bar his appointment in Vienna because he was a Jew. He had had to be baptized before he could aspire to such a high position under the Royal and Imperial exchequer. In any case he had a strong leaning to Catholic mysticism, whereas the Jewish ritual had never meant anything to him. He could never pass a church without going in; he loved the smell of incense and Gregorian chants. But he was not a man who ever deceived himself, and he knew that people would not forget he was a Jew because he was skeptical of the Jewish religion and baptized a Christian. Nor did he wish it forgotten, even though he frequently asked me to warn him when he gesticulated too much, because he hated to see others do so and thought it ill-bred. No one dared tell him funny stories about Jews; they made him seriously angry. And how right he was in this.

His religious chants, the II, the VIII, and all the chorals in the Symphonies are truly his own and not introduced at second-hand. He never denied his Jewish origin. Rather, he emphasized it. He was a believer in Christianity, a Christian-Jew, and he paid the penalty. I was a Christian-pagan and got off scot-free.

After we arrived at Maiernigg, there was the usual fortnight during which, nearly every year, he was haunted by the specter of failing inspiration. Then one morning just as he crossed the threshold of his studio up in the woods, it came to him—*Veni creator spiritus*. He composed and wrote down the whole opening chorus to the half-forgotten words. But music and words did not fit in—the music had overlapped the text. In a fever of excitement he telegraphed to Vienna and had the whole of the ancient Latin hymn telegraphed back. The complete text fitted the music exactly. Intuitively he had composed the music for the full strophes.

He worked with superhuman energy this summer, and often played some of his new compositions to me; he was boundlessly happy and exalted. Unfortunately, he had to break off and go to Salzburg to conduct *The Marriage of Figaro* at a music festival. The performance was given with the whole company from the Opera, but Mahler kept out of the way of everyone, except Roller. Nevertheless, he ran into Lilli Lehmann in the street. She called out to him scornfully that if he wanted to hear true Mozart he must come to her *Don Juan*. Mahler went the same evening with Roller and was both disgusted and amused by the amateurishness of the whole affair. He said to Roller in an undertone (misquoting from *The Magic Flute*):

> "Unless a man their hearts do guide,
> These cows will wander far and wide."

A woman in front of them overheard and turned round. It was Lilli Lehmann.

The following is taken from an article in the *Neue Freie Presse* by Korngold, which appeared in the summer of 1926.

"*Figaro* at Salzburg: the words conjure up an imperishable memory. Gustav Mahler came to Mozart's town in 1906. Visions of a new symphony crowded on him; but he came, happy in these premonitions, in a mood not far from exuberance. A much thumbed volume protruded from his coat pocket: it was *Faust*. The theme of the medieval metaphysician, which was to dominate the first part of the symphony—it was the Eighth—had taken shape. Now the parallel passages from Goethe were waiting. In this mood the director of the Vienna Opera caught sight of his critic in a café and he looked like a willful cherub about to flit in through the open window. It was in this mood too that he was inspired by the tiny theater to perform a miracle of artistic genius in perfect keeping with it. This *Figaro* of his at Salzburg was the ideal *Figaro* in its enchanting grace, its light-winged conversational tone and the incomparable balance of the whole ensemble. No one who was present on that occasion can ever forget it."

Mahler had played and sung to me the chorus *"Alles Vergäng-liche ist nur ein Gleichnis."* I was so utterly spellbound by it that after a few days I sent it to him from memory, fully instru-mented and harmonized. As he was leaving he asked me what I would like from Salzburg, and I said Salzburg marzipan. When I met him at Klagenfurt on his return, he got out dragging a large box after him. Marzipan potatoes had now to be consumed by the hundred and the whole neighborhood rejoiced in his wild extravagance—and absence of mind.

Once back at Maiernigg he worked feverishly at the Eighth, the conclusion of which was the end of Part 2 of *Faust.*

This was our last summer of peace and beauty and content. There followed years of horror, years which swept away the very foundations on which we had built.

We had to return to Vienna at the beginning of September, as usual; and to avoid being in town Mahler went to stay at Dorn-bach with a dear old lady who had been a second mother to me as a child.

Here is a quotation from a letter from Dr. R. Horn about Mahler: "The alarming guest did not make such an upset as they expected. When he found his apples for breakfast, lunch and dinner and the first volume of Bielschowsky's 'Life of Goethe' at Dornbach and the second in Walfischgasse,* he was in heaven; Goethe and apples are two things he cannot live without.

"We had many philosophic walks together; it was all I could do to snatch my afternoon siesta. Mahler is a notable thinker after the pattern of his fiery spirit, a deep and often an inspired one, but usually a thinker by fits and starts, which, I may add, does not worry me in the least."

When Mahler was alone in Vienna, he stayed as a rule with one of our friends or at my mother's. He had to be hedged about or he felt unhappy. After conducting at the Opera he liked going to the café of the Hotel Imperial, where he foregathered with a few of his friends who had been to the Opera. Walter and Roller

---

* Frau Conrat put a room at his disposal in her flat in Vienna as well as in her country villa.

were almost always among them. But he ate scarcely anything and after drinking a glass of beer (in spite of pangs of conscience) he left early. As soon as I returned, the time-table he ordained came into force. And a profound solitude enclosed us both.

In October there was the première of Erlanger's *Le Juif-polonais*, the work of an eclectic, which Mahler produced only because of its use of bells in a manner recalling the opening passage of his own Fourth Symphony. I told him so after the première —an event of little significance—and he freely admitted it.

Our Paris friends, Paul Painlevé, Madame Ramazotti, Georges Picquart, Paul and Sophie Clemenceau and Baron Lallemand, all close friends, paid us a visit in Vienna in October. Mahler got up a galaxy of opera in their honor: *Figaro, Don Juan, Tristan.* He conducted every day for their benefit and all Vienna was open-mouthed at such a gala week. But no one knew the reason of it.

On the night of the 19th of October, just at that breathless moment when Tristan let go the helm at Isolde's bidding and the motif of destiny was heard, a man in one of the boxes got up and, with one nervous look at his watch and one last reluctant look at the stage, hurriedly left the Opera House. It was General Picquart. He had had a telegram in cipher from Georges Clemenceau recalling him instantly to take over the portfolio of Minister for War. Our festivities were upset.

On his card he wrote:

"Dear Master, forgive me. I must leave for Paris immediately. My warmest thanks for your friendly welcome and the rare artistic treat you provided for me.

My kindest regards to Frau Mahler and the Molls—

GENERAL PICQUART"

3, rue Ivon, Villarceau.

He, as well as Paul Painlevé, remained my friends after Mahler's death. I saw Picquart every year in Paris, whither he always came as soon as he knew I was there. And Painlevé paid Vienna several visits and always stayed with us. The last time he complained bitterly of his "nightmare," as he called Hitler. "Hitler," I told him, "was not born at Braunau, but at Versailles," to which he replied with his abrupt: *"Oui, oui, oui—vous avez tout à fait raison."*

Only a man with a great and open mind like his could have said that.

Our elder child used to go to Mahler's studio every morning. They held long conversations there together. Nobody has ever known about what. I never disturbed them. We had a fussy English nurse who took her to his door, as clean and neat as a new pin. It was not long before Mahler brought her back, and by this time she was usually smeared with jam from top to toe. It was my job to pacify the English nurse. But they were so happy together after their talk that I took a secret pleasure in these occasions.

She was his child entirely. Her beauty and waywardness, and her unapproachability, her black curls and large blue eyes, foretold that she would be a danger later on. But though she was allowed only a short life, she was chosen to be his joy for a few years, and that in itself is worth an eternity. It was his wish to be buried in her grave. And his wish was fulfilled.

Mahler often used to say: "An artist shoots in the dark, not knowing whether he hits or what he hits."

Also: "There is only one education—example. To live by example is everything."

He was a foe to all explanations, wranglings and gossiping.

"I must keep on the heights. I cannot let anything irritate me or drag me down. It is hard enough as it is to keep up on that level all the time."

SORROW AND DREAD

1907

*T*HIS YEAR, so blackly underlined in the calendar of our life, began like any other year. There were beautiful productions at the Opera; at home, work and our peaceful routine. Mahler and Roller, from February onwards, made fresh studies of *Die Walküre, Lohengrin,* and Gluck's *Orpheus.* The last was the most successful, the most faultless of all their collaborations.

In the early spring we went with friends to Brünn, where Mahler conducted his First Symphony in the way I always preferred it. Of late he had been passing over the first entrance of the climax and emphasizing its second entrance instead. I could not agree; and for the performance at Brünn he went back to his previous rendering and orchestrated the second entrance of the theme more strongly, recognizing that it was essentially the more important. When he came to it for the first time at rehearsal he turned round and looked at me. I smiled approval. He tapped and had the whole passage played again only for me to hear it once more; for it had gone to perfection.

Nedbal, too, noticed how in the theater one evening Mahler put his arm under mine on the marble balustrade, so that my bare forearm should not rest on the cold stone. Nedbal often told this story afterwards with tears in his eyes. Mahler began at that time to have a new and stronger feeling for me, a conscious feeling in contrast with his earlier self-absorption.

On the next day but one after the performance at Brünn he set off for St. Petersburg; and, meanwhile, before coming to the tragic events in store for us I will relate some of the more cheerful episodes of his early years, as he himself related them to me.

Bruckner had two pupils who made all the piano transcriptions of his symphonies but seem to have bullied and tormented him. They were two brothers called Schalk. Bruckner was very fond of Mahler and entrusted the piano edition of his Third Symphony to him. When Mahler brought him the first movement Bruckner was childishly pleased and said with a roguish smile: "Now I shan't need the Schalks any more!" This saying became a household word with us and was dragged in on all possible, and impossible, occasions.

In those early days he used often to meet with Bruckner at midday. Bruckner stood the beer and Mahler had to pay for his own rolls; but as he generally had no money, he had to make his midday meal on beer alone. Bruckner was always surrounded by large numbers of young musicians, to whom he talked with childlike unrestraint. But if there were Jews present, he always —if he had occasion to say anything about Jews—alluded to them courteously as "the Israelitic gentlemen."

Mahler had a friend whom he looked up to and admired. His name was Hans Rott; it was he whose symphony, although the better of the two, failed to win the prize. Rott's mother once knocked at Bruckner's door on a hot summer day to ask how her son was progressing. In response to a loud "Come in!" she entered the room. Bruckner advanced stark naked to shake her by the hand. She fled screaming, but for a long time he could not understand "what was up with the woman." When engrossed in composition he forgot everything else, and on hot days it was his custom to compose in his tub with the score on a stool beside him.

He was not, strictly speaking, Mahler's teacher, but he had a regard for him as a young man of promise. Very odd stories about his methods of teaching went the round. His methods were simple but graphic. He used to ask his pupils: "Know what a suspension in music is? No? Well, look here." He produced a filthy bit of rag out of his trouser-pocket. "Dirty, eh? That's a discord." Next he pulled out a rather cleaner one. "There, you see—that's better. Been resolved." And now he displayed a snow-white handkerchief. "There you are—and now we're in the tonic."

Bruckner once taught at a girls' school, but was abruptly dismissed on account of improprieties he committed. Nevertheless no one believed him guilty. His innocence only could have been at the bottom of it.

Years later Siegfried Ochs told me a touching story, in which he himself had played a part. Ochs was conducting Bruckner's Mass in Berlin at a music festival, and afterwards he was giving a party in Bruckner's honor. Bruckner telephoned in the afternoon to say that if he could not bring his fiancée he would not come at all. Ochs had a presentiment that something must be very wrong and rushed off to Bruckner's hotel. He found him in despair. The chambermaid had suddenly come in the night before—and, in short, in the morning she sobbed that he had robbed her of her innocence and would have to marry her. So Bruckner promised to do so. Ochs summoned the girl at once and asked her how much she wanted. The sum was considerable. Nevertheless, Bruckner's gratitude was embarrassing in its effusiveness.

Mahler's love of Bruckner was lifelong. He gave performances of all his symphonies one after the other in New York, although they had a very bad press. In Vienna he proclaimed his merits as a matter of course.

In the title-page of his copy of Bruckner's *Te Deum*, he crossed out the words: "For chorus, solos and orchestra, organ ad libitum," and wrote: "For the tongues of angels, heaven-blessed, chastened hearts, and souls purified in the fire!"

When he was eighteen Mahler went to Bad-Hall, where the father of Zwerenz, the *prima donna*, appointed him conductor of the summer-theater orchestra in a unique sense. His duties were to put out the music on the stands before each performance, to dust the piano and to collect the music again after the performance. During the intermissions he had to wheel the baby, Mizzi Zwerenz, round the theater in her pram. He drew the line, however, when he was required to understudy the stage. He regretted later that his pride had stood in the way, as the lost opportunity would have taught him much that was never likely to come his way again.

While there he got into what—for him—was very strange company. The painter, Angeli, was surrounded by an admiring circle of young men of fashion, who invited Mahler to join their gatherings. He was flattered by the attentions of the first persons of birth and breeding he had encountered. He blossomed forth. They went on long expeditions together, which of course withdrew him more and more from his duties, until one day he was so late for the performance that he was dismissed. His new friends escorted him in a body to the station and he parted from them with the promise to look them all up in Vienna. He was delighted to have such fine fellows as friends, and as soon as he heard they were back in Vienna he kept his promise; but every door was closed to him. He felt at once that he was rebuffed as a Jew and, avoiding new acquaintances for the future, fell back on his boyhood friends. (The slight may have been not for the Jew but the holiday acquaintance.)

"I am thrice homeless," he often used to say. "As a native of Bohemia in Austria, as an Austrian among Germans, and as a Jew throughout all the world; everywhere an intruder, never welcomed."

After Hall, Mahler went to Laibach, where his remarkable personality quickly impressed both the public and his colleagues of the theater. He had enormous horn-rimmed spectacles made for him so that he could see well in all directions, and got to work in earnest, rehearsing Margaret (in *Faust*) without the soldiers' chorus—a single soldier marched across the stage, singing the chorus *"feste Burgen,"* and so on. Once during a rehearsal he preached a sermon to a singer on her loose morals, whereupon she swung herself onto the piano and slapping her thighs informed him that the purity of his own morals aroused her utter contempt. (The same thing happened to him in Hamburg. When the singer, Sch.-H., saw that her attentions were thrown away she gave them up and talked malicious scandal about him instead.)

His position at Laibach became uncomfortable. A ring of hatred closed round him. Reading in the newspaper that the conductor of the orchestra at Cassel had absconded, leaving a vacancy, he went straight to the station, without giving notice either of his departure or of his arrival. He was interviewed at once by the director of the opera at Cassel, who asked him whether he could undertake *Martha* without rehearsal. Mahler said yes, although he had never seen a note of it. He asked if he might have the score just to refresh his memory in the course of the afternoon. During that afternoon he learned the whole score by heart, and conducted so brilliantly at night that he was engaged on the spot.

And yet his peace and happiness soon gave out. He fell in love with two singers at the same time, who put their heads together to make fun of him. Tormented by his feelings, he wrote poems to both, not knowing they were friends who showed his verses to each other. If he finished a poem in the middle of the night he despatched it at once by messenger, regardless of the lateness of the hour and the fury these untimely offerings provoked. Driven to distraction at last by gossip and his divided feelings, he left Cassel hurriedly toward the end of the season. Once in the train he was a free man again.

Next he became assistant conductor in Leipzig, with Artur Nikisch as his friend and supporter. It was through him that he met Carl Maria von Weber's grandson, with whose wife—years older than himself—he fell in love. A time of tribulation and bliss began for both. Her influence set him to composing again. He had given it up in the stress of his life as a harried musician. As he had a passionate devotion to Jean Paul Richter, he wrote a symphony, which he called *Titan* and which was given its first performance, with this title, at the Weimar music festival.

Later when he was continually asked to give clues to the various romantic situations in the music, he became convinced of the futility of so-called program-music. So he abolished the title and his *Titan Symphony* became what we know today as the First.

Frau von Weber returned his passion and their mutual feeling was deepened by the musical studies they pursued together. One of these was the picking out from among Weber's manuscript remains the notes and sketches for *Die Drei Pintos*, out of which Mahler pieced the opera together. Its content, however, was as much Mahler as Weber, and yet it was still a patchwork which could not hold its own on any stage.

Finally their love rose to such a pitch that they resolved on flight together. But deep as Mahler's love was, his fear of the final step was deeper. He was a poor man and he had his family to support. Hence his relief was great when the train drew out, and the woman who was to have fled in his company had not appeared.

One summer Brahms and Mahler were out for a walk near Ischl. They came to a bridge and stood silently gazing at the foaming mountain stream. A moment before they had been heatedly debating the future of music, and Brahms had had hard things to say of the younger generation of musicians. Now they stood fascinated by the sight of the water breaking in foam time after time over the stones. Mahler looked up-stream and pointed to the endless procession of swirling eddies. "Which is the last?" he asked with a smile.

Mahler in his own later years was a stand-by to all struggling musicians, particularly to Schönberg, whom he did his best to protect from the brutality of the mob. Twice he took a foremost part in quelling disturbances at concerts.

The first time was when Schönberg's Quartet, Opus 7, was performed. The audience was quietly and by tacit agreement taking it as a great joke, until one of the critics present committed the unpardonable blunder of shouting to the performers to stop. Whereupon a howling and yelling broke out such as I have never heard before or since. One man stood up in front and hissed Schönberg every time he came apologetically forward to make his bow, wagging his Semitic head, so like Bruckner's, from side to side in the embarrassed hope of enlisting some stray breath of sympathy or forgiveness. Mahler sprang to his feet and went up to this man. "I must have a good look at this fellow who's hissing," he said sharply. The man raised his arm to strike Mahler. Moll, who was among the audience, saw this and in a second he forced his way through the crowd and collared the man. Moll's superior strength sobered him and he was hustled out of the Bösendorfersaal without much difficulty. But at the door he plucked up his courage and shouted. "Needn't get so excited—I hiss Mahler *too!*"

The second time was when Schönberg's chamber symphony was performed in the Music Society's hall. People began to push their chairs back noisily halfway through, and some went out in open protest. Mahler got up angrily and enforced silence. As soon as the performance was over, he stood near the front and applauded until the last of the demonstrators had gone. We spent the rest of the evening discussing the Schönberg question. "I don't understand his music," he said, "but he's young and perhaps he's right. I am old and I daresay my ear is not sensitive enough."

I was rung up that night by G. Adler, professor of the history of music: "Gustav made a painful exhibition of himself today. May cost him his job. You ought to stop him. I went home and shed tears when I thought of the way music is going. Yes, I shed tears. . . ." Poor music!

There was undoubtedly more behind the appeal Schönberg's music made on Mahler, or he would not have shown up so prominently as his champion. He felt, even if he did not yet know, the secret of those tortuous paths which Schönberg's genius was the first to tread.

He still leads the way in music and no one has been able to dispute his supremacy. He opens up new paths, which Richard Strauss and others of his contemporaries have explored in their later works.

Mahler's efforts had raised the Opera in Vienna to undreamed-of heights. It was he who discovered the conductor, Franz Schalk, and brought Bruno Walter from Germany. He esteemed Walter highly, and expected great things from the help of a young and extremely talented conductor.

Mahler gave him an engagement at the Opera soon after taking over the directorship of it. The personal and artistic relations between him and the younger musician were congenial from the first and grew into a friendship which was never clouded to the end.

Walter had a full understanding of Mahler during his lifetime as a musician and a composer; after his death, Walter's great and exalted art was at the service of his music throughout the world. He mastered its every subtlety and gave it his own original interpretation. He took the spirit of Mahler's compositions as the keystone of his own work as an interpretative musician.

Roller was now in sole charge of scenery and costume, and Mahler himself moved as supreme as "God over the face of the waters." His chief devotion in the realm of opera was given to Mozart and Wagner. He always conducted *Figaro* himself, also Smetana's *Dalibor,* Gluck's *Iphigenia,* and *Tristan.* He had given up conducting the other Wagner operas.

Fidelio was his masterpiece. I have in my possession a whole production-book devoted to it. He succeeded in making a box-office success of it. When he took over the Opera in Vienna *Manon* and *Werther* were the star performances. When he left, he had put in their place the whole of Mozart, the whole of Wagner and all the masterpieces of classical music.

His conducting of *Die Walküre* on one occasion was such that, from *"so blühe denn Wälsungenblut"* at the end of the first act onwards, no one in the audience dared to breathe. There was a tempo in the orchestra such as I never heard before or since. Bruno Walter, at first awkward and inexperienced, came very near to realizing Mahler's ideals, whereas Schalk, the more proficient of the two, never entirely pleased him.

There was a gala performance on the 11th of March, 1911, in honor of the King of Saxony, and for this Mahler made a fresh study of *Lohengrin.* But only the first act was given. He chose *Lohengrin* so that money should be forthcoming from the exchequer for a superb setting. The fatuous indifference of the whole royal party was a comedy to watch. Mahler sat on the podium with his eye on Prince Montenuovo, who in turn kept his eye on the large royal box, and as soon as my uncle Nepallek, the Master of Ceremonies, gave the signal with his white staff that His Majesty had entered the box, the Prince nodded at Mahler and the overture began. The Emperor talked loudly to his guests and they all noisily sat down. The audience, following high example, also made a great deal of noise, and I was so furious that I left. I told Mahler afterwards that I had a lackey for a husband.

And yet the following true tale shows how little of a lackey he was. The singer, Mizzi Günther, came to him one day with an urgent written recommendation from the Crown Prince, Franz Ferdinand. Mahler took the note and tore it up. "Very well," he said, "and now—sing!"

The Emperor demanded the re-engagement of the singer E.B.-F., with whom he had long since had a passing affair, but whose voice was no longer extant. "Good," Mahler said, "but I will not let her come on." To which Prince Montenuovo replied that it was the Emperor's express wish that she should, and a long-standing promise also, and in any case her salary would come out of his Majesty's private purse. "Then I suppose she'll have to," Mahler replied. "But I shall have it printed on the program 'by command of His Majesty the Emperor.'" He heard no more of it. And it must be set down to the credit of the old regime that his audacity did him more good than harm.

When Mahler was required to hand *Lohengrin* over to Schalk, who had previously conducted it, he was unwilling that this fine production should fall a victim to Schalk's pedestrian style; and so he hit on a Mephistophelian plan. He called a rehearsal and sat on the stage facing Schalk while he conducted the orchestra. Schalk had orders to follow his every nuance and every movement of his baton. A more shocking way of breaking a man's pride can scarcely be imagined, and Schalk obeyed with repugnance. The orchestra hid their grins and no one regretted his humiliation. It was not Mahler's precise aim to humiliate him, but to correct his "tempi"; yet those remained unchanged. But Mahler had made one more active enemy at the Opera, where already he had more than enough.

It was Mahler's wish to hand down his own interpretations as a tradition. His notorious saying: "Tradition is laziness," was meant in quite another sense. When anyone pointed out to him that he took a passage in some opera otherwise than was accepted as traditional, he said: "That is how I hear it. What is called tradition is usually an excuse for slovenliness."

When he found himself in some unpleasant situation he used to say: "Who hath brought me into this land?" and then laughed. It must be a quotation, but I do not know its source.

Mahler's achievement by this time was prodigious:—the Fifth, the Sixth, the Seventh and Eighth Symphonies, the three *"Kinder-totenlieder,"* all his later songs and the sketches for *Das Lied von der Erde,* the numeration of which he wished to dodge in his dread of a ninth Symphony, as neither Beethoven nor Bruckner had reached a tenth. Beethoven died after his Ninth Symphony and Bruckner before finishing his Ninth; hence it was a superstition of Mahler's that no great writer of symphonies got beyond his ninth. At first he wrote *Das Lied von der Erde* as the ninth, but then crossed the number out. When later he was writing his next Symphony which he called the Ninth, he said to me: "Actually of course it's the Tenth, because *Das Lied von der Erde* was really the Ninth." Finally when he was composing the Tenth he said: "Now the danger is past." And yet he did not live to see the Ninth performed or to finish the Tenth.

Our holidays were devoted exclusively to his work and well-being, and his quiet: life went on tip-toe. The poor children might not laugh or cry. We were all slaves to his work—but that was right and I would not have had it otherwise.

During all these first five years of our marriage I had been paying off the load of debts with which Justine's incredible folly had saddled us. Fifty thousand crowns—a tremendous sum, and now at last I had just come to the end of it. Mahler took it all as a matter of course. I existed only as his shadow, paying his debts, making no noise.

One day in the summer he came running down from his hut in a perspiration and scarcely able to breathe. At last he came out with it: it was the heat, the stillness, the panic horror. It had gripped him and he had fled. He was often overcome by this feeling of the goat-god's frightful and ebullient eye upon him in his solitude, and he had to take refuge in the house among human beings and go on with his work there. When this happened I had to hurry through the whole house, which was built in three stories overlooking the lake, and impose silence. The cook must not make a sound, the children were closeted in their nursery, I must not play the piano, or sing, or even stir. This lasted until he reached a pause in his work and emerged to join in our life, beaming, as he always did when his work was over.

I lived his life. I had none of my own. He never noticed this surrender of my existence. He was so self-engrossed that any disturbance, however slight, was unendurable. Work, exaltation, self-denial and the never-ending quest were his whole life on and on and forever.

I cancelled my will and being; like a tight-rope walker, I was concerned only with keeping my balance. He noticed nothing of all it cost me. He was utterly self-centered by nature, and yet he never thought of himself. His work was all in all.

I separated myself inwardly from him, though with reverence, and waited for a miracle. I was blind: the miracle was there beside me—in the shape, at least, of a pure abstraction. In spite of having children, I was still a girl. He saw in me only the comrade, the mother and housewife, and was to learn too late what he had lost. His genius consumed me, although he meant no murder. I have found it so all my life. People say one thing—but they do another.

His productions at the Opera were always gala performances. Mahler was bounded by no horizon. "I can stand people who overexaggerate, but not people who underexaggerate." Roller was always with us every afternoon and every evening, and at last nothing was spoken of in our flat but the problems of stage-management. Alfred Roller was cold and his self-esteem was crushing; he had not a friend in the whole Opera. Mahler backed him up through thick and thin, and his power grew. When it came into his head to design a ballet and be his own choreographer, Mahler at once gave him permission and put all means at his disposal. The lean anchorite became a dancer. All the ballerinas were constantly in his office, and the legitimate ballet-master of the Opera Royal had to put up with encroachments and finally with open defiance on Roller's part. Prince Montenuovo decided to put a stop to these irregularities, of which Mahler would never have approved and was scarcely even aware. Roller, without asking the permission of the ballet-master, Hassreiter, called a ballet-rehearsal in his office; and out of fear of Mahler, who, they supposed, must be behind Roller, all the girls attended it, although the ballet-master had arranged a rehearsal of his own. He arrived to find an empty room. He went in a fury straight to Prince Montenuovo who sent for Mahler.

Mahler at once took Roller's part, and for the first time in the ten years they had worked together, the Lord High Chamberlain expressed displeasure as he concluded the interview. "This is the first time you have condoned an irregularity since you have directed the Opera. My sense of duty will not allow me to overlook it."

Montenuovo did not get over his displeasure. He was only waiting for the opportunity to get rid of Mahler, and the opportunity came. Mahler was in the habit of entering his own engagements in the large engagement book of forthcoming productions at the Opera. And under the heading "After Easter" he innocently wrote: "Rome, three concerts." His leave, however, was only for Easter, and he meant to apply from Rome for a brief extension to cover the third concert. The book was removed by some subordinate official who had a grudge against him and came into the Prince's hands. He sent for Mahler and began by drawing his attention to the fact that the box-office receipts always fell whenever he went on leave. Mahler was able to contradict this on the spot, but the upshot was that his resignation was regarded on both sides as a matter for consideration.

Such was the state of affairs when, half glad to be quit of the Opera, half fearful of the unknown future, we set off for Rome. For even if we were clear of debt, we had saved nothing, and Mahler was very tired.

We left on the 19th of March. The first breakdown occurred at the Semmering. The train came to a stop. I jumped from my bunk and so did all the other passengers; there was considerable excitement, for the train had stopped with a sudden jolt. But Mahler, who now that the train was no longer in motion was at last able to fall asleep, was completely oblivious. He slept for three hours while all the rest of us were in a state of agitation. But the material world he ignored took its revenge, as it always did; for between Bologna and Rome the engine broke down for the second, and just outside Rome for the third time. Our sleeper missed the connection; we lost our trunks, which were left behind somewhere, and with them much of our money. For weeks we had to wear hastily purchased linen, and Mahler, who was used to fine, soft shirts, had to endure a stiff one, in which we both agreed he looked like a candidate for confirmation.

The tragic side of this comedy was that the orchestra scores for the concerts had gone astray with our trunks and Mahler had to conduct from any copy he could get hold of.

Spiro, the historian, showed us the sights very ably. He knew every stone of the Forum by name, and so we passed happy hours between rehearsals. Mahler's favorite expedition was along the Via Appia. I always noticed that he preferred to regard nature from the literary and historical point of view rather than for its intrinsic beauty.

The first concert promised to be a sensation, but Mahler unfortunately had to wear a hired dress-suit, and the one we procured had been made for a tall man. He looked like a small boy in his grandfather's dressing-gown. The proprietor of the *pension* where we were staying for the sake of economy was a German; and seeing Mahler's dilemma he offered him his own dress-coat. But there was a very imposing star (the emblem of an athletic club) sewn on it in front, just as is common among the worthy citizens of Cologne; and, however impressive in its native element, this star would have shown oddly from the podium. It was difficult to convince the German of this and he retired hurt. I was left to do what I could with the very large dress-suit. I made tucks in trousers and sleeves, but Mahler refused to let me stitch up the trousers in front, which flapped open in a very unbecoming way. So I united them from within with a large gold safety pin, which was all I could lay hands on at the moment, and warned him not to touch it until the concert was over. He went ahead, as usual, to see that the chairs and music were all properly arranged for the orchestra. I arrived just before the performance was to begin and only just in time to avert a shocking disaster: the pin was no longer where it ought to have been but extremely visible. When this had been put right he went onto the stage laughing.

Queen Margherita was in her box and summoned Mahler to her presence in the intermission. She jokingly offered to help him find his luggage, but neither she nor the organizer of the concert, Count San Martino, nor the Austrian Ambassador, Count Lützow, nor anyone else could do anything about it.

Mahler in those days was an oddity, whom everyone gave a wide berth and who owed what little awe he inspired to his position as director of the Royal Opera. He was nervous and irritable in Rome. Possibly his imminent resignation affected him more than he cared to show. In any case, everyone we met was astonished at my patience and reproached him to his face for his caprices. For example, I had to unpack our large trunk three times before we left. His rough drafts for the Seventh Symphony were packed, at his wish, at the very bottom. Then, when the hotel porters were waiting to carry our luggage down, he decided he must have the manuscript at the top, so that he could get it out at a moment's notice if required. I had to unpack the whole trunk. We went downstairs escorted by friends and admirers of his, and as soon as we were in the hall he suddenly got into a state of agitation and said he must have the score in his hand. So I had to open the heavy trunk once more almost in the street, and we held the score in our hands by turns all the way to Vienna. However understandable such behavior was, it often made him very difficult to live with.

We never went out at night to any gay party or to the theater all these five years—only to the Opera, and only when he was conducting, which was exactly as I would have wished it to be. There was one exception: we went to *The Merry Widow* and enjoyed it. We danced together when we got home and played Lehár's waltz from memory; but the exact run of one passage defied our utmost efforts. We were both too "highbrow" to face buying the music. So we went to Döblinger's and while Mahler asked about the sale of his compositions I casually turned the pages of the various piano editions of *The Merry Widow,* and found the passage I wanted. I sang it as soon as we were in the street in case it slipped my memory a second time.

Mahler loved cheerfulness and gaiety, as this and many other incidents show, but some dark principle or other held him back. He could laugh uncontrollably, but if anybody else laughed it got on his nerves. He used often to say when we were discussing somebody: "Oh—a beautiful face—marked by suffering," or "An empty face—no suffering in it." It was only in the last year of his life, when excess of suffering had taught him the meaning of joy, that his natural gaiety broke through the clouds.

As a rule Mahler came home from the Opera in solemn mood. After lunch he lay down on our blue divan and I read aloud. It might be *Zwei Menschen* by Dehmel, *Parsifal* by Wolfram von Eschenbach, *Tristan* by Gottfried von Strassburg, or a scientific or historical book. I went to a course of lectures by Professor Siegel at the University: "Astronomy from Aristotle to Kant." I took notes and worked on them at home, and read them out to Mahler in the evenings; he was touching in his eagerness to explain anything I did not understand and was often driven to seek help from his philosophers. In this way we came on Giordano

Bruno and Galileo. I read *Die triumphierende Bestie* and *Das Aschermittwochmahl* aloud, and also the *Geshichte des Materialismus* of Lange, and so on. Someone observed to me once: "Alma, you have an abstraction for a husband, not a human being." It was quite true. But I treasured every single day of my life in those days.

I arrived from Rome feeling very unwell and found that our English nurse in my absence had scalded three fingers of my younger child's hand. She did not look well, and I was anxious; it could not only be the scald. She became feverish and was sick—it was scarlet fever. I waited until she had recovered and then retired to a nursing home to have an operation, but my heart was with my convalescent child. The elder one was with my mother. When I was better and the child too, we all met at the station and went to Maiernigg for our annual holiday. Before this Mahler had resigned and his resignation had been accepted.

On the third day after our arrival in the country the elder of the two children developed alarming symptoms. It was scarlet fever and diphtheria, and from the first there was no hope. We passed a fortnight in an agony of dread; then there was a relapse and the danger of suffocation. It was a ghastly time, accompanied by thunderstorms and lurid skies. Mahler loved this child devotedly; he hid himself in his room every day, taking leave of her in his heart. On the last night, when tracheotomy was resorted to, I posted his servant at his door to keep him in his room if the noise disturbed him; but he slept all through this terrible night. My English nurse and I got the operating-table ready and put the poor child to sleep. While the operation was being performed I ran along the shore of the lake, where no one could hear me crying. The doctor had forbidden me to enter the room; and at five in the morning the nurse came to tell me it was over. Then I saw her. She lay choking, with her large eyes wide open. Our agony dragged on one more whole day. Then the end came.

Mahler, weeping and sobbing, went again and again to the door of my bedroom, where she was; then fled away to be out of earshot of any sound. It was more than he could bear. We telegraphed to my mother, who came at once. We all three slept in his room. We could not bear being parted for an hour. We dreaded what might happen if any of us left the room. We were like birds in a storm and feared what each moment might bring—and how right we were!

Fate had not done with us. A relation took charge of all the hateful affairs death brings in its train. On the second day Mahler asked my mother and me to go down to the edge of the lake; and there my mother suddenly had a heart attack. I contrived cold compresses with the water of the lake and put them over her heart. Then Mahler came down the path. His face was contorted and when I looked up at him I saw, above on the road, that the coffin was being placed in the hearse. I knew now what had caused my mother's sudden seizure and why Mahler's face was contorted. He and I were so helpless, so bereft, that it was almost a joy to fall into a deep faint.

The doctor came to see me. I was suffering from extreme exhaustion of the heart and he ordered a complete rest. He could not understand how I had kept going at all with my heart in that state. Mahler, thinking to make a cheerful diversion and distract us from our gloom said: "Come along, doctor, wouldn't you like to examine me too?" The doctor did so. He got up looking very serious. Mahler was lying on the sofa and Dr. Blumenthal had been kneeling beside him. "Well, you've no cause to be proud of a heart like that," he said in that cheery tone doctors often adopt after diagnosing a fatal disease. This verdict marked the beginning of the end for Mahler.

These events, following his retirement from the Opera, changed our whole existence. We were homeless in feeling and in fact. The verdict pronounced by Dr. Blumenthal took frightful, almost incomprehensible effect. Mahler went to Vienna by the next train to consult Professor Kovacs, who fully confirmed the verdict of the general practitioner.

He forbade him to walk uphill, or bicycle, or swim; indeed he was so blind as to order a course of training to teach him to walk at all; first it was to be five minutes, then ten, and so on until he was used to walking; and this for a man who was accustomed to violent exercise! And Mahler did as he was told. Watch in hand, he accustomed himself to walking—and forgot the life he had lived up to that fatal hour.

I packed the barest necessities and we fled from Maiernigg, which was haunted now by painful memories, to Schluderbach in the Tyrol. We revived to some extent in new and beautiful surroundings and tried to imagine our life in the future. Alfred Roller remarked to me one day on a walk at Schluderbach: "The verdict came as no surprise to me. I noticed during the *Lohengrin* rehearsals, when he was livening up the chorus, motioning them forward and waving them back again, how he stopped to get his breath and involuntarily clutched at his heart." He had thought of mentioning this to me at the time, but had kept on putting it off for fear of upsetting me.

There was an old consumptive friend of my father's, who transferred all the love he had had for him to Mahler; he found his one outlet in seeking out songs for Mahler to set to music and bringing to his notice anything that might be a stimulus to him. It was from him Mahler got hold of *The Chinese Flute,* a recent translation from the Chinese by Hans Bethge. He was delighted with it and put it on one side for future use. Now, after the loss of his child and the alarming verdict on his heart, exiled from his home and his workshop, these poems came back to his mind; and their infinite melancholy answered his own. Before we left Schluderbach he had sketched out, on our long, lonely walks, those songs for orchestra which took final shape a year later as *Das Lied von der Erde.*

AUTUMN 1907

Conried, the director of the Metropolitan Opera, wanted to get Mahler to New York. Cables and letters followed one another. Mahler welcomed the proposal as a providential means of escape from Vienna, which had rejected him, to a new country and a new world. Anything to get away. Germany, too, in spite of many overtures in the past, had suddenly turned its back on him. His immediate need was to earn enough money to enable him to work on in seclusion. He had not accomplished much this summer. The Eighth was completed and awaited a performance; the Ninth, which was later to be known as *Das Lied von der Erde*, was still in embryo.

Conried summoned him by telegram to Berlin and there he signed at once a four months' contract for the season 1907-1908. He told me by telegram how things were going. He was to undertake three new productions at the Opera and conduct at two or three concerts. He returned well pleased to Vienna, and there found a note from Montenuovo asking to see him. I waited for hours in a little tea-shop that afternoon, and at last he joined me in high spirits. Montenuovo had asked him to stay on as director of the Opera and Mahler had made use of the Prince's own words in his refusal.

Montenuovo had said in the spring that he had no use for a director who was always away on concert tours, advertising his own compositions. Mahler had replied to this that it added to the prestige of the Opera if the director had a reputation for original work. The Prince now said he had come round to Mahler's opinion. To this Mahler replied that he too had altered his opinion. He saw now that a director of opera should confine himself strictly to his official duties and be always on the spot.

We knew that Montenuovo had had a number of refusals during the summer. Nikisch had refused, so had Schuch; even Weingartner would have nothing to do with it. Nobody liked to risk being Mahler's successor; nor to undertake such heavy responsibilities for so small a salary. Montenuovo bound Mahler to secrecy and so denied him the opportunity of clearing himself. In the eyes of the public, he had been dismissed and he was reviled accordingly.

That did not worry us. He had his contract in his pocket; and, when late in the autumn he took up his duties again at the Opera for the last time, he was a new man. He conducted farewell performances of his chosen operas, also a wonderful performance of the Second Symphony in the Concert Hall, and finally, on the 15th of October, *Fidelio*. It must be confessed that these final performances were very poorly attended. He was not spared the mortification of being deserted by the public.

Before signing his contract with Conried for New York, he inserted a clause saying that he would not in any circumstances conduct *Parsifal*, as he could not go against the interdict in Wagner's will.

Schönberg and Zemlinsky and their friends wanted Mahler to spend an evening with them before he left Vienna, and so they all foregathered at the Schutzengel at Grinzing. I stayed at home, as I always found such gatherings a weariness. Mahler came back at midnight in great spirits, but his clothes smelt so strongly of smoke that he had to change before giving me an account of the proceedings which kept us laughing until the early hours. He said that as soon as he joined them a religious hush descended on the company; and so to liven things up he called for the bill of fare. The waiter brought the soup with both thumbs in the plate. Mahler sent it back. The waiter next brought a roll in his hand and Mahler demanded another one. The waiter retired to the sideboard, put the same roll on a plate and brought it back again. It dawned on Schönberg's assembled pupils, who had so far watched all this with wonder and awe, that Mahler was making fun of the man; the ice was broken, and the fun became so fast and furious that no one could hear himself speak.

Mahler found the noise worse than the solemn hush and was now eager to get home. He arranged with Schönberg and Zemlinsky that he would jump off the tram at the Restaurant Zögernitz. They were to follow his example and by this means they would be quit of the mob of students; but the students too jumped with one accord from the swiftly speeding tram, and there they all were again, crowded together, enveloped in smoke, and reduced once more to an embarrassed silence, which again gave way to merciless din.

Mahler shouted out above the racket: "What do you fellows think about Dostoevski nowadays?" A chorus of youthful voices replied: "We don't bother with him any more. It's Strindberg now." This evidence of the transience of reputations gave us a lot to think about. Mahler made a vigorous retort; but the young have to have their god of the moment—yesterday Strindberg, today Wedekind, tomorrow Shaw, the day after tomorrow a rediscovered Dostoevski and so on *ad infinitum*. It does not matter that fashion changes their gods. The chief thing is that they have gods of some sort.

We talked it all over while he sat on the edge of my bed, smoking, and eating the supper I had hastily produced for him. He had been too nauseated to eat anything all evening.

The moment of our departure arrived. Schönberg and Zemlinsky marshaled their pupils and Mahler's friends on the platform, to which they had been given private access. They were all drawn up when we arrived, flowers in their hands and tears in their eyes, ready to board the train and deck out my compartment with flowers from roof to floor. When we drew slowly out it was without regret or backward glances. We had been too hard hit. All we wanted was to get away, the farther the better. We even felt happy as Vienna was left behind. We did not miss our child, who had been left with my mother. We knew now that anxious love was of no avail against catastrophe, and that no spot on earth gives immunity. We had been through the fire. So we thought. But, in spite of all, one thing had us both in its grip—the future

"Repertory opera is done with," Mahler observed during the journey. "I'm glad not to be staying on to witness its decline. Up to the last I contrived to hide from the public that I was making bricks without straw."

Our friend Gabrilowitsch, who worshipped Mahler blindly, awaited us in Paris. He and I were alone that evening. He blurted out: "I have a frightful confession to make. I'm on the verge of falling madly in love with you. Help me to get over it. I love Mahler. I could not bear to hurt him." I was too dazed to speak. So I was capable of arousing love: I was not old and ugly, as I had come to think. He felt for my hand in the dark. The light was switched on and Mahler came in; he was affectionate and kindly and the specter vanished. Nevertheless, this episode was my standby for some time in many an onset of self-depreciation.

We traveled to Cherbourg and boarded a tender by night in a choppy sea. Our boat, the *America,* was visible from far off as a great splash of light. Mahler feared the voyage, try as he might to hide his fears. Suddenly the huge ship rose up in front of us; the *Marseillaise* rang out, and all was forgotten. We crossed the gangway in high spirits and were conducted immediately to our staterooms. A wonderful meal was served in the saloon, and I suddenly realized with exultation that we were moving. Mahler was angry when I drew his attention to it: he did not want to know anything about it now that the band was silent and his apprehension had come back.

There was a rough sea, and he endeavored to avoid seasickness by lying rigidly on his back on his bunk like a cardinal on his tomb, neither eating nor speaking until the dread sensation passed. This, in spite of the wonder of ocean and sky, is what I remember best of that first trip.

NEW WORLD
1907~1908

*T*HE arrival in New York—the harbor and all the sights and scenes and human bustle—so took our breath away that we forgot all our troubles. But not for long.

Mahler went to the Metropolitan the morning after we arrived and was informed that *Tristan* was the first opera he was to conduct. I went with him and was able to return to the Hotel Majestic by myself, even going deliberately out of my way, so clear is the lay-out of this divine city.

We had a suite of rooms on the eleventh floor, and, of course, two pianos. So we felt at home. Andreas Dippel, who was then business-manager of the Metropolitan, took us to lunch with the supergod, Conried, who was already a cripple from tabes and showed unmistakable signs of megalomania. This first, fantastic luncheon party, the flat itself and our hosts' utter innocence of culture, kept us in concealed mirth until we were in the street again and could burst out laughing. In Conried's smoking-room, for example, there was a suit of armor which could be illuminated from within by red lights. There was a divan in the middle of the room with a baldachino and convoluted pillars, and on it the godlike Conried reclined when he gave audience to the members of the company. All was enveloped in somber, flounced stuffs, lighted up by the glare of colored electric lights. And then, Conried himself, who had "made" Sonnenthal and was now going to "make" Mahler.

Mahler soon got down to work in earnest and found that things went more smoothly than in Vienna. Here he could devote himself exclusively to the music, which was a blessed change from Vienna in recent years, when owing to Roller's concentration on the staging, pure music had almost been put in the shade.

The orchestra, the singing, the house itself—all was wonderful, and even if the settings, which Conried kept in his own hands, were often—though not always—abominable, Mahler did not care. Fremstad sang Isolde; Knote, Tristan. For the first time in my life I heard the second act sung as pure music. Mahler swam in bliss.

His first appearance in New York had a slightly comic prelude. Just as we were entering the lift Mahler trod on the train of my dress. I had to go back and sew it on again and while I was doing so there was a ring from the Opera. Mahler was too superstitious to go without me, whatever the cost. So we did not answer the telephone. We were both—very oddly for us—quite unmoved, and when we were on our way in the automobile Mahler remarked: "It's their fault. Why didn't they send to fetch me?"

The audience was waiting impatiently by the time he hurried on to conduct one of the finest performances I have ever heard in my life. His triumph was immediate. Americans are very critical and do not by any means receive every European celebrity with favor. They really know something about music. Mottl, for example, was a failure. He had to return to Germany after his first performances had proved a disappointment. Certainly he deserved better, but he made the mistake of not taking the American public seriously.

These days in New York might have been perfect if we had not been annihilated by the death of our child. Mahler spent half the day in bed to spare himself; the child's name was not to be mentioned in his hearing and our days were so disconsolate that often in the early morning, after spending a sleepless night walking up and down, I sat on the stairs on our eleventh floor merely to catch some sound of human life below.

Suffering estranged and separated us. Without knowing it he increased the bitterness of our loss. Moreover, he knew now that he himself was menaced and this put out the light of the sun. He was nervous, wrought up and irritable. It was a wretched winter for me, and indeed for us both. Our saddest evening of all was

Christmas Eve, the first we had spent separated from our children and in a foreign country. Mahler did not want to be reminded that it was Christmas and in the desolation of loneliness I wept without ceasing all day.

Toward evening there was a knock. It was Baumfeld, that kindly silly, whose obsession was a German theater for New York. He read the whole truth in my face and would not rest until we agreed to go with him where we could see a Christmas tree and children and friendly faces. It took us out of ourselves at once; but we were driven away after dinner when some actors and actresses came in. One of these was a raddled female called "Putzi." This renewed our grief, for Putzi was the pet name of the child we had lost.

We went out to dinner several times. The first occasion was at Mr. B.'s, the American director of the Hamburg-America Line. I left the invitation behind and got mixed up between 72 and 27 for the number of the street and so we were nearly an hour late. Our hostess did not hide her anger. At last we sat down to dinner. Mahler was opposite me on the right of our hostess. Suddenly in a momentary silence I heard him exclaim loudly: "What is that? Wagner showed ingratitude to Liszt? And he had a bad reputation? And what does *Tristan* mean to you?" Mrs. B., anxious to calm the storm, said disarmingly that she could never sleep the whole night after hearing a performance of *Tristan*. But Mahler only went on: "And yet you dare to measure Wagner's character with your Philistine yardstick!" Mrs. B. said no more and in complete silence everyone rose from the table. A woman came up to me and asked innocently: "Does your husband always make a scene at dinner?"

One morning I could not rise from my bed. Mahler telephoned for a doctor, who in turn summoned another, and the two diagnosed weakness of the heart and nervous collapse, and ordered a four weeks' rest cure. I was given strychnine and forbidden to move. At long last I was able to give way to my grief and my physical exhaustion. Mahler at once felt his own sorrow less and gave all his thoughts to speeding my recovery.

To dispose of the finest artists and singers in the world, as he did in those days, was an entirely new experience for Mahler. He had Caruso, Bonci, Scotti, Chaliapin, Gadski, Sembrich, Farrar, Eames for Italian opera and Mozart; Burrian, Knote, Burgstaller, Jörn, Goritz, Fremstad, Van Rooy, etc., for German operas. He sent for six pairs of dancers from Prague to rehearse the original Bohemian dances with the corps du ballet when it came to a production of *The Bartered Bride* with Destinn. This opera, however, was not popular and was dropped. Mahler said after a performance of *Tristan* with Fremstad and Burrian: "The stars were kind. I have never known a performance of *Tristan* to equal this."

The whole opera migrated in a body to Boston as soon as the New York season came to an end. We saw a great deal of Van Rooy, who was Wotan in *Die Walküre* and talked of nothing else. He bored Mahler. Speaking of Bayreuth he told a story of Cosima Wagner with special reference, of course, to himself. By a stroke of genius she summoned him to Bayreuth, young as he was and quite unknown, and to his dismay entrusted Wotan to him. They went downstairs together and at the doorway he took leave of her. As he walked away he felt that her eyes followed him with a blessing, under the weight of which he staggered on. At length he could not help coming to a stop and turning round, Cosima had wakened from her trance and was kneeling with her back to him and offering up a prayer at Wagner's grave. And Van Rooy knew that she was imploring Wagner's spirit to help him to fill his role. The best of Van Rooy was his way of regarding his parts as a mission, even if his monomania was wearisome at times. I am astonished when I look back and see how simple and sincere and "modern" a man Mahler was among the stagy solemnities of those vanished days.

Boston itself was dull and sedate compared with other American towns. Here too we lived in isolation for the few days we were there. We had only one invitation. Mrs. Gardiner (the great collector of Italian works of art) asked us to a luncheon party at her house, and we were eager to pay a visit to her palatial museum. Unfortunately we failed to find the entrance. The building resembled a gigantic cistern without windows or doors. We got out of our automobile and made the complete circuit of the house, but found neither door nor bell. So we left it at that and drove back to our hotel, glad to be alone and to do as we pleased. Alone or in company we were always in any case enclosed within a vacuum.

The opera company paid several visits to Philadelphia during the winter. The first time was to perform *Tristan*. I sat in the front row immediately behind Mahler and, as though a veil had fallen, I suddenly saw in his face marks of suffering I had never seen before. The dread of losing him gave me such a pang that I had a heart attack and fell into a dead faint. Professor Leon Corning, who had been observing me, got me out and carried me into Heinrich Knote's dressing-room.

Mahler, who had often turned round to look at me during the performance, now saw my seat empty, but had to go on conducting without knowing what had happened. Corning ran out to a druggist's and by the time Mahler rushed in at the end of the act I was able to sit up. But I remained behind the scenes for the rest of the performance.

It was a new experience for me to be among the singers during a performance. I was talking to Fremstad. Suddenly she became restless and alert and edged her way nearer the wings. "Just a moment," she said and darted on to the stage to sing the *"Liebestod"* with matchless perfection.

Van Rooy, on the other hand, was always Wotan. During the intermission he strode heavily to and fro with his spear, neither speaking nor smiling—every inch a god. Gadski was the very opposite; she cleared her throat, spat, and made silly jokes while waiting for the curtain to go up. Then at the last moment she collected herself and went on as Fricka to the life.

During a performance of *Don Juan* in Philadelphia, Donna Elvira was to come on for her great aria, but could not make the proper entrance because a door had been forgotten. Mahler made one fermata after another, looked round at me with a charming smile and we both enjoyed the delightful impasse to the full. At last Gadski burst boldly from one corner of the chamber in which she was enclosed after the whole structure had heaved and quivered. For a moment the back of the stage was revealed; then the corner was hurriedly closed up behind her and the aria began. She sang it beautifully, far more beautifully than it was ever sung in our Ministry of Music, as we used to call the Opera House in Vienna, with all its hundreds of rooms and corridors. Here it was different. It was a feast for the ear, not the eyes. Don Juan, Scotti; Donna Anna, Fremstad; Elvira, Gadski; Zerlina, Farrar; Ottavio, Bonci; Leporello, Chaliapin.

Or take *Die Walküre:* Van Rooy, Fremstad, Burgstaller. Or *Siegfried:* Knote or Burgstaller or Burrian. *Figaro:* Sembrich, Eames. In short, Mahler had the finest singers in the world. He never had anything of the sort in Vienna.

After this performance of *Don Juan* in Philadelphia, a Mr. Hilprecht asked us to visit his museum the following day, the fruits of diggings he had undertaken in Babylon. Room after room. Sumerian tiles (3000 B.C.) inscribed with cuneiform characters—stock exchange figures from ancient Babylon—remarkable Jewish-Mongolian profiles. His exposition fascinated us. A year after this he was fiercely accused of having forged all his inscriptions. But even so, he did it so well that he led all the experts by the nose for years. In the last resort, what does the "genuine" matter? We both got a great deal from his enthusiastic and learned discourse.

We returned to New York with Knote and Leon Corning. Corning, one of the first users of spinal anaesthesia, was shy and reserved in spite of his great position in the medical world. He scarcely spoke, but there was a constant flicker of lightning in his face, which was the face of a fakir, with leathery furrows. He was very well known and much feared in America; and had the reputation of a miser, in spite of being a millionaire and capable on occasion of sudden generosity. Knote was his brother-in-law. Corning had put 200,000 dollars as a present in his child's cradle. We had made friends with him owing to his help when I fainted; and he sent his automobile for us a few days after we all got back to New York. A gentleman whom we took for a servant stood at the door of the automobile and, as he sat beside the chauffeur, we paid him no further attention. When we arrived at Corning's house, this same gentleman leaped out and opened the door for us and then with a bow accompanied us into the house. He was a guest like ourselves, but a deaf-mute. Leon Corning received us upstairs, casually introduced us to his wife, who vanished immediately afterwards and then took us into his study.

Just as he himself came straight out of a tale by E. T. A. Hoffmann, so this was the chamber of a medieval alchemist. Wires hanging from the ceiling crossed the room in all directions; there were steps leading up and steps leading down. The latter revealed an iron gibbet and some sort of antique machine. He went ahead of us to open a narrow door and we entered an iron-plated cell in which patients were rendered insensible by breathing condensed air. There was a couch, the pillows of which still showed the impress of a human form, and an open book lay on the floor. The space was so confined that we could barely stand erect. All was ghostly. His wife clad in black weeds swept through without a word or look. Her face was a death-mask with hollow eyes. He led us on into his music-room, in which three or four grand pianos stood in a row. Dr. Corning cheered up and walked up and down playing the flute. Finally the door opened and two animate beings came in—his brother with his wife. Up to now, alone with a charlatan or buffoon and his sharp-eyed mute, we felt we had got into some sort of bogey-house.

Dinner was served in a small, square room. Tiny candles guttered on the table and had to be blown out so often that we could scarcely see one another. The fairy electric lights penetrated the haze with difficulty. On each minute plate was deposited an indefinable something equally minute. A half bottle of champagne was opened in our honor and yielded a thimbleful apiece. There were seven of us. His brother asked me in a whisper: "How did you get here? He's a pathological miser and never has anybody in. What's come over him?" We were touched to see that each of us had a small symbolic object made of bronze beside his plate, Mahler a conductor's desk; I, a piano. It was clear that this child with greatness stamped upon his face had prepared for the occasion days before. His wife did not utter a word. If she opened her mouth to speak her husband shut it again with an angry look.

Marie Uchatius, a young art-student, paid me a visit one day in the Hotel Majestic. Hearing a confused noise, we leaned out of the window and saw a long procession in the broad street along the side of Central Park. It was the funeral cortège of a fireman, of whose heroic death we had read in the newspaper. The chief mourners were almost immediately beneath us when the procession halted, and the master of ceremonies stepped forward and gave a short address. From our eleventh floor window we could only guess what he said. There was a brief pause and then a roll of muffled drums, followed by a dead silence. The procession then moved forward and all was over.

The scene brought tears to my eyes and I looked anxiously at Mahler's window. But he too was leaning out and his face was streaming with tears. The brief roll of the muffled drums impressed him so deeply that he used it in the Tenth Symphony.

On another occasion when I was sitting in my room and Mahler in his, working, the silence was suddenly broken by a trickle of sound from far below. It was a tremendous and superannuated Italian barrel-organ. I rang through to the office and begged them to move it on at once at my expense. The noise stopped immediately. Then Mahler burst in: "Such a lovely barrel organ—took me straight back to my childhood—and now it's stopped!"

Mahler in Vienna, whether as director of the Opera or conductor of the orchestra, was extremely intransigent. He permitted no cuts in Wagner, and imposed five- or six-hour performances on the public. He was very severe with late-comers. At first he used to turn his flashing lenses on them, until, wholly cowed, they reached their seats. Toscanini copied him in this. Later he kept a box expressly for these guilty ones, and no one was allowed to enter the auditorium after the performance had begun. They had to stay in the box until the intermission and then hurriedly seek out their seats. When the Emperor Franz Josef was told of this by the superintendent, he remarked: "But after all, the theater is meant to be a pleasure." Mahler was very different in New York. He not only introduced all the usual cuts, but invented new ones in order to abbreviate the operas. He was merely amused, too, by lapses in the settings which in Vienna would have roused him to fury. It was not because his mind was distracted by the anxiety his illness caused him, or that he did not take the New York public seriously —on the contrary, he found the public there entirely of his own way of thinking. The reason was that his whole attitude to the world and life in general had changed. The death of our child and his own personal sorrow had set another scale to the importance of things.

Conried, who was too ill-bred to know what he said or did,

could commit the greatest blunders without annoying Mahler in the least. He once proposed, when a bass was not forthcoming, to let a tenor sing the part. Also, when the scene could not be changed quickly enough after the trio in *Don Juan*, he suggested that the three fairly stout gentlemen should clamber onto one of the wings and simply be hauled off in one operation. These are only two of the many little incidents of which he told me at the time, laughing in spite of his heavy heart.

We spent only three months in New York the first winter. We met Dr. Joseph Fraenkel at the end of the time at the home of Otto H. Kahn, one of the chief financial supporters of the Metropolitan Opera. Fraenkel had a great influence both on Mahler and me during the years which followed. He was a genius both as a man and a doctor, and we both fell in love with him the day we first met him. He was a complete entertainment in himself; dazzling in his wit and a daring thinker—a little splenetic perhaps, but always original. He said, for example, that he divided people into those with whom, and those on whom, he lived. Also, that Prometheus had not brought men fire to make matches of. It was in obedience to this aphorism that he left no records of his great discoveries.

He indoctrinated us so thoroughly with his theory about ears that we could never afterwards see any one without ascertaining the type of his ear. He arrived at the most surprising results by following out Lavater's *Physiognomical Contributions to the Knowledge and Love of Man*. He said that all the organs of the body except the ear were under constant control and that therefore the ear alone revealed the naked truth.

Mahler finally fell so entirely under his sway that he would unquestionably have done whatever he told him.

At first we lived almost in solitary confinement. Mahler was so shattered by the verdict on his heart that he spent the greater part of the day in bed. When he was not having a meal he was reading; and he got up only for rehearsals or for the performance at night, if he were conducting. I, for my part, suffered from hallucinations. Wherever I looked I saw my doomed child. Life for both of us was a misery.

In spite of all, however, the voyage home was better than the voyage out. Mahler had regained much of his old physical self-confidence, and at once the world was brighter for me. Our stewardess in the autumn had struck Mahler with her blooming health and youth. "Oh—to be as young and strong as that girl," he said with a sigh. When we asked after her, we were told that she was dead. She had died on her very next trip back to Europe.

We disembarked this time at Cuxhaven, in May. I saw to the baggage and the customs examination, as I always did. Mahler wanted to help me, but he looked so aged and ill that the German official said out loud: "Your father need not bother. I can help you through." It pained me more than Mahler, who unfortunately heard it.

We spent some days in Hamburg and did not feel at all well there. Mahler had to go on to Wiesbaden and I followed him after a few days. He conducted his First Symphony there and Mendelssohn's *Hebrides Overture*—to a completely empty hall. The public had gone on strike against an increase in the prices of seats, of which the organizers had given notice in their preliminary announcement.

Berliner and Gabrilowitsch came to Wiesbaden to welcome us home and to hear the concert. We three were almost the only persons present. When we all met for supper afterwards Berliner played a practical joke which was not at all well received. Mahler was in the habit of scraping the labels off wine and beer bottles during a meal, and so Berliner told the waiter to have this done beforehand. Mahler took up one bottle after another and put it down again in surprise; and then, catching Berliner's eye, he saw that he was at the bottom of it and was thoroughly put out. He did not recover his temper for the rest of the evening.

We went on to Vienna, and Mahler stayed there while I went to Toblach with my mother. It was May, and in deep snow we looked at every available house until we found the right one, a large farmhouse outside the village. There were eleven rooms, two verandas, two bathrooms—all somewhat primitive, but in a lovely situation. We took it at once for the summer and returned to pack. It was at Toblach in the course of his last three summers that Mahler wrote *Das Lied von der Erde,* the Ninth and the fragment of his Tenth Symphony.

SUMMER 1908

*T*HERE was an amusing scene when it came to allotting the rooms. We followed him proudly from room to room, until, after much coming and going, he had selected the two best and lightest for himself. Next, the largest bed was sought out and moved in for his use, although he was smaller than I was. His egoism was sublimely unconscious, and if he had been aware of it he would have been deeply shocked. As it was, my mother and I followed him about, rejoicing in his innocent pleasure. We had two grand pianos installed and an upright for his studio in the garden.

And now at last there was peace, broken only by occasional visitors. Gabrilowitsch, Gustav Brecher, Oscar Fried, Ernst Decsey all came at different times and there was much music. Mahler got to work once more. His studio stood in a mossy clearing surrounded by woodland; and one night after a warm rain a host of small white mushrooms came up. He returned at midday with tears of delight in his eyes—after picking his way there and back with the utmost care not to tread on a single one of these living creatures, which charmed him as much as if they had been troops of children.

He worked at white heat all the summer on the songs for orchestra, with Hans Bethge's Chinese poems as the text. The scope of the composition grew as he worked. He linked up the separate poems and composed interludes, and so found himself drawn more and more to his true musical form—the symphony. When this was clear, the composition rapidly took shape and was completed sooner than he expected.

He did not, however, venture to call it a symphony, owing to his superstition. And thus he thought to give God the slip.

He expressed all his sorrow and dread in this work—*The Song of the Earth.* Its first title was *The Song of the Affliction of the Earth.*

One day he came into the house in a transport of fury. He told me to dismiss our servant on the spot and flung himself on his bed, almost insensible. This was the story. The representative of a large American piano firm knocked and asked for Mr. Mahler. In obedience to strict orders, the girl refused him admittance and said that the director was working and could see nobody. The man asked where he was working and the silly girl pointed in the direction of the woods, whereupon he advanced to the fence and shouted at the top of his voice: "How do you do, Mr. Mahler?" Mahler, who was lost in his work, came out and sent him about his business, but the shock gave him a heart attack. He came to me sobbing and said he had felt as if he had been flung onto the pavement from the spire of St. Stephen's.

This agitating scene had an amusing sequel. On our arrival in New York in the autumn we found six grand pianos drawn up in the hall of our hotel, which meant that two firms had to be grievously slighted. Our visitor had said nothing of his reception but merely reported to his chief that Mahler prized their make of piano beyond all others.

In the meanwhile I sold our villa at Maiernigg on Wörther-see. We could never have gone there again. I returned there once in the autumn by myself to see to the removal of our possessions, including furniture belonging to Mahler's childhood—dear to him for that reason—and said good-by to the scene of our bitterest sorrows.

This autumn too, being overrun with visitors, it occurred to us to escape them by going away simply for a holiday—a thing we had never done during our whole married life. We decided to take the recently opened Tauerbahn and traveled by it to Salzburg, where we put up at the Hotel Nelböck in a large garden-room. We felt that we were on our honeymoon and regretted very much that I had promised to go and see Burckhard the next day. Mahler stayed in Salzburg and I went out to Sankt Gilgen, where Burckhard was. I had heard he was seriously ill. Almost his first words were: "I must be in a very bad way for Mahler to let you come and see me." He was right; Mahler had always been jealous of him, but only as a spiritual influence. I had always gone to him for advice during the years before I married. In temperament and attitude to life they were complete opposites. Burckhard preached Nietzsche's doctrine of the superman, and he had the right to, for he lived up to it in all his many activities. He ran the Burgtheater, he was a Privy Councillor and judge of the High Court, he loved sailing when the lake was stormy, he was a daring climber. He had no equal in strength and courage, and nothing whatever could stop him. He was a pagan and hated Christianity. He could live among brigands in Sicily, disguised as one himself, and pick up any dialect so quickly that he was at home in any company. "Death," he used to say, "exists only for those who believe in it, and therefore it has no existence for me."

It was impossible for Mahler, who saw everything from the opposite point of view, to get on with him, and Burckhard felt the same about Mahler. Whenever they met there were fierce arguments. During our last winter in Vienna I noticed that Burckhard used to open a window to cool his heated head. This alarmed me. I told Mahler that there must be something seriously the matter, and from that moment Mahler was an altered man as far as Burckhard was concerned. He avoided all controversial subjects, and the moment ill feeling entered a perfect understanding followed.

When I saw Burckhard at Sankt Gilgen he was in a sorry state. "Do you know," he said, "I'm on the way to going blind? It takes fifteen or twenty minutes before I can open my eyes in the morning. One day I shan't be able to and then I'll be blind."

He spent his nights mostly in a hut in the woods. "We ought to do as the animals do. When their end is near, they creep into the undergrowth to die."

He had a drawbridge made for his villa at the edge of the Wolfgangsee and laid in a stock of provisions. If he did not wish to see anybody (not even his old housekeeper) he drew up the bridge and broke off all intercourse with the world.

Mahler was going to send a motor-car to fetch me back next day, but to my great joy he came in it himself; and we persuaded Burckhard to come back with us to Salzburg. Just before we got

Mahler's studio at Toblach
1907-1910

there he grew uneasy and asked to be put down then and there. This was the last time they saw each other.

We went out to many lovely places from Salzburg, to Königsee among others; but we avoided strenuous walks owing to the ever-present anxiety about Mahler's heart. Once we knew he had valvular disease of the heart we were afraid of everything. He was always stopping on a walk to feel his own pulse; and he often asked me during the day to listen to his heart and see whether the beat was clear, or rapid, or calm. I had been alarmed for years by the creaking sound his heart made—it was particularly loud on the second beat—and I had always known that it must be diseased.

I had often implored him to give up his long bicycle rides, his climbing and also swimming under water, to which he was so passionately attached. There was nothing of that sort now. On the contrary, he had a pedometer in his pocket. His steps and pulse-beats were numbered and his life a torment.

This summer was the saddest we had ever spent or were to spend together. Every excursion, every attempt at distraction was a failure. Grief and anxiety pursued us wherever we went. Work was his one resource. He slaved at *Das Lied von der Erde* and the first drafts of the Ninth.

The first performance of the Seventh Symphony took place in Prague in September. Mahler went ahead and I remained behind to see to all the practical arrangements for our autumn migration.

There were many of Mahler's friends in Prague, Neisser, Berliner, Gabrilowitsch, and also several youthful musicians, Alban Berg, Bodanzky, Keussler, Klemperer. They all helped him to record corrections in the score and the parts. Even at the final rehearsal he was aware of lack of balance and never ceased making alterations in the proofs up to the time of printing. On all the various occasions when his symphonies were performed for the first time, younger musicians had gathered round to give him their help, as they did now.

I arrived in time for the last rehearsals; and as I was alone he sent Berliner to meet me instead of coming himself, which very much alarmed me. I found him in bed; he was nervous and unwell. His room was littered with orchestral parts, for his alterations were incessant in those days, not of course in the composition, but in the instrumentation. From the Fifth onwards he found it impossible to satisfy himself; the Fifth was differently orchestrated for practically every performance; the Sixth and Seventh were continually in process of revision. It was a phase. His self-assurance returned with the Eighth, and although *Das Lied von der Erde* is posthumous I cannot imagine his altering a note in a work so economical in its means of expression.

But now he was torn by doubts. He avoided the society of his fellow musicians, which as a rule he eagerly sought, and went to bed immediately after dinner in order to save his energy for the rehearsals. On one occasion Artur Bodanzky went up to his room with him, and I spent an hour or so with the rest. He came back with tears in his eyes and said to me in an undertone: "I shall never love a woman as I love Mahler."

Mahler's health and spirits improved as the rehearsals went on, and his self-confidence rose.

The Seventh was scarcely understood by the public. It had a *succès d'estime*. Mahler went to Munich shortly after to rehearse and conduct it there. He asked my mother to join him. I was unable to go, as we were soon to return to America and I had to make use of his absence to pack; and so I missed precious moments of our common life.

We were to sail from Hamburg this time, but before we set off there was one more unpleasant scene between Mahler and Justine. When she married she took away a number of books and papers with her; among them there was the libretto, *Rübezahl*, which Mahler had written in rivalry with Hugo Wolf. She may have carried it off by accident or from the desire to possess anything he had written, but in any case it was without his permission, for he wished to destroy it. He made a search for this and other manuscripts which had also vanished, but found no trace of any of them. One day when we were lunching with the Rosés he chanced to see a manuscript of Lipiner's in Justine's book-case. He accused her of being in possession of other papers of his, but she swore she had nothing else whatever. But one day Roller said to us: "Justi gave me a youthful work of Mahler's to read yesterday." The sequel was very odd, for Mahler insisted that I should demand the return of the manuscript on the ground that he refused to speak to her until it was in his possession.

I did as I was told, but Justine took her solemn oath that she had burned it. I told Mahler this, but he refused to believe a word of it. I had to go to her again, armed this time with the threat that unless she handed it over she would not see him again before he set off for America. Nevertheless, she swore, as she loved her husband and children, that she had burned it, and added numerous embellishments to her tale, such as that Arnold had had to tear it up to get it into the stove because it was so bulky. Mahler was obdurate and stuck to it that she was lying, and he left Vienna without having seen her. I remained behind for some days. Justine paid me a visit and I brought the matter up once more. "Of course I didn't burn it," she said abruptly. "I sent it after him the moment he had left and he'll find it waiting for him at Bremen when he gets there."

We met in Hamburg and went on board at Cuxhaven. We had been given a rousing send-off from Cherbourg to the strains of the incomparable "Marseillaise," but the sentimental Germans made our departure this time a very melancholy affair. All the passengers, including ourselves, wept aloud as the band played: " 'Tis God's decree that we must part, From all that's dearest to the heart, Must pa-a-art, must pa-a-art." It was too much.

We had our three-year-old child with us for the first time and I had engaged as nurse an elderly Englishwoman, who was always inculcating the stoicism of a samurai in her charge. When we were on the tender and the large ship loomed up, the little girl gave a cry of delight, whereupon this lady advanced, held her tightly by the hands and said sternly: "Don't get excited—don't get excited!" Mahler heard this and instantly snatched her up and sat her on the taffrail with her feet dangling over the water. "There you are, and now be as excited as you like. You shall be excited." She was.

We did not go back to the Majestic but stayed this year and the next year at the Savoy, where nearly all the stars of the Metropolitan, Caruso, Sembrich, etc., stayed also.

Mahler was now in the best of health. He conducted *Figaro, Pique Dame* and *Fidelio* during this winter, 1908-1909, and made fresh studies of them all. It was the first performance of *Pique Dame* in New York. Sembrich, Farrar, Eames and Scotti sang in *Figaro*. Slezak made his début at the Metropolitan in *Pique Dame.*

For *Fidelio,* Mahler had Roller's scenery sent over from Vienna, and he played the *Leonora Overture* before the last act, as in Vienna.

Mrs. Minnie Untermyer and Mrs. Sheldon, both leading lights in New York society, left together after one of these performances. Both were full of enthusiasm, and on their way home they had an inspiration. They determined to put an orchestra at Mahler's disposal and within a few days they collected a hundred thousand dollars. This came in very opportunely for Mahler. His relations with the Metropolitan were no longer very good. Conried was at death's door. Gatti-Casazza, who had been sent for from the Scala, was now director of the Metropolitan, and he had brought Toscanini over with him. The good old days of German supremacy were over. It is fair to say that Mahler was offered the post but declined it.

Toscanini had gone so far as to make it a condition that the first production at which he was to conduct should be *Tristan,* an opera Mahler had already rehearsed. Weary of conflict he gave *Tristan* up. Toscanini immediately took it in hand and rehearsed it all over again in an entirely different manner. Mahler bitterly resented this and took no further pleasure in opera in New York. We had all read the cables between the Metropolitan and Gatti-Casazza. The Metropolitan wanted Toscanini, and he made *Tristan* his supreme object and an indispensable condition. So Mahler resigned it to him. Instead of thanking him, Toscanini from the first moment contemptuously ignored him. He even went so far as to hold him up to scorn during rehearsals. He was always telling the orchestra that Mahler "could not do that" and that he had no understanding of *Tristan.* We went to the first night of this production of Toscanini's. The nuances in his Wagner were distressing. His style has been simplified since those days.

And so Mahler joyfully welcomed another outlet. A committee was formed immediately, the active members of which were Mrs. Draper, Mrs. Untermyer, Mrs. Sheldon and Mrs. Schelling. The contract was signed before we left for Europe and the engagement, which was to begin when we returned, was by no means exacting. He was to give a series of concerts with an orchestra of his own. This had always been his dream.

One consequence was that I was invited to a luncheon at a

women's club. It was a beautiful building with a swimming-pool and the costliest furnishings. All the women were of that incredible elegance to be seen only in America, but last of all there arrived a little person in an ill-made coat and skirt which was very much the worse for wear. She was received with acclamation and nobody appeared to notice her odd attire. She was Natalie Curtis, an amazing creature, of whom I shall have more to say. Thus I got to know and to love the truly democratic America. Wealth bowed down to poverty if it clothed a creative, gifted mind.

We also met the sculptor, Bitter, who lived on the Palisades. We crossed the Hudson and arrived—how I no longer remember—at the summit. His studio and his house, which was separated from it, overhung the abyss in a breath-taking manner. He received us dressed in white as a chef, and grilled a fish for us in the Indian fashion on an ebony slab turned to the open fire. Mahler was so charmed with this device and with everything he saw that it was difficult to tear him away, and before leaving it was agreed that we should return for a New Year's party in the studio.

Friedrich Hirth, the great Sinologist, spent Christmas Eve with us and told us wonderful stories of China the whole night long. We felt as though we had stepped out of the real world.

Marcella Sembrich invited us to a Christmas party. Caruso was there and others of their circle at the opera. We liked them all, even though intercourse with them was rather superficial. Caruso had genius even as a human being. They all had an instinctive perception of Mahler's importance and treated him with the greatest respect in private life as well as on the stage. Sembrich's Christmas tree caught fire and we were within an ace of being burned to death.

New Year's Eve came and the long expected party in Bitter's studio; but Mahler had to go alone as I was not feeling well. A terrific blizzard blew up during the evening, and I was so anxious that in spite of a high temperature I could not leave the window. Far and wide there was no one to be seen, not a vehicle, not a cat or a dog. Only at intervals a solitary man lurched across the square, holding on desperately to the bushes of Central Park, or edging his way along the face of the buildings.

Mahler arrived at last at two o'clock, utterly exhausted. He had left Bitter just after twelve. He got onto an omnibus at the ferryboat landing. Everybody in it was drunk and he was so nauseated that he got out and with much difficulty found a hansom. A few minutes later it was blown over and he had to creep from under it. While he was paying the fare his pince nez was blown into a snow-drift. He was blind and the cabby tipsy, but between them, in the howling gale, they fished the pince-nez out of the snow. He was now two streets away and after clawing his way along for half an hour was blown into the entrance of the hotel.

NEW WORLD
1909

*T*HUS in a foreign land we built up a world of our own which was more European than Europe itself. One evening we had five people in, all of whom had come over in the steerage—Bitter to evade conscription, Fraenkel for lack of money, and all either destitute or in flight. They had thrilling tales to tell of their early days in America. Mahler was younger and less oppressed, his grief was dying down; and when we arrived in Paris in the spring we were able to take a certain pleasure in life.

They were days of blissful repose.

Karl Moll had had the wonderful idea of commissioning Rodin to do a bust of Mahler, and Sophie Clemenceau had contrived to represent it as Rodin's own wish to model a head which interested him so much. Mahler believed this—though with reservations—and agreed, as he never otherwise would have done. The sittings which followed were a marvelous experience.

Rodin fell in love with his model; he was really unhappy when we had to leave Paris, for he wanted to work on the bust much longer. His method was unlike that of any other sculptor I have had the opportunity of watching. He first made flat surfaces in the rough lump, and then added little pellets of clay which he rolled between his fingers while he talked. He worked by adding to the lump instead of subtracting from it. As soon as we left he smoothed it all down and next day added more. I scarcely ever saw him with a tool in his hand. He said Mahler's head was a mixture of Franklin's, Frederick the Great's and Mozart's. After Mahler's death

Rodin showed me a head in marble, which he had done from memory, and pointed out how like these it was. A custodian of the Rodin Museum in Paris actually labelled it "Mozart."

One of his mistresses was always waiting patiently in the next room while he worked. This singular arrangement held good in whichever of his numerous studios he happened to be; some girl or other with scarlet lips invariably spent long and unrewarded hours there, for he took very little notice of her and did not speak to her even during the rests. His fascination must have been powerful to induce these girls—and they were girls in what is called "society"—to put up, unabashed, with such treatment. But then, his own wife waited in Meudon all her life.

Picquart, then Minister for War, invited us to lunch in the Ministry, where he lived. His old friend, Madame Ramazotti, was hostess. Painlevé, the Clemenceaus, Baron Lallemand and we were the guests. We first met Picquart in Strassburg in 1905. He made a very deep impression on us. Now we heard his story from his friends.

He went to Tunis when a young officer on the General Staff. While there he received a document from Paris with an urgent memo. He read it through and finding flaws in it sent it back for correction. It soon came back, again with instructions to deal with it immediately. Again he sent it back at once without having signed it, giving as his reason that an injustice had been committed. This document was the sentence passed on Dreyfus. Colonel Henry, who was the real culprit and had the plot in hand, was now compelled to take steps against Picquart. He had a search made in the hope of finding some excuse for having him dismissed and putting an obedient tool in his place. All he could find in Picquart's desk were a few ancient and trifling love-letters to the wife of the president of the Law Court at Rennes. He sent them to the unsuspecting husband, and Picquart, in spite of the lack of incriminating evidence, went to prison. The wife was divorced although the whole story belonged to the past. Picquart treated her as his wife in spite of her being by then an elderly woman.

Picquart had no wish at all to make Dreyfus's acquaintance, eager as Dreyfus was himself. He had acted solely from humanity and a burning sense of justice. Dreyfus was nothing to him per-

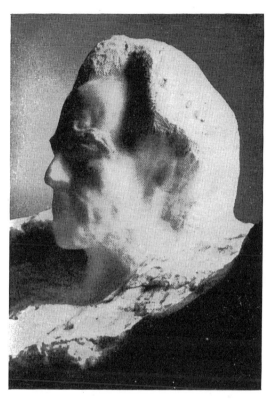

Mahler: Portrait head in marble, made by Rodin for himself

sonally. As with Zola, who also was unacquainted with Dreyfus, it was a question of upholding the truth.

The rest is history: Dreyfus was declared innocent and brought back after years on Devil's Island. Colonel Henry committed suicide, and Picquart, after three years' imprisonment, was set at liberty. He and Dreyfus were rehabilitated and promoted before the whole army. Picquart added that he had not at all liked having to share the ceremony with Dreyfus.

When we drove up to the Ministry the gates opened and a guard of honor drawn up to left and right in full-dress uniform presented arms as we passed through. Picquart was standing at the top of the steps, as happy as a child over this idea of his.

"It is the rule in the case of royalty. You are the same in my eyes," he called out to Mahler.

Each of us was given his or her favorite dish, of which Picquart had taken private note in anticipation. After lunch he showed us a small gold box. He pressed a spring, the lid flew open and a bird set with jewels sprang out of the box, sat on the lid and sang enchantingly. He gazed at this bird, which had diamonds for eyes, and said with emotion: "It was the only music I heard during my three years of imprisonment. An American, who has remained anonymous, smuggled it in. I was not allowed to have any music or books from my friends. I might receive visits one day a month, when for ten minutes I could speak with friends or relations from behind a grill—overheard, of course. Attempts to poison me were made twice. Knowing this I made it my habit to hold up every morsel of food I ate against the light, and so I was never tricked. Another time there was ground glass in my food. Thank God, it's over."

He carefully put the box away again in another room.

His love for Mahler was both reverent and paternal, for although he was only his elder by a year or two he was more detached and set. After the fall of the Government he commanded a division at Amiens. A thoroughbred reared with him and only great presence of mind kept him in the saddle. The same thing happened at a parade soon after and during the last march past his horse reared for the third time and fell with him. He was fatally injured and taken to Paris, where he died in the arms of the devoted friend who had been as a mother to him. His funeral procession gave rise to one of the most impressive demonstrations Paris has ever known. Is it possible that a nation understood the greatness of a soul like his?

I happened to be in a cinema when his funeral procession was shown. It seemed incredible that the man we loved was passing by in that coffin. This was after Mahler's death.

The Chief of the Police invited us to his box at the Opera for a gala performance of *Tristan*. General Picquart and the Clemenceaus were there too. Madame Grandjean and Van Dyck were singing. In the great scene between Tristan and Isolde in the second act, Van Dyck jumped up time after time and advanced to the prompter's box and there, embracing the audience with extended arms, he addressed to them instead of to Isolde his intimate discourse on the dear little word "and." This was too much for Mahler. He could not bring himself to sit it out a moment longer; so disregarding the feelings of our host and the surprised glances of General Picquart and the rest, we got up and went out.

By the time we got back to Vienna my nerves were in a critical state and I was ordered to take a rest-cure at Levico. I first took Mahler to Toblach and then went to Levico with my child. I was in a state of profound melancholy. I sat night after night on my balcony, weeping and looking out at the crowd of gay and happy people, whose laughter grated on my ears. I longed to plunge myself into love or life or anything that could release me from my icy constraint. We exchanged letters daily on abstract topics. Mahler grew anxious about me and at last he came to see me.

I met him at Trient, but when he got out of the train I failed to recognize him. Wishing to look his best he had gone to the barber at Toblach before he left, and he had been given a close crop while he read the newspaper without giving a thought to what was going on. The sides of his head were shorn as close as a convict's and his excessively long, thin face, deprived now of all relief, was unrecognizably ugly. I could not get used to the transformation and after two days he sadly departed again.

Mahler was quite without vanity about his personal appearance. He grew a beard in his earlier years to give him an older look. He also had enormous horn-rimmed spectacles made "so as to see in all directions." The lenses were round and gave him a very menacing appearance. Later on, at Maiernigg, he used to let his mustache grow because he found shaving a nuisance.

He had been working at full pressure during the summer and had finished the Ninth, but without venturing to call it so. In the winter too he had kept to his usual Vienna program, devoting every morning to revision and orchestration.

Erich Wolfgang Korngold had played his fairy-tale cantata, "Gold," to Mahler for the first time at Easter, 1908. I was not present, but Mahler told me afterwards with great enthusiasm what an impression the music of this ten-year-old boy had made on him.

Now, a year later, Julius Korngold, a musical critic and a friend of ours, and his wife, paid us a visit and brought their son, Erich with them. He at once engrossed all our attention. At Mahler's request he played some of his own compositions and played them so perfectly that it seemed incredible he had only just begun to learn the piano. He did not welcome the attention paid him. He slipped out to play with our little daughter on the top of a haystack. I went out to call them in to tea. "Don't want to," he said. "Why not?" " 'Cause I don't eat nicely."

He was not to be persuaded and so the two children ate their cakes out of doors. They got on quite well together as both were laconic and morose. Indeed, my daughter Anna, who was five, begged him not to go but to spend the night with her.

As soon as we were alone again we talked for hours of Erich's unbelievable talent.

Happy that he could work again and, as he felt, better than ever, Mahler was in excellent spirits. The summer was interrupted only by a visit from the Strausses, preceded by an exasperating exchange of telegrams from either side of the Alps. What was the weather like with us? What did the glass say? At last the omens were favorable. They arrived at Toblach and expected us to dinner. But first Mahler went down at midday. Frau Pauline greeted him in the square in front of the hotel by shouting out at the top of her voice: "Hello, Mahler. What was it like in America? Filthy, eh? Hope you got a pile anyway."

Mahler hurried them inside and up to their room, and leaving them as soon as possible came to meet us. He had no stomach for such situations. And besides he grudged every hour of his time.

My mother, Roller and I were included in the invitation to dinner and the Strausses had a neighbor of theirs at Garmisch with them, whom they had brought along out of gratitude for his kindness in shutting up his dogs, and himself too, while Strauss was working. We fully understood. We too had had neighbors at Maiernigg, an amiable but utterly uninteresting family, with whom we had to be on friendly terms as our only defense against their live-stock of all descriptions—poultry, geese, dogs, of course, and against a brother of the lady of the house, who was a baritone and sang most execrably. In addition to all this, the master of the house was deaf, and it took the combined lungs of the whole family to arouse in him a gleam of comprehension. The massacre of Mahler's music had to be bought off with visits, theater-tickets, boxes for the opera and, in general, at the cost of eternal vigilance. We understood very well.

This gentleman of Garmisch was a colonel and quite scatterbrained. He constantly mixed everything up. He took my mother to be Mahler's wife and Roller to be my husband.

Mrs. Strauss was very much wrought up that evening. Her son, who was still a boy, got first a slap on the head and next a glass of milk. We all stood awkwardly round and Strauss, to get the company seated, motioned to Mahler to sit next to his wife. At this Pauline exclaimed: "Yes, but only if he doesn't start fidgeting, because I can't put up with it." Mahler, who was just about to sit down, went instead to the far end of the table. Strauss joined him and they both left us to deal with her. She excelled herself that evening. We trailed home exhausted in mind and body.

On the 1st of October we made a move. Our Vienna flat in Auenbruggegasse was superfluous now that we spent so much of every winter in New York; and so I packed all the books and china, and stored all our movable possessions. Mahler said goodby to the rooms where he had spent eight years of his life and went to Mähren to put the final touches to *Das Lied von der Erde*.

I always did my utmost to save Mahler all the drudgery of life. When we moved or went away anywhere he knew nothing of what went on behind the scenes. The only exception was our honeymoon journey. He said there was nothing in packing and piled everything into a trunk in a heap. As soon as the trunk was turned on one side all was confusion. From that day on I took sole charge.

He did not return from Mähren until my child and I had recovered from an operation on our tonsils, and after spending a few days at my mother's he went to Amsterdam to conduct his Seventh Symphony. Mengelberg's preliminary rehearsals were so thorough, on this occasion as on all others, that Mahler was able to conduct this difficult work almost without rehearsing it himself. He arrived in Paris the day I did.

October found us in America once more. We could no more restrain our tears now than the first time at the sight of the magnificent spectacle which the arrival in the harbor of New York unfolds. No one who was near and dear to us ever awaited us on the pier and yet this scene, unequalled of its kind in the whole world, moved us so deeply that our knees shook as we walked down the gangway; and not even the highly unpleasant customs examination could dash the feeling of eager suspense.

This time Mahler came to conduct his own concerts and he was glad to have no more to do with the operatic stage. The arrangements made allowed him every other week in New York for the rehearsal of one or two programs, which the week after he gave twice in New York and twice in Brooklyn. Later when he had a number of programs ready there were to be longer tours to Philadelphia, Springfield, Buffalo and all the cities which looked to New York to provide their music.

He conducted once only at the Metropolitan by permission of the new committee, which was responsible for all the expenses of this year's trip. He conducted Smetana's *The Bartered Bride,* with Destinn as Marie, Jörn as Hans. It was a marvelous performance. Americans, however, were no lovers of rusticity in opera. Nor were they of the starkly Germanic: they could dispense with the *Ring*. Their favorite Wagner operas were *Tristan* and *Meistersinger*.

Mahler took four particularly lovely pieces from the Bach suites and strung them together for one of his concert programs. He worked out the figured bass and played it marvelously on the cembalo, with his baton clipped tightly under his arm. Schirmer, the publisher, offered to print this arrangement of Bach's music for him and Mahler took the keenest pleasure in working on it.

He played it at many of the concerts, more for us than for the audience. He altered his cembalo accompaniment according to his fancy every time and cross-examined me afterwards about the effect of each. It was hardly likely that any change would be lost on me. The critics did not raise the cry of sacrilege. This was reserved for the pundits of Europe.

When Marcella Sembrich bade farewell to the stage every artist was eager to take part in the great occasion and so, instead of a single opera, acts and scenes from several in which she particularly shone were performed. Caruso, Bonci, Farrar, Eames, Scotti and all the conductors, including Mahler, offered their services as a tribute to this incomparable singer. Mahler conducted an act from *Figaro*. She herself sang all her parts for the last time with a perfection unsurpassed even in her best years. At the end, after she had been called before the curtain thirty or forty times, the curtain went up and revealed a grove of laurel overhanging the whole stage. The whole company stood in a half-circle round a table, at which the Mayor of New York was seated. He rose immediately and advanced toward Madame Sembrich, who retreated in embarrassment as he presented her with a large rope of magnificent pearls, while the audience stood and clapped. After he had made a speech in praise of her merits as an artist and a woman, all her colleagues came forward with their presents. She had invited us to a ball after the performance, and we all proceeded there laden with the costly tributes of silver and gold which were heaped upon her; there was no other means of transport. The orchestra of the opera surprised her on her arrival at the hotel with a flourish of trumpets and played at the ball throughout the night, to show their gratitude for her generosity after the San Francisco earthquake in which all their instruments had been destroyed and she had given up her salary until they were replaced. She opened the ball by dancing a mazurka with Paderewski.

Shortly afterwards the whole opera company gave her a farewell party on her leaving New York. Everyone connected with the opera was present and a few others, including Paderewski. It took place in the Plaza Hotel with the greatest pomp and ceremony. Caruso drew his masterly caricatures and showed them to all save the victim. They were often too telling to be borne with equanimity. He did several of Mahler and showed them to me, but could not be persuaded to let Mahler see them. "People say beforehand they won't mind," he said. "Then you let them see and they're very angry. That's happened to me too often already."

We saw a good deal in those days of the aristocratic families whose ancestors had come over in the *Mayflower*. Our circle had become so large that every day was filled up. Anglo-Americans are quite unlike the Latin races, among whom one remains a foreigner forever. They genuinely take you to their hearts. You are at home and share in all their pleasures. They are at your service if they see any opportunity of serving you, as I was to learn very often later on. Mahler accompanied me whenever he felt inclined and enjoyed himself more than I should ever have thought possible. He never missed a dinner party; and they were very different, certainly, from those we knew at home. The invitation was for seven-fifteen or seven-thirty; the dinner was excellent, far better, needless to say, than at the hotel; the talk was lighter than in Europe, but whether it was trivial or profound depended naturally, as in Europe, on whom one was placed next to. The men retreated to the smoking-room after dinner and the ladies were left to themselves. By ten one was at home again without fatigue. New faces had been seen, new personalities encountered, and these new acquaintances did not fail to invite us in their turn, and so our engagements lengthened out in an unending chain. We used to sit up for an hour afterwards and talk over our impressions.

On the 15th of November, a date I noted because we enjoyed the day so much, we went out to Oyster Bay, a stretch of coast owned almost entirely by the Roosevelt family. It was a day of cloudless weather. We traveled by a little railway and were met at the station and driven in a pony-trap across sand dunes to Mrs. West Roosevelt's house. We stopped in front of a high terrace wall, onto which we stepped from the trap, and saw in front of us a lovely old frame house standing on its terraced eminence and surrounded by the sea. The sight was so overwhelming that we forgot to greet our hostess.

The hall and every room were as perfect as the surroundings. We felt at home immediately. Mrs. Roosevelt took us to see the house of her brother-in-law Theodore Roosevelt, who was shoot-

ing big game in Africa at the time. It too, although it had less
character than the old farm-house, was beautifully situated on
rising ground, surrounded by blue sea. We could see through
the house from outside because every room opened onto a
veranda of glass. Mrs. Roosevelt observed that this was symbolic
of Theodore, whose life was as clear and open as his house.

One evening after dining with Otto H. Kahn we went to a
séance of Eusapia Palladino's. Mahler, the Kahns, an Englishman, Fraenkel and I drove there in two automobiles. We got out
on Broadway at a building of dreary proletarian aspect and
ascended in the elevator to what might be called the attic-floor.
There was no one to be seen. After a search we discovered Palladino's spacious room, where the séance was to take place, but she
was not there. Next door a riotous drinking party was in progress.
There was a great bawling and smashing of glasses against the
walls; but we were none the wiser. There was a flat opposite,
which was vacant except for the litter of its recent occupants. Next
to it, there was the shining brass plate of an agency for mechanical
pianos. We heard trills and roulades, but when we looked through
the keyhole there was nobody there. We began to feel very queer.
Mrs. Kahn was wearing a white satin dress with white slippers and
strings of pearls nearly to the floor and the sight of her finery in
these surroundings added to the incongruity. At last Palladino
appeared.

She had a kind of peasant's shawl round her head and a face
which was red and puffy and vinous. She gave us a brief and
casual greeting and went on with a reeling gait into the large
and dimly lighted room. We followed. Before her arrival we
had been invited by her two secretaries, who later took notes of
the proceedings, to examine the room and in particular the alcove,
curtained off by a black hanging, which was immediately behind
her chair. Its walls were papered black. It had a window looking
out onto a roof illumined by the moon and covered with snow.
There was nothing whatever to arouse suspicion.

She sat down without ceremony and the two secretaries and a
girl turned out the lights, leaving only a red one in front of each
secretary. We sat down uneasily and held hands. Within a very
short space she went into convulsions. Her face began to flicker

wanly, her breath came in quick pants. The Englishman and Fraenkel sat on each side of her, gripping her hands and knees. Fraenkel felt her pulse, counting out loud at a terrific rate when she rose to a crisis. She insisted on us all repeating *"va bene"* without interruption, and if any of us stopped he was angrily told to go on. The Englishman went into a trance from the perpetual repetition of *"va bene"* and so was out of the running.

The rest of us all felt we were being touched: phosphorescent bodies which we saw moving about came into contact with us. I grasped at one of them and had something and then nothing in my hand. Palladino commanded Mahler to look into the alcove behind her. He drew the black curtain aside. Everything in there was bathed in phosphorescent light and everything was in movement. A mandolin flew through the air and bashed him lightly on the forehead. He let the curtain fall hastily in his confusion and Palladino murmured that he was in danger. She summoned him almost compassionately to come and sit beside her. The table shot up to the ceiling, but if any one of us spoke a word in an unsympathetic tone it abruptly descended. The black curtain swept the table as though waved by an unseen hand; the mandolin and light objects of wood glided about above the table, on the edge of which our hands were resting with interlinked fingers. Although warned not to, I caught at the bellying, balloon-like curtain and again I felt something palpable and impalpable.

We went away in silence, pondering deeply; and for many days after we were still pondering. After a week Mahler said: 'Perhaps there wasn't any truth in it and we only dreamed it." This seemed to me very remarkable, since for the first two or three days he had done nothing but fish out fresh details from his memory, and now suddenly it was all a dream.

We often went to Mrs. Havemeyer's. She lived in a fairy-palace, built by Tiffany, and gave musical afternoons. We did not, however, go to hear the Haydn and Brahms quartets. We went straight to her gallery of masterpieces. She had eight Rembrandts, and a large number of Goyas; but the cream of the collection was El Greco's only landscape, "Toledo," and his "Cardinal." My stepfather, Moll, had so often shown us this painting of the "Cardinal" in photographs and described its coloring that when Mrs. Havemeyer first displayed it Mahler broke in: "I've seen that before somewhere." She went pale, for there is nothing so terrible to a collector's ears as the suggestion that any object in his collection, whatever its merits or beauty, is not unique. I tried in vain to recall to Mahler's memory Moll's description of the picture: he obstinately stuck to it that he must have seen the picture before. I then explained his mistake to the poor woman, who was beginning to think she had been cheated and that somewhere, unknown to her, there was a duplicate Cardinal in existence.

We spent many an hour walking up and down in this long gallery, in which the concealed lighting fell smoothly on the pictures, while snatches of music came to our ears from far away without fatiguing or enlisting our attention. Mahler had no native feeling for painting; his mind was too much under the dominion of literature. Yet by degrees, through much looking and an exorbitant desire to know all that was to be known, he began to derive pleasure from pure painting and the ability to judge it. Moll, Klimt, Roller and Kolo Moser disputed the right to be his master.

One day after Mahler had got his orchestra, a card arrived from Louis Tiffany requesting permission to attend the rehearsals in concealment owing to his shyness. Shortly afterwards he invited us to his house and Mrs. Havemeyer, the link between us, took us there. We stopped before a palatial building and ascended an imposing flight of steps; thence we proceeded upstairs. Sudanese native huts with all their furnishings were let into the wall all the way up on either side. At the top we entered a room so enormous it seemed to us immeasurable. Colored lusters shed soft, flowerlike light through the gloom. The overture to *Parsifal* was being played on an organ. We were told later that the organist was a grandson of Shelley. As far as we knew we were quite alone. A black fireplace in the middle of the room had four colossal hearths, on each of which a fire of a different color was blazing. We stood stock-still in amazement.

Then a man with a remarkably fine head came up to us and murmured a few incomprehensible words. It was Tiffany, the man who spoke to no one; and before we could collect our wits, before Mahler, indeed, could have had time to make any reply, he vanished. We heard afterwards that Tiffany was a hashish addict and never quite in his right senses. Like everything there, he made the impression of being enchanted. The chimney went up and up forever, no roof was visible, but high up in the walls panels of stained glass, designed by Tiffany, were let in, and lighted from without. We spoke in whispers and felt that these panels of flowerlike light might be the gates of Paradise. The music stopped and it was now apparent from the murmur of voices that a large company was assembled. Silent footmen perambulated with costly glasses, filled with champagne, which although on trays, never clinked. Palms and sofas, beautiful women in odd shimmering robes—or did we dream? It was the thousand and one nights—in New York.

We went to the opera a great deal, and the theater too. Boxes and seats were, naturally, always at Mahler's disposal. Once we went to a play by a young and unknown playwright named MacKaye. This play—*The Scarecrow*—was based on a symbolical use of fairy tales; it was extremely talented and marvelously produced. We saw it three times and would have seen it ten times, but as we were the whole audience it was taken off.

The Manhattan Opera, for a long time superior to the Metropolitan itself, was the creation of Hammerstein, the cigar merchant. We saw Mary Garden there as Salome; she was unrivaled also as Mélisande and Louise, with Perrier and Dufranne as Pélleas and Golo. Hammerstein sent to Paris both for the scenery and for the conductor for *Louise*. A German could never have put on such a production. Mahler conducted *Louise* himself in Vienna, but I never appreciated it to the full until I heard a quite ordinary conductor conduct it in Paris. The orchestra in Vienna was too heavy-handed—the waltz predominated; Paris has its own unaccented, ever wakeful music and it is on this that the melody and drama of *Louise* are worked.

This was the reason, no doubt, why Mahler always had Italian conductors for Italian operas—Spetrino and Guarneri. It is only natural that they should have a better command of the Italian verve and the *brio* in *rubato* than the most gifted of Germans, whether of the north or the south. However polished

Toscanini's conducting of *Tristan* might be, we always felt that his Wagner suffered from an excess of Italian accent. Perhaps this is the key to the future of all those opera houses which wrestle in vain with their repertoire of the eighty classical operas. Perhaps there will be national seasons, Italian opera companies visiting Germany, while the whole strength of German opera migrates to Paris or Milan. Thus there would be a constant interchange of genuine art between one country and another.

STORMS
1910

WE MET Joseph Weiss, the pianist, through the painter, Groll, a necessitous artist who lived among Indians, spoke their language and told us a lot about them. Weiss had a square, bald skull, with the merest tuft in the middle, and brown eyes wedged in slits, which could mean only insanity or genius. He was the greatest pianist Mahler, according to his own account, had ever heard. He played to us for the whole of New Year's night. We sat for hours without moving.

He made piano transcriptions of some of the loveliest songs of Brahms and they sounded more songful than any singer could make them; Bach's "Passacaglia" too—and yet his strongly original interpretations did no damage to the original composition. Mahler was so enthralled that he arranged a trio in our room. He asked Reiter, who played the horn so marvelously in the Metropolitan orchestra, and Spiering, his own first violin, to come, and Weiss was to play the piano parts. Mahler and I sat on the sofa, feeling like King Ludwig of Bavaria.

The first movement was exquisite, but as soon as the second began Weiss started playing in a willful manner, apparently from annoyance at having to subordinate himself even for a moment. This soon brought them to loggerheads and the other two declined to play with him any longer. Weiss refused to listen to reason and simply got up and left. Mahler then played the piano part of the whole trio, and Brahms' Horn Trio cannot often have been given such a perfect performance.

After the other two had gone, Weiss, who had been keeping a lookout, came back to apologize. He was very amusing in the scorn he poured on the two others. He said their faces had put him off, and he did all he could to remove the bad impression he had made. Mahler, who had promised to help him on in New York, felt encouraged; but, as events were to prove, he had better have left matters alone.

We asked two friends of ours, Franz Kneisel, the well-known violinist, and Karl Bitter, the sculptor, in to hear him play. But it was a fiasco. When he was asked to play after dinner he first of all refused and then played some perfectly frightful compositions of his own for half an hour without stopping. Mahler asked him gingerly whether he would mind playing some Brahms. This was too much for Weiss. No one who slighted his compositions could possibly understand Brahms. We had to listen a little longer while he hammered away madly and then we began talking, which Weiss apparently did not notice. The whole evening was ruined, but when Weiss joined us he was so witty and entertaining that Mahler again forgave him. In spite of warnings from all sides he agreed to let him play the A Minor Concerto of Mozart at his next concert. He had a quite extraordinary urge to break in this unbridled colt.

Weiss was starving and Mahler had induced the committee to pay him a big fee. Weiss appeared to be pleased and the rehearsals passed off unexpectedly well. Then came the dress-rehearsal. He was rather more nervous than usual, but he played the first movement well, even if without his true *élan*. This and a few willfulnesses in his tempo annoyed Mahler, whereupon Weiss made some impertinent remarks under his breath, which Mahler purposely did not hear. He wanted to help him. Weiss recovered his self-control and began the second movement. Mahler called out to him: "Good!" This was the end of Weiss. He seized the music and hurled it on the floor at Mahler's feet. "As good as you any day," he shouted, raving like a lunatic. The orchestra, thinking Mahler was in need of protection, flung themselves on Weiss. Mahler begged them not to touch him, but now it had gone too far and Weiss had to leave the concert hall.

The rehearsal was broken off and Mahler came home, half-enraged and half-amused. But his strongest feeling was pity for Weiss. And now a search began for someone to play the concerto. The only pianist available was a young man who undertook to play it without rehearsal, and played it so badly that Mahler from anger and shame could scarcely go on conducting. The concert was unusually well attended, because the morning papers had made a head-line sensation of Mahler's fight with Weiss. There were blood-curdling pictures with the caption: "Weiss hits Mahler on the head." Sparks were depicted flying out of it. It was all extremely unpleasant. Immediately before the concert began Weiss turned up accompanied by a lawyer, to prove that he had presented himself with the purpose of playing, but had not been allowed to, and therefore his fee would have to be paid. "I ought to have let him and called it quits," Mahler said later. This concluded our friendship with Weiss. He retired soon after this to a mental home, but has apparently recovered since.

Mahler, at the request of the ladies of the committee gave a performance of his First Symphony. After thorough rehearsal he arrived with his mind at peace. He had a rude awakening. To do him honor these ladies had wreathed and also heightened the podium, distributed the strings in an outer circle around and beneath him, and massed the brass in a tight circle at his feet. He came onto the platform suspecting nothing and was so taken aback that he could only stand and gasp. The performance was a veritable martydom for him, and for me too. The brass was deafening and drowned all else. We were amazed at the audience who sat it out quietly and even applauded dutifully at the end, the credit for which must be divided between Mahler's prestige and their own unawareness.

He had invited the orchestra to the Arion Club afterwards, and stayed with them (seventy in all) until the small hours. He came back in a very jolly mood, and said he felt like a father among his children.

Our box at the opera was the resort of many friends and acquaintances: Kneisel, leader of the best quartet in New York; Hassmann, the gadabout Viennese painter; Fraenkel; the beautiful Crosby, the Schellings—he, an extremely gifted composer, she, a charming woman; Prince Troubetzkoy, brother of the sculptor, a wild, handsome Russian, whom one almost feared when he strode through the streets with his pair of wolf-hounds; Schindler, a really gifted musician, always eager to manage us; and many others whose names have escaped me. If we made an agreeable acquaintance we took him along, and so our box acquired a special character of its own. Carlo di Fornaro, a journalist, turned up from Mexico and told us many tales of Porfirio Díaz, who was still President of Mexico at that time, his cruelties, his overbearing arrogance and his ruthless and dictatorial oppression of his fellow-citizens. For example, after a strike when the men were returning to work, he had soldiers posted in ambush inside the open gates to shoot them down. Fornaro was now traveling about the States investigating prisons in order to expose their short-comings. He effected an entry into these closed fortresses by disguising himself or by acquiring the papers of someone convicted of a political offense, and serving his sentence instead of him. Fornaro was a journalist with an excess of conscience.

There was Poultney Bigelow, too, who had gone to school with Kaiser William II. He was living in New York in princely style and introduced us to many literary people there. We could not make much of this opportunity owing to the insurmountable barrier of language; and even when we got to speaking English of a sort it did not help us to join in serious conversation; we were soon out of our depth.

We also knew Natalie Curtis. She was quite fearless, and lived for years among Indians with her brother, camping in the open. She wrote an excellent book on Indian music.

All these people were friends of ours. We were more at home than in Vienna. They loved Mahler and—with the exception of a malignant critic named Krehbiel—he was not harried by hostile criticism as in Vienna, where up to the very last he was always being rapped on the knuckles.

The work he was called upon to do was child's play compared with his official duties in Vienna. There were rehearsals only every other morning. I often picked him up afterwards and we walked home. He performed a great deal of music merely to hear it himself and to get to know it, without bothering whether it went down with the public or not. He conducted the overture to *The Flying*

Dutchman and the Paris version of the *Tannhäuser* overture six times in succession, merely because he had fallen in love with them.

I was introduced by friends to Charles Dana Gibson, the celebrated creator of the "Gibson girl." His wife was a beautiful and very empty woman. She showed me portraits of her sisters, each lovelier than the last. She and her sisters had always been her husband's only models. I was shown her very sophisticated bedroom, her carved antique bed with a canopy lined with looking-glass, and I was not at all surprised when she asked me, in her sumptuous automobile of original design, how such a beautiful girl as I had brought myself to marry such a hideous and old and altogether impossible man as Mahler. To all I said she replied merely with a contemptuous smile. She was a beauty of spun gold, untarnished and vacant. Wealth and luxury were the only setting she could imagine for beauty like hers.

The première of Strauss's *Elektra* took place at this time in the Manhattan Opera House. Mahler disliked it so much that he wanted to go out in the middle. We sat it out, but agreed afterwards that we had seldom in our lives been so bored. The public decided against us. It was a success and some, very characteristically, described it as "awfully nice." The production was a brilliant success, as Hammerstein's always were. The youthful Labia, the *décor*—all superb!

We sailed early in April and went on to Paris, where rehearsals began for the performance of the Second Symphony at the Châtelet. Pierné had pledged himself without knowing the music. General Picquart, Lallemand, the Clemenceaus and Painlevé were with us daily to our great joy.

The rehearsal of the symphony interested Mahler greatly. The chorus was lazy but incredibly talented. No one came in time for the rehearsals and they left again when they felt inclined. On the day of the performance they sang flawlessly with a fine metallic tone.

While the rehearsals were on, Pierné gave a party in Mahler's honor and invited Debussy, Dukas, Gabriel Fauré, Bruneau and the Clemenceaus. Debussy's strong personality and the beauty of his head were very impressive. He brought his second wife, who was said to be very wealthy. He sat next to me at dinner, and I noticed that he took only the minutest helping of any dish. When Madame Pierné tried pressing him, his face took on a look of pain. But his abstemiousness had no ill effects: he was a broad-shouldered, ponderous man.

Dukas told me in an undertone that when they were schoolboys together and provided by their mothers with money to buy their mid-morning lunches, they all selected the largest confections except Debussy; he always chose the smallest and most expensive, for even as a child he was nauseated by bulk. That evening, too, we were told that Debussy's ill-treatment had almost been the death of his first wife. It was a youthful marriage on both sides and they were very poor. She couldn't endure her life with him, or life without him. So she took poison. Debussy came in and found her apparently unconscious on the floor. He went up to her very calmly and took what money she had on her before sending for a doctor. She heard and saw it all, for she was not unconscious but temporarily paralyzed. She recovered from the poison and was cured too of her love of Debussy, from whom she was divorced. This was the story she herself put in circulation. What truth there is in it, no one will ever know.

Mahler was not happy or at ease that evening, and he had good reason. The day of the performance came. It was a matinée. I was sitting with the Clemenceaus and my mother, who had come to Paris to meet us. All eyes were on the Countess Greffulhe's box, where she was to be seen with Abbé Perosi. This for the public was the one thing that mattered.

Next, I suddenly saw Debussy, Dukas and Pierné get up and go out in the middle of the second movement of Mahler's symphony. This left nothing to be said, but they did say afterwards that it was too Schubertian for them, and even Schubert they found too foreign, too Viennese—too Slav.

The success he had with the public was no consolation for the bitterness of being so misunderstood and indeed condemned by the foremost French composers.

We had been present the night before at *Ariane et Barbe Bleue*. Mahler was enchanted by the first act, and so he gladly acted on

Lallemand's suggestion and went behind the scenes to compliment Dukas. By the time the piece was over he was so bored that he was glad he had obeyed his impulse when he had. His generosity in expressing his appreciation met with no return from Dukas.

We went this time from Paris to Rome. Mengelberg was there, waiting to see Mahler, for his own concerts were over. In the kindness of his heart he was unwittingly responsible for an extremely unpleasant incident. He warned Mahler not to stand any nonsense from the orchestra. They were a job-lot and quite undisciplined. He was to be stern with them. Even menaces and abuse were needed to rouse them from their lethargy.

Mahler did not need telling twice. It was never, as Mengelberg was not aware, a failing of his to err on the side of gentleness. Armed with a dictionary, he pitched into the orchestra in a manner not really undeserved; for it was late in the season and the good orchestra Mengelberg had had in his earlier concerts had gone on leave to South America. But undeserved or not, when it came to Mahler's saying that he was uncertain whether to describe their behavior as *"stupidità"* or *"indolenza,"* they leaped to their feet as one man and left the hall. It was only with great difficulty that Mahler could get through his concert at all, for the whole orchestra took to passive resistance. The success of the concert was accordingly very moderate, and immediately it was over he cancelled the second one. We arrived in Vienna in very bad humor to find a garbled version of the story in all the papers and everybody talking about it.

SUMMER 1910

I took Mahler to Toblach and then, following medical advice, I had to go to Tobelbad for a complete rest. Mahler remained at Toblach, looked after by an old and reliable man-servant, and began sketching out his Tenth Symphony. I was very ill. The wear and tear of being driven on without respite by a spirit so intense as his had brought me to a complete breakdown.

I lived an utterly solitary life at Tobelbad, as I always did whenever I was by myself anywhere. I was so solitary and so melancholy that the head of the sanatorium was worried and introduced young people to me as company on my walks. There was a painter, X, whom I found particularly sympathetic, and I soon had little doubt that he was in love with me and hoping I might return his love. So I left. Mahler met me at Toblach station and was suddenly more in love with me than ever before. Perhaps the reason was that my submerged self-confidence had been brought to the surface again by the flattering attentions of the young painter. In any case, the future seemed brighter and I was happy. I had no wish at all to exchange my old life for a new one.

After a week had gone by a letter arrived from the painter saying that he could not live without me; and therefore if I had the slightest feeling for him I must leave all and go to him. The letter was clearly meant for me, but the envelope was very distinctly addressed to Mahler. Whether the young man made a mistake in the stress of emotion, or whether it was his unconscious wish that it should come to Mahler's hands, remains a mystery.

Mahler was seated at the piano when he opened the letter. "What is this?" he asked in a choking voice and handed it to me. He was convinced at the time, and remained convinced ever after, that X had deliberately addressed the letter to him as his way of asking him for my hand in marriage.

And now—at last—I was able to tell him all. I told him that I had longed for his love year after year and that he, in his fanatical concentration on his own life, had simply overlooked me. As I spoke, he felt for the first time that something is owed to the person with whom one's life has been linked. He suddenly felt a sense of guilt.

We sent for my mother to come to our help, and until she came we could do nothing but walk about together all day long in tears.

After we had laid bare the causes of our division with the completest honesty, I felt as strongly as I ever had that I could never leave him. When I told him so, his face was transfigured. His love became an ecstasy. He could not be parted from me for a second.

The letters he wrote me at this time say all that I pass over here in silence. He caught me to him—but I had never really gone away. He was now jealous of everything and everybody, although he had always shown a wounding indifference to such feelings before. The door of our two rooms, which were next to each other, had to be open always. He had to hear my breathing. I often woke in the night to find him standing at my bedside in the darkness, and started as at the apparition of a departed spirit. I had to fetch him from his studio every day for meals. I did so very cautiously. He was often lying on the floor weeping in his dread that he might lose me, had perhaps lost me already. On the floor, he said, he was nearer to the earth. We spoke to each other as we had never spoken before. But the whole truth could not be spoken. My boundless love had lost by degrees some of its strength and warmth; and now that my eyes had been opened by the impetuous assaults of a youthful lover, I knew how incredibly ingenuous I was. I knew that my marriage was no marriage and that my own life was utterly unfulfilled. I concealed all this from him, and, although he knew it as well as I did, we played out the comedy to the end, to spare his feelings.

We were brought back to earth by an accident of a different **kind.** My English nurse was suffering from a severe sore throat but said nothing about it for fear of being a nuisance. But as she was always about with us we caught it one after the other. Finally Mahler caught it too, less severely than any of us or so it seemed. He soon recovered and started to work again.

One night I awoke suddenly. I called out to Mahler. There was no answer. I ran to his bed and found it empty. I rushed onto the landing and there found him lying unconscious with a lighted candle beside him. I carried him to bed, called my mother and sent our servant on his bicycle to fetch a doctor (a friend of ours who lived at Schluderbach), and meanwhile gave Mahler what stimulants for the heart I had in the house. He came round quickly, but was cold and white for a considerable time. We wrapped him in warm blankets, massaged him, and heated water for hot water-bottles and also to steep his hands and feet in. By five o'clock when the doctor came, all had been done that could be done and all he needed was rest.

One day after this when we were out driving I caught sight of X hiding beneath a bridge. He told us later that he had been lurking in the neighborhood for some time, in the hope of coming across me and insisting on an answer to his letter. My heart stopped, but only from fright, not joy. I told Mahler at once, and he said: "I'll go and bring him along myself." He went straight down to Toblach and found him at once. "Come along," he said. Nothing more was said by either.

It was night by this time, and in silence they walked all the way up to our house, Mahler in front with a lantern and X following on behind. It was pitch dark. I was waiting in my room. Mahler came in with a very serious air. I hesitated for a long time before going to speak to X, and I broke off our brief interview after a few minutes from a sudden alarm on Mahler's account. I found him walking up and down his room. Two candles were alight on his table. He was reading the Bible. "Whatever you do will be right," he said. "Make your decision." But I had no choice!

Next morning I drove down to Toblach, as X was to take his departure. I saw him off at the station and drove home again as fast as I could, but Mahler had come halfway to meet me in his dread lest I had gone with X after all. X sent me a telegram from every station on his return journey. They were succeeded by lengthy appeals and adjurations, and all these Mahler wove into the beautiful verses he wrote during those days.

I could never have imagined life without him, even though the feeling that my life was running to waste had often filled me with despair. Least of all could I have imagined life with another man. I had often thought of going away somewhere alone to start life afresh, but never with any thought of another person. Mahler was the hub of my existence and so he continued to be.

He, on the other hand, was churned to the very bottom. It was at this time he wrote those outcries and ejaculations addressed to me in the draft score of the Tenth Symphony. He realized that he had lived the life of a neurotic and suddenly decided to consult Sigmund Freud (who was then living at Leyden in Holland). He gave him an account of his strange states of mind and his anxieties, and Freud apparently calmed him down. He reproached him with vehemence after hearing his confession. "How dared a man in your state ask a young woman to be tied to him?" he asked. In conclusion, he said: "I know your wife. She loved her father and she can only choose and love a man of his sort. Your age, of which you are so much afraid, is precisely what attracts her. You need not be anxious. You loved your mother, and you look for her in every woman. She was careworn and ailing, and unconsciously you wish your wife to be the same."

He was right in both cases. Gustav Mahler's mother was called Marie. His first impulse was to change my name to Marie in spite of the difficulty he had in pronouncing "r." And when he got to know me better he wanted my face to be more "stricken"—his very word. When he told my mother that it was a pity there had been so little sadness in my life, she replied: "Don't worry—that will come."

I too, always looked for a small slight man, who had wisdom and spiritual superiority, since this was what I had known and loved in my father.

Freud's diagnosis composed Mahler's mind, although he refused to acknowledge his fixation on his mother. He turned away from notions of that kind.

One day during this time of emotional upsets I went for a walk with our little girl, Gucki. When we were nearly home again I heard my songs being played and sung. I stopped—I was petri-

fied. My poor forgotten songs. I had dragged them to and fro to
the country and back again for ten years, a weary load I could never
get quit of. I was overwhelmed with shame and also I was angry;
but Mahler came to meet me with such joy in his face that I could
not say a word.

"What have I done?" he said. "These songs are good—they're
excellent. I insist on your working on them and we'll have them
published. I shall never be happy until you start composing again.
God, how blind and selfish I was in those days!"

He played them over again and again. I had to sit down then
and there—after a ten years' interval—and fill in what was missing.
And that was not all; but since he was over-estimating my talent,
I suppress all he went on to say in extravagant praise of it.

When I returned to Toblach that summer after leaving the
sanatorium, Mahler told me that Hertzka of the Universal Edition
had been to see him. He had taken over Mahler's first four symphonies from Waldheim and Eberle. The terms of publication
were that the symphonies were to earn 50,000 kronen ($10,000)
before yielding Mahler any royalty. They were now within 2,500
kronen of doing so, and Mahler was therefore just about to profit
from them. Having made this clear, Hertzka went on to ask Mahler
to forego his profits until a second sum of 50,000 had been earned,
on the ground that the Universal Edition would like to take over
the works of Bruckner also and advertise them at great expense.

Mahler agreed at once. He thought it only right that he should
sacrifice his profits for another fifteen years out of love of Bruckner, without of course receiving, or expecting, a penny from the
sale of Bruckner's works. This was a great sacrifice to make to
Bruckner's memory and shows how deeply he revered him.

Oscar Fried paid us a visit this summer, little as Mahler wished
to see him. He did not want to see any one, and the least thing
upset him. He had so little control over himself that while Fried
was with us he went to bed the moment he finished working in
the morning and again when he came in at dusk. One day he
called out to me from his bed to play my songs to Fried. I did so
on compulsion, and as soon as I had played one he wanted to know
how Fried had liked it. When Fried replied in his impudent way

that it was "very gifted" or "very nice," Mahler flew into a passion; and my mother, who was sitting on the edge of his bed, had great difficulty in preventing him from jumping up and telling Fried what he thought of him. I could plainly hear his abusive remarks through the wall, and Fried, who was sitting beside me at the piano, no doubt heard them too. Mahler had not recovered his temper when I went in to see him later on. He called Fried an idiot, who might think himself lucky if he ever composed anything half as good; there was no calming him down. Fried was not allowed to say good night to him, as he usually did, and in the morning he observed to my mother in Berlin-cockney that he might as well go. "Just as well, my dear Fried," she replied quietly.

This brief visit of Fried's was something new as well as comic. Mahler had always liked him hitherto, for Philistine though he was he had a streak of genius; but now suddenly Mahler could not put up with him. It had never worried him before that Fried never opened a book, but this time he made frequent sorties from his studio to catch him lounging in a chair, while I with my back turned was trying to work at my writing-table—in spite of being continually interrupted by his desire to talk. He took him for a walk and scolded him for not reading more, not thinking things out, not taking himself and his work seriously enough. Fried felt that things were getting too hot for him, and departed.

There was also a dispute about Hugo Wolf of whom Fried spoke very warmly. "Of Wolf's one thousand songs," Mahler said in reply, "I know only three hundred and forty-four. Those three hundred and forty-four I do not like."

From this, I remember, we went on to auricular confession. I had been brought up as a Catholic, but in those days I was inclined to be skeptical. Burckhard and many another had seen to that. Mahler defended the confessional, and Fried became quite lyrical in praise of it. I, a Catholic, was the only one who had mild reservations. But then, I was the only one who had so often been to confession.

One night I was awakened by an apparition by my bed. It was Mahler standing there in the darkness. "Would it give you any pleasure if I dedicated the Eighth to you?" Any pleasure! All the same I said: "Don't. You have never dedicated anything to any-body. You might regret it." "I have just written to Hertzka now—by the light of dawn," he said.

A long correspondence with Hertzka followed. Mahler was not satisfied with the type and spacing of the page of dedication, to which he wished to have every honor done. In this, as in all else during these days, there was the same note of passion. When the time came for him to go to Munich for the rehearsals of the Eighth, we parted as if for years, although I was to follow him in a week. He took my wedding-ring and put it on his finger. I was happy—and yet not happy. I had been through too much. Old wounds ache.

He wrote poems to me daily and telegraphed them; and when I arrived at Munich I found him in a fine suite of rooms at the Hotel Continental. Every room was smothered in roses in my honor. My mother found the piano edition of the Eighth on the table in her room. The dedication ran as follows: "To our dear mother, who has ever been all in all to us and who gave me Alma—from Gustav in undying gratitude. Munich. September 9, 1910.

He met me at the station, looking ill and run down; he had had a recurrence of his sore throat on his arrival in Munich. He had taken to his bed, and I had not been there to look after him.

This concert, the rehearsals for which made Mahler very happy, would never have taken place at all but for the high-handed and unscrupulous conduct of Emil Gutmann, who organized it. He cabled to Mahler in New York, telling him that the score was already printed and that the preliminary rehearsals had long ago begun in Vienna. In fact, none of the parts had been printed. As soon as Mahler knew this, he wanted to cancel the performance immediately, but by that time rehearsals were actually in progress.

Numbers of friends of ours were there, but we kept mostly to ourselves.

I, too, found a copy of the Eighth with its dedicatory page on my table. Mahler was eager now to hear what his old friends would have to say; for, egocentric though he was, he expected his friends to enter into and share his pleasure. But his friends kept silent. He found himself alone; his feelings and his happiness were of no account; he was of importance to them only in so far as he reflected credit on themselves. Justine excited his wrath on this account. He drove her from my door when she came to pay me a visit. "Alma has no time for you," he told her. He gave short shrift to a certain Countess, who regarded me as her enemy for the droll reason that Mahler refused to give an audition to a certain singer. She sent a gilded basket of roses up to my room an hour later as a propitiatory offering. But he was blind no longer. On the contrary, he was ready to take offense at the slightest sign that I was not paid enough honor or not received with enough warmth.

EIGHTH SYMPHONY
September 12, 1910

THE WHOLE of Munich as well as all who had come there for the occasion were wrought up to the highest pitch of suspense. The dress-rehearsal provoked rapturous enthusiasm, but it was nothing to the performance itself. The whole audience rose to their feet as soon as Mahler took his place at the conductor's desk; and the breathless silence which followed was the most impressive homage an artist could be paid. I sat in a box almost insensible from excitement.

And then Mahler, god or demon, turned those tremendous volumes of sound into fountains of light. The experience was indescribable. Indescribable, too, the demonstration which followed. The whole audience surged toward the platform. I waited behind the scenes in a state of deep emotion until the outburst died down. Then, with our eyes full of tears, we drove to the hotel. Several of our friends were waiting for us in the entrance, among them Reinhardt, Roller, the Neissers, Erler, Berliner, the Clemenceaus, and Paul Stefan. Beyond them in the doorway a wealthy and eccentric American from New York barred our passage. "Since— since—since Brahms, nothing has been written to equal it," he gasped out. We pushed past him by main force. Mahler detested flattery of any sort, and to appreciation by people who understood nothing about music he was unmerciful.

A large room had been reserved, and Mahler's guests were assembled there to celebrate the occasion. He and I were just going to sit down when we found ourselves surrounded by all the members of his family. So he scribbled a note, saying it was not a family party—I was to find a seat somewhere else and he would follow. I sat with the Neissers and Berliner; Mahler soon joined us laughing. We spent a very jolly evening and Mahler was acclaimed and honored on all sides.

It was a lovely warm night and we ended it up by talking until morning, with Gucki, our dear child, sleeping beside us.

Next day Berliner said to me: "Alma, everybody's paying tribute to Mahler. But you've suffered for the Eighth and you deserve something too. Now, tomorrow evening you and Gustav are to come to Frau Neisser's room at the Hotel Vier Jahreszeiten, and there'll be a surprise waiting for you."

We did as we were told and found a large display of costly knickknacks, all designed by Fritz Erler. I did not like any of them at all. They were much too modish. There were heads of John the Baptist carved out of ivory and strung together to form—a necklace; or a head of Christ as—a pendant. Out of the corner of my eye I caught sight of three baroque pearls on a gold chain, and I chose this.

Mahler and I went out for a motor-drive in the country immediately afterwards. Unfortunately, he was now in a bad humor. He grudged Berliner this idea of his and wanted to buy the pearls from him so as to give them to me himself. I said this would not do; it was Berliner's idea and a very charming one. "Then it really does please you?" he asked me over and over again. "Is it really such a pleasure?" It certainly was and I could not help it now. It was the first piece of jewelry I had ever received in my life.

Mahler had no notion what gave a girl pleasure. When we became engaged he said: "Other people give each other rings. It's very bad taste and I'm sure you don't want it any more than I do." I hastened to say that I thought it a ridiculous custom.

The wedding came but no wedding-present. He had no idea that a wife expected such a thing from her husband, and no one told him. After the children arrived such extravagances were out of the question. In any case, I was in charge of finance from the first and had my work cut out to pay off his debts. I could not think of jewelry or of any luxuries whatever. His American earnings changed all this—but now Berliner had stepped in.

A rather painful incident took place before the first full rehearsal. Mahler wanted Rosé as first violin for this special occasion and so he asked the manager of the concert to make this known to the orchestra; he, however, was afraid to do so. Mahler, thinking it was all arranged, telegraphed to Rosé, who came from Vienna at once. We went to the rehearsal with him in all innocence; but as soon as he took his seat, the whole orchestra rose and deserted in a body to show their resentment of the affront to their own leader. Mahler was dumbfounded.

Rosé got up slowly and after begging Mahler not to be upset, he left the platform and walked solemnly the whole length of the hall, with his violin under his arm, to where we were sitting. This would have covered him with shame if his dignified forbearance had not at once shifted the blame onto the other side.

As soon as we were back in Vienna, Mahler saw a doctor about his throat. As he was very sensitive to pain, it was not considered advisable to remove his tonsils; and so they were cauterized, a procedure which had had good results in my own case a year before. We believed he was now safe from further attacks and Mahler himself did not want a more radical cure.

We took up our quarters with my mother, as usual. One evening we asked Zemlinsky and Schönberg in. Schönberg took me aside. "I promise you," he said, "never to argue with Mahler again. From today on he can shout at me as hard as he likes. I shall never take offense." I was more alarmed than pleased. "My mind is made up," he went on. "And it is because I love him."

I remember a discussion Mahler once had with Schönberg about the possibility of producing a melody from the variations of a single note played successively on different instruments. Mahler denied that it could be done.

We met on board the boat at Cherbourg in November 1910, for our last outward voyage, he coming from Bremen and I from Paris. The voyage had no terrors for us now. We sailed on the 15th and arrived at New York on the 25th. We used the ten days to have a complete rest. The weather was perfect, as it was on all our voyages.

I took two photographs of Mahler on the voyage, the last times he was ever photographed. Ever since the summer he had taken the greatest care of his appearance. He wore smart waistcoats, beautiful suits and shoes. It was easy enough for him—with his fine face and alert, well-proportioned figure—to look well dressed.

He had taken to saying: "Spitting on the floor doesn't help you to be Beethoven."

His American concert tours were now extended as far as Seattle. Usually a week's rehearsal was followed by two weeks of concerts in New York and Brooklyn, and a third to cover these more distant places. The same program served for all, so that a new one had only to be rehearsed every third week and more use was made of each. This would have been a relief to most conductors, but not to Mahler, who could not bear traveling.

He left with his orchestra for Springfield on the 7th of December, and on the 9th I joined him at Buffalo. I arrived early in the morning; he sent Spiering, the first violin, to meet me. I found Mahler at the hotel, and after a short rest we took the train to Niagara and drove from there in an antediluvian carriage to the Falls.

It was a day of wintry sunshine. Every twig was coated with ice. When we got right up to the Falls and then beneath them by means of the elevator, the strength of the greenish light hurt our eyes. The thunder of the water beneath the roof of ice, the trees mantled far and wide in frozen foam, and the distant view over the snow-covered plain all had a dreamlike beauty.

We turned away with reluctance and looked for somewhere where we could eat. Surprisingly, there was nowhere at all inviting and we could do no better than follow the other pilgrims into a little restaurant, heated by an iron stove and smelling of galoshes and steaming clothes. An old waiter came forward. "It is a pleasure, Mr. Mahler," he said beaming, "to see you here. The last time I had the privilege of waiting on you was at the Hartmann in Vienna, but that is long ago now." We were in good hands, for the old man could not do enough for us.

It was not easy for Mahler to be one of the crowd after being recognized in Europe as a celebrity wherever he went. He was so used to being singled out that he had forgotten the poverty and obscurity of his early years.

We got into the little carriage and into the little train and arrived at last at Buffalo with hands and feet frozen. Mahler went straight to bed, as he had to conduct that evening. He got up after an hour, completely refreshed. I did not go to the concert, as I had heard the program four times already and, besides, had traveled all night and arrived in the early hours.

He came straight back after the concert in high spirits to a simple and belated meal. "I have realized today," he said, "that articulate art is greater than inarticulate nature." He had been conducting the *Pastoral Symphony* and had found it more tremendous than all of Niagara Falls.

Mahler had his third concert to conduct next day at a city not far away; so I went back to New York, because I did not want to leave my little girl alone too long with her nurse. At his suggestion I reread *The Brothers Karamazov* on the journey, and I telegraphed from New York: "Splendid journey with Aliosha." He telegraphed back at once: "Journey with Almiosha much splendider."

It was a habit of his to repeat for days and weeks, even months together, some thought which particularly pleased him, turning it over in his mind and introducing variations. At this period it was: "All creation adorns itself continually for God. Everyone therefore has only one duty, to be as beautiful as possible in every way in the eyes of God and man. Ugliness is an insult to God."

When the Committee was first formed I warned Mahler not to allow these ladies too free a hand in the choice of the programs. He laughed and said he did not at all mind being relieved of the burden. It would give him less to do. But he was to pay dearly for this.

A member of the orchestra named Jonas wormed his way into Mahler's confidence by describing his sufferings as a consumptive; but soon he talked more about the orchestra than his ailment and kept Mahler informed of everything that was said against him. Jonas was always at his elbow, and Mahler used to come back at the end of the morning feeling thoroughly annoyed. The orchestra also was indignant when he had appointed Jonas personnel manager, and so ill will increased on both sides. Jonas may have been inspired by devotion to Mahler, but the results could not have been worse. Several of the orchestra complained to the ladies of the Committee and all demanded Jonas's dismissal. Mahler refused. I advised him to give his unqualified consent, but he would not listen. Jonas, he said, was his only friend. If he lost him he would be alone among enemies, for the whole orchestra hated him. Jonas had done his work well.

Mahler had a slightly septic throat before Christmas. It passed over very quickly and did not alarm us. But it might well have done so.

CHRISTMAS 1910

SOME days before Christmas Mahler went out with a very solemn air, taking his check-book with him, a thing he never did for fear of losing it. I knew what it was: it was the Christmas feeling, the giving of presents, the thrill of expectation—everything I had missed so sorely for ten long years. Christmas came and, as usual, I had a large Christmas-tree, lots of candles, and presents for him and Gucki, which I was just going to give them when Mahler drove me out of the room, saying he had something he wanted to do. A moment afterwards Gucki came out and said Papa wanted a lace cover. I was surprised but gave it to her. Next they both came in arm-in-arm and requested me to follow them.

I entered the bright and festal room—but what words are there for the awful premonition, the pang of icy dread which gripped me, when I saw, on a table all for me, that long mound of presents covered with a white cloth and smothered in roses. I snatched off the covering. Mahler stood sadly by. But his sadness soon vanished and my dread premonition also, for I was touched to the heart by all the lovely things he had thought of without any regard for his own likes and dislikes. There was scent, for example, which he hated and I loved. There were also two drafts, which I give verbatim:

Good in the amount of 40 dollars
for a fine spree
along
Fifth Avenue
For Herr Gustav Mahler on a country ramble with his Almschili

Good
for the purchase of a
Solitaire
to cost over 1000 dollars.

Gustav Mahler
New York
Christmas
1910

The whole room was soon full of the pink roses. We spent this Christmas—by our own choice—quite alone.

We often went for walks together arm-in-arm that winter, or sometimes, as I had to spare myself fatigue, I sent him out alone with Gucki. It was good too that he should get to know his little daughter, of whom he grew more and more fond. I could see them nearly the whole time from my ninth floor window, walking together in Central Park and snowballing each other.

He always worked on his compositions of the summer during the winter. This time it was the Ninth Symphony, for the Tenth was not completed and he had a superstitious fear of working on it. He played bits of *Das Lied von der Erde* to me almost daily during these last two years. I knew it by heart before it was first performed. One day while he was working Gucki stood beside him, watching with engrossment. He was scratching out one note after another. "Papi," she said, "I wouldn't like to be a note." "Why not?" he asked. "Because then you might scratch me out and blow me away." He was so delighted that he came at once to tell me what she had said.

Our drawing-room was a corner room. It had three enormous windows, one of which was a bow-window occupying the whole corner. Immediately below there was the Plaza, but the noise of its ceaseless traffic reached us only as a murmur. In front we had a magnificent view over the vast Central Park, studded with lakes and ponds.

Fraenkel was with us on New Year's night—our last. New York stretched on out of sight in a milk-white haze. Sirens opened up at five minutes to twelve from every factory in the city and from every boat in the harbor. The bells of all the churches united in an organ-note of such awful beauty that we three who loved each other joined hands without a word and wept. Not one of us—then

knew why

Page from score of *Das Lied von der Erde*

THE END

1911

I SAW a lot of a young American woman who tried to imbue me with the occult. She lent me books by Leadbetter and Mrs. Besant. I always went straight to Mahler the moment she left and repeated word for word all she had said. It was something new in those days and he was interested. We started shutting our eyes to see what colors we could see. We practiced this—and many other rites ordained by occultists—so zealously that Gucki was once discovered walking up and down the room with her eyes shut. When we asked her what she was doing, she replied: "I'm looking for green."

It was at this time also that I had a visit from the singer, Alda Gatti-Casazza. As soon as she was announced by telephone from the office I went to fetch Mahler, but she said that her visit was to me and me only. She had seen my book of songs and wanted to sing one of them at her next recital. Mahler went up in the air at once. He urged her to sing all of the five songs in the book. This she could not do, as her program was already settled. He became quite angry, and said she ought to leave out some of her other songs. I protested and the conclusion was that Mahler agreed to rehearse this one song with her.

A few days later we went, as arranged, to the Waldorf-Astoria, where she was staying, and Mahler rehearsed the song with her most carefully. "Is that right?" he kept asking me from the piano. I was so nervous I could scarcely open my mouth. I begged him in a low voice not to ask me any more, as he knew better than I. We were very closely united in those days.

It was quite a different matter between him and his committee of ladies. Storms were brewing, although he paid no attention. They were now dictating programs he had no wish to perform and they did not like it when he declined. Jonas had set the whole orchestra by the ears and they were so refractory that Mahler no longer felt secure in his position. His habit of shutting his eyes to what was unpleasant prevented him from seeing his danger, until one day in the middle of February, he was required to present himself at Mrs. Sheldon's house. She was chairman of the Executive Committee. He found several of the male members of the Committee there and was severely taken to task. The ladies had alleged many instances of mistaken conduct. He rebutted these charges but now at a word from Mrs. Sheldon a curtain was drawn aside and a lawyer, who (as came out later) had been taking notes all the time, entered the room. A document was then drawn up in legal form, strictly defining Mahler's powers. He was so taken aback and so furious that he came back to me trembling in every limb; and it was only by degrees that he was able to take any pleasure in his work. He decided to ignore all these ladies in the future. The only exception was Mrs. Untermyer, his guardian angel. She was away at this time; otherwise nothing of all this could have happened.

And so now Jonas was dismissed in the middle of the season—which Mahler took as a personal affront—in response to unanimous representations from the orchestra. Mahler went on conducting but with rage in his heart against the orchestra and the Committee. But the ladies were in the right.

On the 20th of February he was suffering once more from inflammation of the throat and fever. On the 21st he was to conduct and insisted on doing so. Fraenkel, he said, would pull him through. Fraenkel warned him not to attempt it, but Mahler insisted that he had conducted time after time with a temperature and Fraenkel had to give way. We wrapped him up carefully and drove to Carnegie Hall. Among other works he conducted that night was the first performance in public of Busoni's "Cradle Song at the Grave of my Mother."

He felt very exhausted when the intermission came, and his

head was aching. But he pulled himself together and conducted the rest of the concert. His last concert. We drove back, taking all possible precautions, accompanied by Fraenkel, who examined him as soon as we arrived. His temperature was normal again and Mahler was very merry about conducting himself back to health. We all parted from each other much relieved. He was given aspirin. Next morning he seemed better and in a few days the inflammation of the throat had vanished. But the fever had come back. At first it was slight, but it kept on rising in zig-zags. By the end of a week Fraenkel had no doubts left about the nature of the disease. I called him in one evening when Mahler had a sort of collapse. He reassured him and me too, but when he returned in the morning his hair had gone gray. Thus Mahler and I saw with our own eyes that hair can turn white in a few hours. Fraenkel told me years later that he had buried his dearest friend that night.

I did not know how great the danger was. If I had, I could never have got through the next three months. Even so, they were terrible. His ups and downs kept us on the rack; he was often convinced of his recovery; often again he despaired and was in mortal dread. When he felt better he joked about his approaching death. "You will be in demand when I am gone, with your youth and looks. Now who shall it be?"

"No one," I said. "Don't talk of it."

"Yes, but let's see, who is there?"

He went through his list, and always ended up with: "It'll be better, after all, if I stay with you."

I had to laugh with tears in my eyes.

He entrusted his annotated scores of Beethoven and Schumann and other symphonies to me. "They're valuable," he said. "Have them printed."

Sometimes he got up and went into our large corner sitting-room. He lay on a comfortable sofa and I read aloud to him.

When I went out, the policeman on duty in the Plaza, a busy spot, asked me again and again: "How is Mr. Mahler?" Then he took me safely across and gave me his good wishes. Never in my whole life have I met so much genuine warmth of heart and delicacy of feeling as in America.

One day Schindler, who was to accompany Alda, came to ask me about the tempi of the song of mine she was going to sing.

Mahler who was in bed in the next room was enraged at the dilet-
tante way he went to work, and when Schindler went on to play
me some Mussorgsky songs he whistled for me to come in and told
me to send Schindler about his business. He said it was tactless
of him to start playing something else immediately after my song,
and said it so emphatically that there was no contradicting him.

I was often taken out for drives by friends as a relief from constant attendance at his bedside; and one afternoon Fraenkel came
unexpectedly to take me for a walk. This was very opportune, as
it was the afternoon of Alda's recital and I had a ticket for the
back of the gallery. Fraenkel was very much astonished when he
found I was going to a concert, a thing I had not done for weeks.
I did not say what the concert was, let alone that a song of mine
was being sung, and I parted from him speedily before he had time
to ask. Meanwhile, Mahler was awaiting my return in the keenest
suspense. He said he had never been in such a state of excitement
over any performance of his own works. When I told him it had
been encored he said: "Thank God," over and over again. He was
quite beside himself with joy.

I looked after him now just as if he were a little child. I put every
bite into his mouth for him and slept in his room without taking
off my clothes. We got so used to it that he said more than once:
"When I'm well again we'll go on like this. You'll feed me—it's
so nice."

Delicacies of every kind were sent us in a constant stream, by
strangers as well as friends. Every day he was delighted by some
fresh surprise, and as nourishment was all-important he was fed
almost every hour of the day and night. In the early stages Fraenkel
had suggested a blood test, and it yielded the verdict: streptococci.
Neither Mahler nor I had ever heard the word before and in our
innocence were not at all alarmed.

This was done on two occasions. The first time we had a surgeon
from the Montefiore Hospital, who must have been rather incom-
petent, for the bed, the floor and the bathroom were covered with
blood. Mahler shouted to Fraenkel that if another blood test had
to be made, it would have to be done differently or he would throw
the man downstairs. The second was carried out by a doctor from

the Rockefeller Institute and there was no sign a minute after it
had been done at all.

It was remarkable that his temperature went down both times
and his state of mind was better for several days. Probably it would
have been a good thing if he had been bled.

There was a weekly consultation between leading doctors of
New York. On their advice Kollargol injections were tried. Mahler
joked about his little bugs, which were always either dancing
or sleeping.

Fraenkel often said that if it had not been a case of the celebrated
Mahler, but just some ordinary person, lots of things might have
been tried. Blood-transfusion, for example, or saline injections.
"But you daren't try experiments on Gustav Mahler. We must
wait in the hope that nature herself will give him the strength to
pull through. I could not take the responsibility."

Finally, after a consultation at which Fraenkel was present, it
was decided that Mahler must be sent at all costs to Europe to
some great bacteriologist in Paris or Vienna. There was talk of
Metchnikoff. When I heard this my strength gave out and I fell
in a faint at Mahler's bedside. Fraenkel and Dr. Brettauer, an
eminent doctor and a friend of ours, carried me to my bed. They
both insisted on my cabling at once for my mother. I did so and
Mahler was delighted. He consulted the newspaper. "She'll be
here in six days," he said. We knew she would leave Vienna the
same day and take the fastest boat, undeterred by any fatigue or
difficulty, as soon as she heard his cry for help. She did in fact arrive
by the very boat we reckoned on.

The relation between them was very close. I used to say as a joke
when I was first married that if Mahler had gone to my mother
and said: "I've had to put Alma to death," she would simply have
replied: "I'm sure you were right, Gustav." It was a foolish jest,
because I was pleased he was always right in her eyes, even if sometimes it made things awkward for me. It was the utmost happiness
when we were all three together.

Now that my mother was there I could spare myself a little, as
she took part of the day-nursing. I still watched at his bedside all
night as before. We tried three male nurses in turn, each of whom
he dismissed at once; one's shoes squeaked, another snored. At last

we tried a female nurse. He forbade her to look at him. It was more than he would endure. If she must attend to him, then she must look sideways. But this woman was a necessity. I had forty pieces of luggage to pack—without his knowledge and with dread in my heart. So every time I went out of his room I unobtrusively took an armful of things with me. He had no idea his room had been entirely emptied when the time came for him to leave it.

My mother was once stewing fruit over a spirit-stove between two open windows. There was an explosion, and instantly the curtains, window-sill and carpet were on fire. I promptly lost my head. There was Mahler in bed in one room, our daughter asleep in another, and a blazing curtain blowing out right across the room toward her door. And we were on the ninth floor. I rushed to the telephone, but could not get out the word "fire." The girl at the telephone, hearing the terror in my voice, at once sent some men from the office and some hotel servants, who forced the doors, which were all locked as it was late at night. My mother and our English nurse tore the curtains down and poured water on the flames as fast as they could. They had nearly put them out by the time the men were on the scene. When I went in to see Mahler, he was lying quietly in bed and could not understand why I got so excited about a fire.

My mother always cooked his favorite dishes on this spirit-stove, but this time—for once—it was for herself. "Poor Mama," was all he said. "Cooking all day for me. Then—for once—she thinks of herself, and has a disaster. Poor thing!"

No one in the hotel reproached us by word or look. All was put right next day and we did not have to pay a cent for the very considerable damage we had caused, for the hotel was insured, and moreover, the Americans did everything on an incomparably generous scale.

Our cabin was booked, the packing was done, and Mahler was dressed. A stretcher was waiting, but he waved it aside. He looked as white as a sheet as he walked unsteadily to the elevator, leaning on Fraenkel's arm. The elevator-boy kept out of the way until the last moment, to hide his tears, and then took him down for the last time. The huge hotel lounge was deserted. Mrs. Untermyer's automobile was waiting at a side entrance; Fraenkel helped him in and drove to the pier with him. I went back to the office to pay the bill and to thank the office-staff for all they had done for us without a thought for themselves during those weeks. They all came out and shook hands. "We cleared everyone out of the lobby—we knew Mr. Mahler wouldn't like to be stared at."

Blessed America! We never met with any such proof of true sensibility during our subsequent weeks in Europe.

When I arrived on board Mahler was already in bed and Fraenkel was at his side. He gave me his last instructions and warned me not to call in the ship's doctor. Then he bade Mahler a brief and sad farewell. He knew that he would never see him again.

Our cabins were heaped with presents and flowers from friends as well as from people we didn't even know.

The voyage began. My mother and I shared the nursing; he would not allow anyone else near him and we gladly, though with heavy hearts, took entire charge. What he suffered from most was the alternation of a sub-normal with a high temperature, which he reduced by violent perspiration. So our cabins had at one moment to be over-heated, the next icy cold. I had a temperature myself every evening, but I could not think of that. My bunk was under the window, and when Mahler wanted it open the ice-cold air blew straight in on me. It was the end of April.

He got up nearly every day and between us we carried rather than helped him onto the boat-deck, where the captain had had a large space screened off so that he should not be seen by the other passengers. We dressed and undressed him, lifted him up and fed him by hand; he was not obliged to make a single movement for himself.

Busoni was on board. He sent Mahler crazy specimens of counterpoint to amuse him, and also bottles of wine. Busoni had a really good heart. He and I walked on deck together one day while Mahler was sleeping. He loved him and talked of him all the time. We stopped at the taffrail and looked over the sea. "The Germans," he said, "are a funny lot. Even now they have not absolutely put the stamp on Mahler's genius. They blow hot and cold. They don't really know anything about him. But if he—if he were taken from them, ah, then———!"

Mahler's beauty was staggering. "Today, you're Alexander the Great again," I used to say. The beauty of his black shining eyes, his white face, his black hair and blood-red mouth struck terror to my heart.

The voyage went well, and when it came to embarking in the tender at Cherbourg we found that the captain still had us in his thoughts. He gave us time to board the tender and settle Mahler down in seclusion before allowing the other passengers to leave the ship.

There was a great stampede on the pier; and so, as we had reserved a compartment, we sat quietly where we were until the crowd dispersed; then we helped Mahler slowly along to the train, which was a long way off. An official of the Hamburg-America Line asked if he might take my place as I looked so ill. I accepted his offer with Mahler's consent, and left my mother to accompany them while I hurried back to the customs shed, where our forty pieces of luggage were waiting. As soon as I said that my husband was dangerously ill, it was all done in a moment and I hurried to the train. But as I did not know the number of our compartment, I had to go the whole length of the train, coach by coach, and they were all vacant. There were two drunken porters at the end of one of them who said they had lifted a sick man into the train. They demanded a tip. I opened my handbag in my desperation, and they forced me to give them all I had in it. I did not care. I ran on and at last found Mahler lying comfortably in an improvised bed my mother had quickly made.

Busoni had told me there was a young Austrian on board who wished to offer his services to Mahler and me. I sent back word that we did not need to trouble him while we were on board, but that he might be of help when it came to landing. There was no sign of him then, however; although in the tender he was the only person who spied on Mahler over the barrier of our luggage. Mahler had had to turn away to avoid his stare. Again at Cherbourg we saw him hurrying to the customs shed, and when I got there his baggage had just been examined. Now, I thought, he will give me his help. Not a bit of it. He vanished. I next came on him with Gucki, telling her a fairy-story in a very loud voice. Mahler found it disturbing and asked me to tell him to stop.

We reached Paris at five in the morning. My stepfather had come from Paris to meet us and got on our train at an intermediate station. Rooms were reserved and ready for us at the Hotel Elysée.

We all went to bed, utterly worn out. When I woke at seven next morning, Mahler was sitting on the balcony. He was fully dressed. He was shaved. He rang for breakfast. I could not believe my eyes.

"I always said I should recover as soon as I set foot in Europe. I'll go for a drive this morning and in a few days, when we've got over the voyage, we two will set off for Egypt."

I stared at him in utter astonishment. It seemed literally to be a miracle. He had not done anything for himself for months. My mother and I had almost had to carry him from the boat. And now! I sent for Mama and Moll, whose love for Mahler was nothing short of idolatry. We all laughed and wept for joy. It seemed he was saved.

He talked with great excitement about future productions during breakfast. *The Barber of Bagdad*—it would be marvelous; and he began to develop his ideas for making it go. He jumped up (a pang of dread clutched at my throat) and abruptly ordered an electric automobile. He got into it as a man recovered, and got out, after an hour's drive, as a man at death's door.

He got paler and paler from the moment we reached the Bois, although at first the beauty of the day roused him to raptures. He leaned his head on my mother's shoulder and the drive ended without his uttering a word. We urged the chauffeur to drive as fast as possible. We were in mortal dread. At last—at last we were back in the hotel.

He was put straight to bed. He had a shivering fit. Then a collapse. A doctor was summoned by telephone. He gave him a camphor injection. And so ended our first day in Europe—after so wonderful a beginning.

I left him alone with my mother and spent the time with our little girl, who had been sadly neglected in our terrible alarm. He did not want me to hear what he said; and although my mother sat by his bed and tried to rouse him from his despondence she did not succeed. He wept, and begged her if the worst came to have him buried beside his daughter at Grinzing, in a simple grave, with no pomp and ceremony, and a plain headstone with nothing but "Mahler" on it. "Any who come to look for me will know who I was, and the rest do not need to know. I cannot talk to Almschi about this. It would be too painful for us both."

My mother and he wept bitterly. It was the only time during the whole of his illness that he was so utterly disconsolate. When Moll came in, he said again that he wished to be buried in the same grave as our daughter and asked him never to desert me.

As soon as I came in he fell silent. But I saw his tears. Soon he began to talk again and at length about his early associations and the companions of his youth; his complaints of them were bitter. "They spun webs round me like spiders. They stole my life away. They kept me apart, from jealousy and envy. But I am to blame too. Why did I let it happen? My life has all been paper!" He said this again and again, as though speaking to himself: "My life has all been paper!"

We now endeavored to get in touch with the doctors whose names Fraenkel had written down for us, but it was just before Easter and not one was available. The only bacteriologist we could get hold of was Chantemesse. When he came he insisted on instant removal to a nursing-home of Dr. Duprès' in Rue Dupont. This was the best and most up to date of all the clinics in Paris at that time, but somewhat primitive compared with our hospitals in Vienna. There were wonderful rooms overlooking a garden, but no nursing to speak of. However, my mother and I needed no help in our devoted care of him.

There was no shutting our eyes now to the unmistakable signs. His growing weakness was arrested only by a feverish excitement. Yet he was glad to talk and he talked a great deal. He read works of philosophy all through his illness and up to the very end. The last book he read was *The Philosophy of Life* by Eduard von Hartmann. By the end it was in fragments. He tore the pages from the binding, because he had not the strength to hold more than a few at a time.

During his last days and while his mind was still unclouded his thoughts often went anxiously to Schönberg. "If I go, he will have nobody left." I promised him to do everything in my power. Moll too promised to stand by Schönberg.

After Mahler's death Moll told friends of ours what he had said and they resolved forthwith to collect a considerable sum and to put it at my disposal year by year for the benefit of young musicians. I chose Strauss, Busoni and Walter as trustees of the fund, and at my request the proceeds frequently went to Schönberg. War and inflation have unfortunately made it worthless.

Chantemesse, who was a celebrated bacteriologist, now made a culture from Mahler's blood and after a few days he came to us in great delight with a microscope in his hand. I thought some miracle had happened. He placed the microscope on the table. "Now, Madame Mahler, come and look. Even I—myself—have never seen streptococci in such a marvelous state of development. Just look at these threads—it's like seaweed." He was eager to explain, to shine his light abroad. But I could not listen. Dumb with horror, I turned and left him. The shock it gave my mother did her serious harm.

Once when Mahler was feeling better I sat on his bed and we discussed what we should do when he had recovered. "We'll go to Egypt and see nothing but blue sky," he said.

"Once you are well again," I said, "I shall have had enough of suffering. Do you remember when you first met me you thought I was too happy. I've suffered enough now. I don't need any more chastening. We'll live a careless, happy life."

He smiled tenderly and stroked my hair. "Yes, you're right. God grant I get better and then we can still be happy."

But he got worse, and in my anguish I telegraphed to Professor Chvostek, the most celebrated doctor in Vienna, asking him to come at once. He arrived next morning. I told him first how to behave with Mahler and then he went into the sick room and began in a loud, jovial voice: "Now then, Mahler, what's all this about? Working too hard, that's what it is. You'll have to knock off for six months or a year. You've brought it on yourself—you can't treat your nerves that way, you know."

Mahler gazed at him with growing astonishment.

"Shall I ever be able to work again then?" he asked, his face lighting up with joy.

"Of course. Why not? Keep your heart up, that's all. This evening we'll be off to Vienna together."

Chvostek told me to make preparations for leaving as soon as possible. Anything might happen and then it might be too late to move him. All the same, I did not lose all heart, and when I went back into Mahler's room the joy in his face was such as I had never seen. He cried out again and again: "Oh, the lovely man, the lovely Chvostek! Oh, for tonight—how soon can we all start?"

And it seemed that his overwhelming joy made a new man of him. He could not endure delay. We packed madly. Moll hurried out to reserve sleepers. Mama was to follow us to Vienna with her granddaughter. Mahler was dressed long before it was time to start, blissful, transfigured.

Chvostek and I accompanied him in the ambulance and then he was carried to the train on a stretcher. His traveling-cap was awry—so helpless he was. I took it off; his beautiful face showed he understood. It was horrible to see him manipulated into the train on a stretcher along the narrow corridor. He went straight to bed, and Moll, Chvostek and I took turns in watching through the night. "Are you there? You're an angel," he said, and after a pause: "We're coming home in poor trim this time. But we'll soon be on our feet again." I was sitting on a suitcase beside him. I laid my head on his hand and kissed it.

Chvostek called me out in the middle of the night and made Moll take my place.

"No hope," he said solemnly. "And may the end come quickly. If he did pull through, which is not likely, he'd be condemned to a bath-chair for the rest of his life."

"Better that than nothing," I said. "I can't face life without him."

"Yes, but then the whole nervous system will go too and you don't want to wheel a senile idiot about."

I refused to submit and asked Moll to let me return to my post. Journalists came to the door at every station in Germany and Austria for the latest bulletin, and so his last journey was like that of a dying king. They all knew his importance and had to hear how he was at half-past ten, at eleven and twelve. Mahler asked who each of them was and what paper he represented, and it seemed to do him good. He said to me over and over again: "My madly adored Almschi."

Vienna—and by ambulance to the Löw nursing home, where an enormous room with a veranda was ready for him. Not only the room but the corridor too were wreathed in flowers, and Mahler was obviously delighted. More and more flowers arrived. I had to bring them all for him to see and to arrange them with care. A white basket of flowers arrived with a card: "From the Philharmonic."—"*My* Philharmonic," he said again and again.

After a time he lay completely still. His mind was becoming confused. Justine paid him another visit and at the sight of her his eyes dilated unnaturally:

"Who is this lady?" he stammered. She fled.

Berliner arrived from Berlin, true to their old friendship, and Mahler recognized him and grasped his hand. "My dear friend," he said, and then turned to the wall, perhaps to hide his emotion.

During his last days he cried out: "My Almschi," hundreds of times, in a voice, a tone I had never heard before and have never heard since. "My Almschi!" As I write it down now, I cannot keep back my tears.

When Gucki came to his bedside he put his arms round her. "Be my good girl, my child."

Did he know? Or not? It was impossible to tell. He lay there groaning. A large swelling came up on his knee, then on his leg. Radium was applied and the swelling immediately went down. On the evening after, he was washed and his bed made. Two attendants lifted his naked emaciated body. It was a taking down from the cross. This was the thought that came to all of us.

He had difficulty in breathing and was given oxygen. Then uremia—and the end. Chvostek was summoned. Mahler lay with dazed eyes; one finger was conducting on the quilt. There was a smile on his lips and twice he said: "Mozart!" His eyes were very big. I begged Chvostek to give him a large dose of morphia so that he might feel nothing more. He replied in a loud voice. I seized his hands: "Talk softly, he might hear you."—"He hears nothing now."

How terrible the callousness of doctors is at such moments. And how did he know that he could not hear? Perhaps he was only incapable of movement?

The death-agony began. I was sent into the next room. The death-rattle lasted several hours.

That ghastly sound ceased suddenly at midnight of the 18th of

May during a tremendous thunderstorm. With that last breath his beloved and beautiful soul had fled, and the silence was more deathly than all else. As long as he breathed he was there still. But now all was over.

I was not allowed in the death-chamber. Moll was with him to the last. I was removed that night from my room next to his. The doctors insisted. But I felt it a humiliation not to be allowed to stay near him. I could not understand it. Was I alone? Did I have to live without him? It was as if I had been flung out of a train in a foreign land. I had no place on earth.

I went up to the Hohe Warte, in Heiligenstadt. The bells tolled without ceasing. I had Mahler's photograph beside me and I lay in bed and talked to him. He was still there—not yet in the earth.

Chvostek came to see me, unasked. "Your lung is touched—and badly too. If you don't look out, you'll very soon follow him." Mama came in and for the first time for many days I smiled. It was my one hope to follow him. But—I have lived on.

I can never forget his dying hours and the greatness of his face as death drew nearer. His battle for the eternal values, his elevation above trivial things and his unflinching devotion to truth are an example of the saintly life.

Letters

1901

28 November, 1901

I have hastened, dear Miss Alma, to collect for you all my songs that have so far been published. My only consolation for not being able to bring them is the pleasing thought that you will now have to give me a little of your attention and will have me in your thoughts.—When I come on Monday (I count the hours till then with eager impatience) I will play any of them you want to hear.

How happy we were yesterday in spite of all; that is what I felt as soon as L. left me to go on my way home alone. Those delightful hours echoed on and on in my heart, and accompanied me even into my dreams.

In haste, dear Miss Alma, from

Yours,

Gustav Mahler

5 December, 1901

Dearest friend,

I hope Hoffmann afforded you some pleasure yesterday—although the opera gives little but the dregs of him, from which the spirit has fled. Madame Schoder brought out much that lies on the surface (unfortunately in this whole work there is only the surface to retrieve) but the triviality of poor Schrödter and his son-in-law was too leaden a weight on the wings of poetry. It is only with a struggle I can get to the end of the first two acts. But yesterday I was buoyed up by the joy of doing it for you! The third act is better. There at least I find something that helps me to evoke the demonic character of the original.

If you want to know how much the opera loses, read Hoffmann's story, *Rath Krespel.* The Schoder was moving, and not far from seeing eye to eye with me. But even she left me in the lurch rather when it came to the subtleties of interpretation, for which her tendency to realism is to blame. Antonia does *not* die of consumption, as the Schoder suggested by her cough—that cursed cough so beloved on the stage. It is the demonic principle of art, which pushes anybody who is possessed by it to relinquish his own personality; and in this case so penetrates a nature peculiarly disposed to give up the ghost that it snatches her out of life. One might say it is not the ghost she gives up, but the body. Or—in one of those images you love so much—she takes her way into the realm of night, from which there is no return. But these are only the elements of a powerful drama, the dark perspectives of which might be lighted up in the grisliest fashion by a composer of genius. That is how I felt it yesterday, hoping in my heart that it might come home to you.—If you will turn a sympathetic eye on Hoffmann's Tales, you will find a new light on the relation of music to reality; for music, mysterious as it is, often illumines our souls with a flash of lightning, and you will feel that the only true reality on earth is soul. For any one who has once grasped this, what we call reality is no more than a formula, a shadow with no substance.—And you must not, please, take this for a poetical metaphor; it is a conviction which can hold its own at the bar of sober reason. We'll discuss it when I see you again. I write rather at length on the subject because it has so close a bearing on my earnest desire, which is not, as you may think, just a piece of pedantry, to set up my God in the place of the idols of clay.

To my great sorrow, I cannot come on Saturday. I will tell you the reason when I am back from Berlin. For the moment, rather than make polite excuses, may I just say—as I find it hard to do so laconically—that I must refuse your charming invitation?

I have grown so fond of our talks in this short time—or our squabbles for that matter, or even our silences, that the dearest wish I cherish before going away is that you will still be my dear comrade and help me a little to be yours too. Don't forget our favorites: Evchen—and Hans Sachs!

                                          Au revoir,

                                                    G.

8 Dec., 1901

Dearest Almschi,

Here is a fairy-tale belonging to my youthful days. You were a true joy to me yesterday. You listened so charmingly and answered so charmingly too. What a pity that such an afternoon should be so short—and the coda at night almost sad.—Today brings me the evening when we shall be in the deepest sense at one—I shall think of you in every beat, and conduct for you. It shall be as it was yesterday at the piano when I spoke to you so gladly and from my heart. And sometimes I shall pause and have that mistrustful look which has so often surprised you. It is not *mistrust*, in the ordinary sense, but a *question* addressed to you and the future. Dearest, *learn to answer*. It is not an easy thing to learn—you have first to know yourself thoroughly. But to *ask* is more difficult still. Only by asking can one learn one's whole and inmost relation to others. Dearest, dear one, *learn to ask!*

Your response to me yesterday was so different and so much more mature. I feel that these last days have opened—unlocked so much for you.—How will it be when I come back again?—I shall ask you again: Are you fond of me? Fonder than yesterday? Did you know me before? And do you know me now? And now, *Addio,* my dear one, my comrade!

Your

Gustav

Berlin, 14 Dec., 1901

Dearest,

Full rehearsals begin tomorrow. If only you were here! I find now (particularly since my thoughts have been bound up in you) that I am getting quite vulgarly ambitious in a way that is almost unworthy of a person like me!

I should like now to have success, recognition, and all those other really quite meaningless things people talk of. I want to do you honor. I have always had ambition, but I have not coveted the honors my contemporaries can confer. To be understood and esteemed by men of like mind, even if I were never to find them (and indeed they are only to be found outside space and time) has always been the goal I have striven for; and so it shall be all the more from now on. In this you must stand by me, my beloved. And to win this guerdon and to be so crowned, I must deny myself the applause of the crowd and even of the Great and Good (even they can't always follow me). How gladly up to now I have suffered myself to be slapped in the face by the Philistine, to be scorned and hated by the immature. To my sorrow I know only too well that what little notice I have had must be put down perhaps only to misunderstanding, or at least to a dim perception of some unintelligible ideal.—I am not, of course, speaking of my activities in opera or as a conductor: they after all are of an inferior order. Please let me have your answer to this, whether, that is, *you* understand and are willing also to follow me. Alma, could you endure hardships with me, and even ignominy and shame, and gladly take up so grievous a cross? If this is to go today I must stop!

I could talk on to you for ever!

I think of you every minute, my dear, beloved Alma, and I will make use a thousand times over of the permission you give me in the postscript of your last letter.

Yours, darling girl,

Gustav

Program of the Second Symphony by Gustav Mahler

We are standing beside the coffin of a man beloved. For the last time his life, his battles, his sufferings and his purpose pass before the mind's eye. And now, at this solemn and deeply stirring moment, when we are released from the paltry distractions of everyday life, our hearts are gripped by a voice of awe-inspiring solemnity, which we seldom or never hear above the deafening traffic of mundane affairs. What next? it says. What is life—and what is death?

Have we any continuing existence?

Is it all an empty dream, or has this life of ours, and our death, a meaning?

If we are to go on living, we must answer this question.

The next three movements are conceived as intermezzi.

SECOND MOVEMENT. ANDANTE.

A blissful moment in his life and a mournful memory of youth and lost innocence.

THIRD MOVEMENT. SCHERZO.

The Spirit of unbelief and negation has taken possession of him. Looking into the turmoil of appearances, he loses together with the clear eyes of childhood the sure foothold which love alone gives. He despairs of himself and of God. The world and life become a witch's brew; disgust of existence in every form strikes him with iron fist and drives him to an outburst of despair.

FOURTH MOVEMENT. THE PRIMAL DAWN. (ALTO SOLO.)

The morning voice of ingenuous belief sounds in our ears.

"I am from God and will return to God! God will give me a candle to light me to the bliss of eternal life."

FIFTH MOVEMENT.

We are confronted once more by terrifying questions.

A voice is heard crying aloud: "The end of all living beings is come—the Last Judgment is at hand and the horror of the day of days has broken forth."

The earth quakes, the graves burst open, the dead arise and stream on in endless procession. The great and the little ones of the earth—kings and beggars, righteous and godless—all press on —the cry for mercy and forgiveness strikes fearfully on our ears. The wailing rises higher—our senses desert us, consciousness dies at the approach of the eternal spirit. The

"Last Trump"

is heard—the trumpets of the Apocalypse ring out; in the eerie silence that follows we can just catch the distant, barely audible song of a nightingale, a last tremulous echo of earthly life! A chorus of saints and heavenly beings softly breaks forth:

"Thou shalt arise, surely thou shalt arise." Then appears the glory of God! A wondrous, soft light penetrates us to the heart— all is holy calm!

And behold—it is no judgment—there are no sinners, no just. None is great, none is small. There is no punishment and no reward.

An overwhelming love lightens our being. We know and are.

Palace Hotel, P. H. Kons. Berlin W.
Monday morning, 17 Dec., 1901

Dearest Almschi, don't empty out the baby with the bath If, after I have struggled for fifteen years against stupidity and misunderstanding and endured all the toils and afflictions of the pioneer, a work of mine should at last be understood, particularly in Vienna, where people have come to have some idea of me without knowing it, there is no reason to mind it any more than you would mind misunderstanding and ill-will, or to feel that it would tell against my work. The point is not to take the world's opinion as a guiding star, to go one's way in life and work unerringly, neither depressed by failure nor decoyed by applause. It does seem to me now that some of the seed I have sown is coming up, and, apart from all else, I rejoice that it should happen just in time to remove a few thorns from your path. Not that I would spare you them if it was a question of being true to my destiny—and yours, for they are now the same. And so we shall now support and encourage each other in facing the world with equanimity—which is the highest honor we covet.

Alma—we shall not be able to utter a word for the first hour—we shall have too much to say. Your mother knows now, doesn't she? Tell her everything before I come. I must meet her from the first moment as her son. I cannot face any formalities. Tell her everything. As you know, I did at first mean to speak to her myself—but that was before I, and still more you, had seen the whole truth. My idea was to consult her as the person who knew you best.—But now that our minds are irrevocably made up, there is nothing I could say to her except: "Give me what is mine—let me live and breathe," for your love is as much a condition of my life as my pulse or heart. The more I think of it the more I feel how important for our whole future it is that at this solemn time (the true solemnity of marriage, when souls recognize their affinity and flow into one channel) we should be together not in the body but in the spirit.

My beloved,

Your

Gustav

Hotel Bellevue, Dresden A.

19 Dec., Wednesday morning

Dearly beloved!

The last of our Stations of the Cross! I am nearer to you now, and think only of Saturday when I shall hold you in my arms. It will be the supreme moment of my life.—The Second is being given here today. My Almschi! Justi did not tell you, then, that I only drew up the program as [printed after letter of 14 Dec.] as a crutch for a cripple (you know whom I mean). It only gives a superficial indication, all that any program can do for a musical work, let alone this one, which is so much all of a piece that it can no more be explained than the world itself.—I'm quite sure that if God were asked to draw up a program of the world he had created he could never do it.—At best it would say as little about the nature of God and life as my analysis says about my C Minor Symphony. In fact, as all religious doctrines do, it leads directly to misunderstanding, to a flattening and coarsening, and in the long run to such distortion that the work, and still more its creator, is utterly unrecognizable.—I had a serious talk with Strauss in Berlin and tried to show him the blind alley he had got into. Unfortunately, he could not quite follow what I meant. He's a charming fellow, and I'm touched by his attitude to me. And yet I can mean nothing to him—for whereas I see over his head, he sees only up to my knees.—He is coming to Vienna very soon. Perhaps I'll bring him out to see you.—Here I am, writing to you again until late at night. It is so moving, so delightful now to think over and plan our future life in every detail—with you as the center of my whole existence—always beginning afresh from you and returning to you again—when I wake at daylight or when I go to bed—or if I get up in the night or in the early morning. I sleep little owing to an indisposition which usually afflicts me when I travel; but I don't mind, because my thoughts fly at once to you.—How I wish you could be here for the C Minor. The piano score gives no idea of it. And it is so important you should know it—for my Fourth will mean nothing to you.—It again is all humor—"naïve," as you would say; just what you can so far understand least in me—and what in any case only the fewest of the few will ever understand to all futurity. But you, my Alma, you will be guided by love and it will light your way into the most secret places. My love and my longing, my hope and faith—a thousand thousand times yours,

Your

Gustav

21 Dec., 1901

My beloved Alma,

I am back in the air you breathe, my native air; and I had scarcely entered my room (how glad I am you know it now) before I saw your dear handwriting. I was touched by your affectionate welcome, even though it was written before you got my letter of yesterday.—That letter weighed on my heart when I thought of the impression it could not fail to make on you at first. For my sake and yours, I trust you read it in the light of my love and truth and recognize how strong and deep they were. For you do understand, I know, how hard and implacably truthful I am where love is concerned.—And everything must be clear between us before we hold each other in our arms—for this afternoon I could never have enough control over myself to discuss with you what all the same must be decided between us. I await the answer my servant will bring in a state of suspense and anguish such as I have never known.—What will your answer be? But do not misunderstand me. The decision rests with what you are, not what you say. The passion which fetters us must be momentarily overcome (and this can only be, if we do not meet face to face—and that is why I write while there is still time). Otherwise, we cannot with the inward composure and certainty of love enter those bonds which shall indissolubly unite us as long as life lasts.

"He stands the test who binds himself forever" and "burst the girdle, rend the veil, tear the lovely craze in two."

No more now, for my heart overflows at the thought of our meeting again. I will come as soon as I can. But I do not know how long I may be kept at the Opera. Also I have to see the Manager today and often I don't get away from him before 3 o'clock.

Au revoir, my dear, my love!

Your

Gustav

24 Dec., 1901

My Alma!

For the first and last time I send you Christmas greetings on Christmas Eve; for in the future we shall spend Christmas together. Once united—soon, I hope—we shall need no messenger. You will be there beside me, ruling the household. The love which has ripened our happiness so quickly that it falls from the tree at our feet may have been unguarded, but it was trustful and looked with hope to the future. Today, a day that would have united us, as it does all mankind, even if we had known nothing of each other, in a children's festival, shall remain a symbol, a sign that, happy and united in our love, our hearts must be open to all others too—for a love we may call divine binds us together and links us also with all humanity.

I bless you, my beloved, my life, on this day, the children's day, in whom the seed of earthly as well as divine love strikes root.

1902

The Semmering, 2.02

Beloved!

Your dear little letter came just at breakfast time to my indescribable joy. I too have been painfully awaiting the first word from you. It was not the parting only—I found the whole evening uncomfortable. Strauss sheds such a blight—you feel estranged from your very self. If these are the fruits, how is one to love the tree? Your comment on him hits the nail on the head. And I am very proud of your penetration. Better, by far, to eat the bread of poverty and follow one's star than sell one's soul like that. The time will come when the chaff shall be winnowed from the grain—and my day will be when his is ended. If only I might live to see it, with you at my side! But you, I hope, will see it for certain and remember the days when you discerned the sun through the mist—as on that day we were in the Park and it looked like a nasty red blot. For the moment all I think of is to get well and be yours, body and soul. I am much better already after a good night's sleep. Perhaps I may see you up here? If you come on Saturday afternoon we could go back to Vienna together on Sunday. But let your mother decide. Don't urge it on her. If I want one more day I shall see you at any rate on Sunday evening. I am getting on now. I'll write again this evening. And, by the way, Alma, my child, do write a proper, legible address, if only for the sake of the poor postmen. How are they to make head or tail of your scrawl? I should tease you about it if you were here.

You said I did not join in the conversation this day before yesterday, and I will now tell you why. How could I take any part in his vulgar talk? I was elated by a performance which had aroused my creative energy. I was not going to be dragged down to his level and talk about royalties and percentages, of which he is for ever dreaming as though they were the food of imagination itself and part and parcel of his inspiration.

I send you a thousand kisses, in spite of Strasser (who, by the way, tells me I suffer from a dilated vein, owing to a congestion of the blood-vessel, which has been going on for months—very much the same as I had last time). Never mind. Fortunately I noticed it in time and will soon be all right again.

Your
Gustav

3.2.02

Almschi, dearest!

I am just back from the station. There was just the chance you might be coming. It is snowing hard and we shall soon be snowed under—you would love it as much as I do. I'm enchanted with it —but miss you all the more. I seem to catch sight of you everywhere I look. I have had a glorious idea—I'll come out to you for lunch on Monday—as early as I can. I'll try to be with you by one. We should have time for a little walk. I could stay until a quarter to six. You could take me to Zögernitz and I could go by train from there to the Opera, to conduct that tiresome show. Would that do? We should see more of each other than if you came to us. I feel as fit as ever now. I knew it would put me right to come up here. And so, Almschi, we set off on our travels on the 10th of March, if all goes well. The snow here whets my appetite for St. Petersburg. How you will love it—that is the best of it. Do you love me a little? I can hardly bear to wait. It is only "on grounds of health" I stay on up here. It puts new life into me. Almschi! Do you still love me?

Always your

Gustav

Almscherl, are you being good and behaving properly? Make good use of my being away to have a real rest. Am eager to hear what you make of the Abbazia idea. It is quite comic, by the way, how well known I am. Even on my travels, and in towns where I've never been before, people address me as "Director" at every turn, and are so civil and obliging that I am often quite put to shame. I look forward to Monday already. I don't in the least mind, you know, if we have some good walks at Easter in the Wiener Wald and the Hinter-Brühl instead of taking expensive rooms at Abbazia or the Semmering. But perhaps it would do you good. Discuss it, anyway, with Mama.

A thousand kisses,

from your

Gustav

1903

Hotel George, Lemberg

1903

My dear Almscherl,

Here is the card from Justi you wanted; also a clipping from the *Berliner Tageblatt*, wherein you may read what Helmholtz thinks upon a matter very puzzling to many.—Nothing better could be said in few words about all that balderdash (Maeterlinck, etc.). Oh, these people—one of them as bad as another—

seeking after those things of which there are more in "heaven and earth, Horatio," as if they were searching for lice.—And that blessed word, occultism, they have invented for them! What on earth is not occult, metaphysically speaking, I should like to know. Flat-heads! I am certain they devour the whole of Nietzsche for breakfast and follow it up by Maeterlinck for supper, and have never digested a word of sense from any source whatever.

Last night there was my visit to the Opera. *Tosca*, as I told you. An excellent production in every way; quite an eye-opener, for a provincial town in Austria. But as for the work itself! Act I, papal pageantry with continual chiming of bells (specially imported from Italy). Act. II. A man tortured; horrible cries. Another stabbed with a sharp bread-knife. Act III. More of the magnificent tintinnabulations and a view over all Rome from a citadel. Followed by an entirely fresh onset of bell ringing. A man shot by a firing-party.

I got up before the shooting and went out. Needless to say, a masterpiece. Nowadays any bungler orchestrates to perfection.

> Your
>
> Gustav

Hotel George, Lemberg
1903

Dearest,

My days here are divided between sublimest contemplation and earthly tumult (due to rehearsing in primitive conditions). At intervals I read Zend-Avesta with engrossing interest; it comes home to me with the intimacy of what I have long known and seen and experienced myself.

Remarkable how close in feeling Fechner is to Rückert: they are two nearly related people and one side of my nature is linked with them as a third. How few know anything of those two!

The first concert comes off tonight. I find it hard to understand at times why I should be playing my symphony to the people of Lemberg. But as it can't be helped now, I do my best. There is no knowing where a grain of seed may fall.

And it is a thousand kronen in my pocket and brings me one step nearer to independence—although the independence is merely a word unless the soul itself is free. And that freedom a man must win for himself. So help me to attain it. I went for a fine walk today, which had moments all its own (both in landscape and my inward meditation). I will tell you all about it when we meet. By the end, however, I was back in the traveler's prevailing mood; *sic transit gloria mundi!*—*What* a dirty town Lemberg is—the thought of eating anywhere except in the hotel nauseates me.

Your devoted

Gustav

Hotel George, Lemberg

1903

My dearest Almscherl!

Thank God, it's nearly over. It is frightfully cold here now and I wish I had my winter clothes. I am frozen to the marrow. The symphony, yesterday, made a great impression. There was a general desire for a second hearing, and so I am giving it again at tomorrow's concert. So there's a success for you. The audience would have pleased you, they were so breathlessly still and listened so intently. I went to lunch today with the director of the concerts. A very comical fellow, wife to match—so true to type as a provincial theater director who has money and most ostentatiously gilds his poverty with it.—He lives in a disused theater and has turned the foyer into his drawing-room—every pillar and alcove adorned with fans, photographs, laurel-wreaths and other trophies; all in an exaggerated profusion such as I have never seen. His wife insisted on singing to me; in the hope, I believe, of future professional contacts. To the same account is to be debited the presentation, to which I had to submit *coram publico*, of a silver—or was it even golden? I didn't know—laurel wreath. You can well imagine the face I made on the occasion.—The audiences have behaved charmingly and with great respect (after maintaining at first a certain reserve).

I was much distressed yesterday, Almscherl, at having no letter from you. I nearly sent you a telegram.—

Last night was also the night on which my Second was performed in Düsseldorf. I wonder very much how that went off.

*   *   *

Your old

Gustav

Vienna-Kahlenberg
29.8.03

Dearest A. Cannot run to a letter today. Only this card as a
sign of life. Capital journey! Very conscious of my 70 kilos in
a jolting train—on arrival, straight to theater, changed, whereafter played hell with everybody and made myself felt, had a
word in passing, too, with Arnold and Walter, whereafter lunched
with Moser at the Leidinger, coffee with Roller, and then to the
Leopoldsberg. Walked with Roller up the Kahlenberg, furious
thirst, tea and peaches—stung by a wasp, sucked it quickly,
bandaged by Roller with muslin, hurried down again to the
theater, where bound to pay due credit to playing of orchestra,
then rattled up here by train at 9.30. Room very charming (only
seen its windows from outside, as no time). All my—— Off with
Roller now!

Your

Gustav

1904

Mannheim, 29.1.1904

My darling Almschili!

*   *   *

. . . . The journey came to an end at last. I made use of every stop
to have a "walk." Kähler, the conductor, met me at the station
and rehearsed my symphony that evening with the orchestra. I
preferred the theater, where *Romeo and Juliet* was being played

and—in spite of all the obtusenesses of the performance—Shakespeare, greatest of all poets and almost of all mankind, put his spell on me completely; and my spirit opened its wings again.

My darling,

Yesterday, as I told you, to *Liebesgarten*. A very good performance and, all told, a confirmation of my impressions on reading the score. I gained no fresh outlook and my opinion of Pfitzner remains unaltered. Great emotional appeal and very interesting in color. Frog-spawn and slime with a continual urge towards life, but the urge as continually defeated. Creation stops short at the molluscoid level. No sign of the vertebrates. It makes one wish to cry out with Calchas in Offenbach's *La Belle Hélène*: "Flowers, nothing but flowers." The audience, with the best will in the world, wilted in the close air of a stagnant mist and was lost in the mystical maze.

Had supper with Kähler and Wolfrum afterwards and then with the latter to Heidelberg, where I spent the night.

Nodnagel turned up suddenly with an analytic program of the Third. Now we come to the final rehearsal.

Neisser went everywhere with me, and he stays on until I go. I like him a lot better now (he came for the Symphony and only arranged his lecture to fit in with it). He has a great enthusiasm for my music and knows the Third by heart.

I hope the Neckar will prove as kind to me as the Rhine. All the auguries suggest it. There are signs of the liveliest interest on all sides and the concerts in both places are sold out (which does not occur even with Strauss, I'm told). But it shows me how important it is for me to be there in person on all occasions in the future—it is too appalling what they make of my work in my absence. Strauss is perfectly right to conduct his own works on all occasions.

And now, my deepest love, dearest. (All yesterday without news of you. I hope all is well!) How is my sweet Putzi?

Your

Gust

From Maiernigg to Vienna
23 June, 1904

My dearest Almschili,

So the first day is over. Simply frightful! That horrible smell in my bedroom, followed by miserable efforts to assemble the scattered fragments of my inner self (how many days will the assembling take, I wonder), followed by confabulations with Theuer and then a bath and lunch; read the Wagner-Wesendonck letters all day and find deep refreshment in them; they give an insight into an important, perhaps the most important, aspect of this unique and precious great man's life. I meant to go out for a walk over hill and dale, but a hailstorm came on which continued until night and brought all my plans to naught. So for a change I played the piano—Brahms chamber music—but, alas, most of it utterly barren music-making, and if I had not come unexpectedly on a charming sextet in B-flat major I should have given him up in despair, as I do myself at present. Then back to Wagner-Wesendonck, which after Brahms seemed all the more transcendent and superhuman. Looked occasionally into Tolstoy's *Confessions*; terrifyingly sad and savagely flagellant; a fallacy in his very way of putting the question and in consequence a withering blight on all human achievement whether of the heart or head. Occasionally I ventured out in rain and shower; I got as far as Maiernigg Café, but left the muddy coffee undrunk. Oafs to right of me, oafs to left of me, ancient, unappetizing crones knitting, and cheese-eating bald-heads soon drove me home again. Thus the day passed by at last and I tumbled into bed (still the stink of glue) and slept until half-past eight.—Today I have revived slightly; your postcard in particular, dear Almscherl, refreshed my dreary existence. Now I've walked the well-known old road to Klagenfurt and am sitting in the Kaiser von Österreich, as the Café Schieder has been made odious by the introduction of waitresses—drinking coffee and chocolate and writing to you. The boat arrived today too. It looks like new. I am doing some shopping and then walking to Loretto, where Anton will pick me up with the boat.

Keep your heart up, my Almschi. I count the days until you

come. Does Putzi ask for me? A thousand greetings and kisses to you all from

Your
Gustl

Almschi, don't do any more copying! That can't be good for you.

My darling Almschel,

*   *   *

I'm beginning by degrees to get used to my solitude, as one always does to the inevitable. But never in my whole life have I felt so *lonely*!

I have gone all through Brahms pretty well by now. All I can say of him is that he's a puny little dwarf with a rather narrow chest. Good Lord, if a breath from the lungs of Richard Wagner whistled about his ears he would scarcely be able to keep his feet. But I don't mean to hurt his feelings. You will be astonished when I tell you where I get more completely bogged than anywhere else—in his so-called "developments."

It is very seldom he can make anything whatever of his themes, beautiful as they often are. Only Beethoven and Wagner, after all, could do that.

Look after yourself and Putzerl. And now for Bach (with two candles). I must clear the air a bit after Brahms. Eagerly looking forward to seeing you all.

Gustl

My dear one,

*   *   *

The Wilde is quite a thrill, but spurious. He has got hold of a good idea and ruined it with caprice and dilettantism. I should not bother to read it if I were you. Now that I've worked my way through Brahms, I've fallen back on Bruckner again. An odd pair of second-raters. The one was "in the casting ladle"* too long, the other not long enough. Now I stick to Beethoven. There are

* *Peer Gynt.*

only he and Richard—and after them, nobody. Mark that! You can count on enjoying the Wagner-Wesendonck letters! It was a positive necessity to disinfect the mind of those paltry "fol lowers of.

I kiss you many times,

Your

Gustav

Saturday night.   Mid-July

My Almschel,

I cannot bear this sultry heat any longer, so I am off to the Dolomites. One of those lightning-excursions I am so fond of. I shall drive to Toblach early—half-past six—on Sunday morning, then by Schluderbach to Misurina, go for a walk there and spend the night. Next day (Monday) home again the same way, arriving at Maiernigg that evening. Then on Wednesday, God willing, I shall expect you at Klagenfurt. Be sure to write exactly when you arrive. Have had your very dear letter just in time before I start and am rejoiced to the heart by your absorption in those wonderful pages [Wagner-Wesendonck Letters] and your comments on them. The analogies with one's own life, which continually crop up in one way or another in a correspondence of this kind, give it a peculiar fascination. On the one hand, one is able to follow the performances of the works with understanding and appreciation: on the other, there is the supreme gratification of finding oneself related in destiny and sufferings with those whose habitat is on the heights. It will always be so for you, Alma, into whosesoever life you look. Outside space and time there is a select company of solitary persons who are drawn to share an all the more intense life together. And though you find merely a poor counterfeit, still you search those effaced features for the look you understand so well, a look which only the elect can have. Your having this sympathetic insight I consider to be the most precious of blessings on your earthly course and mine.

All my love, my Almschili,

Your

Gustav

1904

My darling Almschili,

The job is done, and you'll open your eyes wide when you see what a fine playground we've made for our Putzel. It's like Columbus's egg. There's still room for a number of improvements, but they shall wait until you come. I have just been tinkering at it a bit myself.—I can hardly wait for the moment when we inspect it together for the first time and put our Putzi inside. She will have her heart's desire before her very eyes.—And *still* I don't know when to expect you! Do write at once and tell me what the doctor's decision is. It must be insupportable now in the flat.

From your

Gustav

My beloved,

Your dear letter was a real comfort to me. It shows me you're now on the right road. When we're alone for a time we achieve a unity with ourselves and nature, certainly pleasanter society than the people one sees every day. Then we become positive (instead of getting stuck fast in negation) and finally productive. The commonplace takes us farther and farther from ourselves, but we are brought back to ourselves by solitude, and from ourselves to God is only a step. Your whole temperament is steeped in this feeling and it gives me infinite joy, for I never doubted it was in you.

How petty our ordinary life, stuck fast in negation and criticism, seems to us then.—You find the same thing in your reading, don't you? Shakespeare is the positive, the productive; Ibsen merely analysis, negation, barrenness. Now you can understand why it is I strive to rescue the positive and productive mood from the clutches of the commonplace, and hence often take a birdseye view.—Don't be led astray when negation comes down on you again and you cannot see your way on for a time. Never believe that the positive is not there or is not the one reality. Think simply that the sun has gone behind a cloud, and is bound to emerge again.

Your

Gustl

P.S.—I have come on another piano quartet of Brahms, the one in C minor we played four-handed last year. The first two movements wonderful. Apart from the G minor it is the only work of his I can wholly accept. A pity that the last two movements fall off so sadly.

I drop Tolstoy for the while. You need a rest from him. I speak of the publicist and prophet. His stories and novels—that is another matter!

Frankfort, 1904

Here I am, you see, my darling Almscherl, taking a cosy quarter of an hour to talk to you over a cup of coffee, after the exhausting rehearsal (from 9:30 to 11:30) followed by a very frugal meal in an ale-house. I always take your letters to the Central Station and they go off at half-past four to reach you in bed next morning.

I shall be conducting the final (public) rehearsal of the Third at the same time as you are reading this letter. It went much better today. The orchestra has got down to it now and appears to take a real interest in the business.—The chorus of the opera makes a very good job of it (no beauties amongst them, so you need not pass any sleepless nights after perusal of this letter)—and the contralto (not only alto but old too) is likewise quite adequate. So I hope all will go well tomorrow night. After that my hopes are set on a pleasant journey, which, thank God, will take me back to your arms. I arrive in Vienna, West Station, at 5:26 on Thursday.

*   *   *

Your

true Gustl

First Performance of the Fifth Symphony

Cologne, Friday afternoon, after the first
rehearsal, 16 October, 1904

How blessed, how blessed a shoemaker to
be! With Variations.

Almschi dear,

According to my calculations, you ought to get this first post tomorrow if I take it to the station to catch the mail. And so, today was the first rehearsal!

It all went off tolerably well. The Scherzo is the very devil of a movement. I see it is in for a peck of troubles! Conductors for the next fifty years will all take it too fast and make nonsense of it; and the public—Oh, heavens, what are they to make of this chaos of which new worlds are for ever being engendered, only to crumble in ruin the moment after? What are they to say to this primeval music, this foaming, roaring, raging sea of sound, to these dancing stars, to these breath-taking iridescent and flashing breakers? What has a flock of sheep to say but "baaa!" to the *Brüdersphären Wettgesang?* How blessed, how blessed a tailor to be! Oh that I had been born a commercial traveler [Demuth] and engaged as baritone at the Opera! Oh that I might give my Symphony its first performance fifty years after my death!

Now I'm going for a walk along the Rhine—the only man in all Cologne who will quietly go his way after the première without pronouncing me a monster. Oh that I were "quite the mama, quite the papa!"*

How blessed, how blessed a locksmith [Slezak] to be and to become a tenor at the Vienna Royal Opera House. I have to go to the Opera tonight to hear the prima donna. It's *Fedora*, produced by Giordano. Oh that I were an Italian roast-chestnut man!

Oh that I were a Russian police agent!

Oh that I were town councillor of Cologne with my box at the Municipal Theater and also at Gürzenich, and could look down upon all modern music!

Oh that I were a Professor of Music and could give lectures on Wagner and have them published [Guido Adler].

I expect you without fail on Sunday. I must have one person anyway to whom my Symphony will be a pleasure. If you were here now we should take a taxi and drive along the Rhine; as it is, I must go on foot in case you should be envious. The weather is glorious. A thousand greetings from your Oh, so blessed

Gustl

* *Domestica* by Richard Strauss.

But this is horrible! My Almschl, I was really angry at the first moment and nearly hit the telegraph-boy on the head. And now— after venting my rage—I still can't give up all hope. Leave nothing undone—sweat it out—swallow brandy—gobble aspirin—you can get over a chill in two days and still travel on Monday night and be here for the concert on Tuesday! Almschili, please—do all you can. It would be too, too ghastly—to be all alone at this—the first —performance. It's enough to kill the funeral.—The rehearsal today, as far as that goes, was a great deal more reassuring. The worst of it is that on the top of all I'm worried lest there's something serious the matter with you. For what else could stop you?

Write by return. I won't give up hope. All my thoughts! I take this to the station and send it by special delivery—you may still get it tomorrow morning!

Your speechless

Gust

Hotel Dom, Cologne
19.10.1904

Almschel dear!

Only a word! I'm in a spin! Public rehearsal yesterday went very well. An excellent performance. Audience breathlessly attentive— even if dazed by the first movements! There was even a hiss or two after the Scherzo. The Adagietto and Rondo seemed to get home. A whole crowd of musicians, conductors, etc., from outside. Hinrichsen is *enthusiastic* and has already booked my Sixth with the utmost eagerness, adding humorously: "But now—don't put up your price on me"—as I certainly shall not; he's such a good fellow. Walter and Berliner, the two stalwarts, turned up; Walter yesterday, for the final rehearsal. Berliner only this morning—he's in his room now, weeping because you haven't come. I believe he only came for your sake.

So tonight's the concert. I'll wire tomorrow and then off to Amsterdam. Write next time to Amsterdam, Concertgebouw.

That's all you need put.

Your not being here, Almschi, spoils everything. Turns it to dust

and ashes, I can almost say. You would have taken a pleasure in it, a pleasure all your own!

Kiss the little angels for me. And, God above, see you get well again!

Your old

Gustl

Amsterdam, 19 October, 1904

Almschl dear,

In Amsterdam, as you see. The Mengelbergs met me at the station and insisted on carrying me off with them.—So here I am again—as last year. Very charming, unassuming people. Not to lose time, I rehearsed the solos with the singer here last night. Short stout little woman, like Cilli, [the Mahler's cook] but sings beautifully—voice as clear as a bell. Why are you not here? You would get so much from it.

I hope Walter has told you all about Cologne.—I think it answered all our expectations.

I'm off now to the first rehearsal (they start at 9 here) and am only writing these few lines in a hurry, so as not to leave you without news of me. Write to me at the Concertgebouw, it's simpler and it will be brought to me at once.

A thousand kisses in haste.

Your

Gustl

Amsterdam, 20 October, 1904

My darling Almscherl,

I'm staying with Mengelberg. He seemed so set on it that I couldn't refuse and I have given up my other (much finer) abode. Now I'll tell you all my adventures from the beginning.—I traveled with the King of the Belgians! To my utter astonishment, I observed as I was boarding my train symptoms of the wildest excitement in the officials of the railway, not to mention a laying down of carpets and a thronging of uniforms and shakos. We ordinary travelers were herded and hustled like cattle and our tickets were examined with calculated rudeness. The rumor

spread like wild-fire and there was an excited stampede to the
carriage windows—I of course sat where I was, but from a sudden
increase of noise (presumably due to beating hearts of blissful subjects) I deduced that the chattering event was in progress. But I
was not to be left out of it. After a short time, thinking myself
safe, I looked about me with composure and saw an imposing
personage, who fixed me with a piercing eye, pass the carriage
window. It was His Majesty, I realized a moment later. And I
regretted for the first time since starting on the journey that my
Almscherl was not there; it would have thrilled her, I'm sure.

*   *   *

Your old

Gustav

Amsterdam, 21 October, 1904

My darling Almschili,

It is really vexatious this time how hard it is to get a letter written. I literally have to steal away.

Yesterday, then (to resume), I strolled about all afternoon with
my host along the canals and streets. In many ways I am reminded
of Hamburg, only that there it is so much nobler and more open.
Mengelberg is very kind, and he and his wife do all they can to
make life and even the very earth a cushion to me. The only part
I don't like is being forever entertained. In that way it was much
better at Lemberg, where at least I was always alone. At night,
thank God, I was left to myself and rummaged about in a vast
accumulation of Dutch, Belgian and French scores. What a fantastic crowd, yet how sterile! Another rehearsal this morning. The
orchestra were off their heads with delight. Its beauty fairly winded
me. I can't tell you what I felt when I heard it again. Only, it
makes me very sad that you should not be here, dear heart. It will
be a fine performance. Better than at Crefeld. Final rehearsal this
evening. Now I am going to have a look at the docks. And tomorrow morning, having nothing else on, to the Museum.

On Sunday, as now decided, I shall conduct *only* my First. Is
that a compliment, or not? Mengelberg claims the rest of the program. But I'm in a fix about the ham and cheese to bring back
with me! I'm so terribly clumsy! And if I asked my hosts, they

would take it as a hint, which would be most painful, as they provide all they possibly can. They even produced a bottle of Asti for me today. God knows where they got it from. I would rather bring you the money when I come, and then we'll have a jaunt in the town and buy something nice for you and Putzi. When all's said and done, it's a ghastly sacrifice to make to one's work —this traveling all over the place! I'm just not cut out for it. Almscherl, I kiss you many times, my beloved, and embrace you.

Your

Gustl

I saw the Bourse too yesterday. It is very imposing. People here, however, don't appear to think much of it—just like in Vienna!

Amsterdam, 1904

Dearest,

I enclose the notice from the *Kölnische Zeitung*, which was sent on to me here. That's all I've seen so far. I can imagine how they are letting off steam. The *Neue Freie Presse* in particular will show what it can do.

I'm really delighted by the people here.

Just imagine the program for Sunday:

1. Fourth Symphony by G. Mahler.
   Intermission.
2. Fourth Symphony by G. Mahler.

How do you like that? They have simply put my work twice over on the same program. After the intermission, it starts at the beginning again! I'm really curious to know whether the audience will be warmer the second time. It must be the record for a new work. I rehearsed the Fourth today and the orchestra plays it so cleanly that I'm enchanted. In Cologne too I found my chief (if not my only) supporters in the orchestra. I must go to the rehearsal.

A thousand greetings, my dearest,

Your

Gustl

Don't worry if the critics are abusive.

Amsterdam, 23 October, 1904

My precious Almschili,

I can't understand your not having had a letter yet after four days! I write every day! —I don't waste an hour here. This morning I went for a lovely walk in the country. This Dutch countryside —enchanting roads, paved, and lined with trees, leading out in all directions, and the long undeviating canals, converging from every quarter, shining like streaks of silver, and the little green-washed houses; and, above it all, the gray-blue, cloudy sky and flocks of birds! So lovely—I think to myself all the time how you will love it next year, when you come to hear my Second and Fourth performed. Everyone here talks about you. Your beauty is renowned throughout Holland and everyone wants to know you. They're a splendid lot, now I know them better, and so hospitable you feel completely at home. I'm very glad I'm staying with the Mengelbergs. It means I make such good use of my time that I never waste an hour. I think of you always whatever I am doing, and of you all.

And now for yesterday evening. It was magnificent.—At first they were a little puzzled, but with each movement they grew warmer and when the contralto came on (I haven't told you yet that the Dutch singer was ill and *la* Kittel was sent for and sang very well) the whole hall was gripped, and from then to the end there was the familiar rise of temperature. When the last note died away the tumult of applause was almost daunting. Everyone said nothing like it could be remembered. I have beaten Strauss, who is all the rage here, by yards. The second performance comes off tonight (not a seat to be had).—This morning there was the first rehearsal of the First.—The orchestra in the utmost enthusiasm. Too bad you're not here.

This afternoon I'm going to the Museum to see the Rembrandts. Tomorrow to The Hague and Scheveningen. Day after tomorrow, Sunday morning, to the sea at Haarlem. And early on Monday, at half-past six, back to you again, my one and only one.

Gustl

Amsterdam, October, 1904

Almschl dear!

Enclosed is a photo taken by an admirer during a concert. It will amuse you, I think, and I send it as a glimpse of my present existence. (At the moment, I'm listening to a first-rate performance of Schumann's D Minor Symphony, Mengelberg conducting.)— Today, the final rehearsal of the Fourth.—Last night, rehearsal with chorus of the Second.—They sang magnificently, almost as well as the Basel chorus.

I wish it was Friday and I was in the train again. I was not born to be forever on the move—however necessary it may be. The only moments of a trip like this when I feel at ease are the rehearsals. If only conductors had grasped by now how my work ought to go, I should leave them to it and take my ease at Heiligenstadt!

I see now, anyway, what folly it was to set about the first performance of a work of mine in Cologne, where the audience gave my Third such a cool reception.—The response of the audience always affects the newspaper-scribblers, who have no more mind of their own than a weather-cock. And so all the upset and fatigue of a long journey was to no purpose. I could have got it cheaper in Vienna.

I'll try and manage things more cleverly with the Sixth. I think of you with tenderness, my Almscherl. See that you're thoroughly rested by the time I come home!

Your much harried

Gustl

Amsterdam, 25 October, 1904

Dearest!

It was an astounding evening! The audience from the very start was so attentive and understanding, and the response was warmer with each movement.—The enthusiasm increased the second time, and at the end it was something like it was at Crefeld. The singer sang the solo with moving simplicity, and the orchestra accompanied her as though with rays of sunshine. It was a picture on a gold ground. I really believe now I shall find in Amsterdam the musical home for which I hoped in that stupid Cologne.

Today the final rehearsals of the Second begin. There's still a hard nut to crack there. The orchestra here is as charming to me as ever! I kiss you many times, my Almschi.

Your (in great haste)

Gustl

Amsterdam, 1904

Dearest!

I send you with this a critique (from the leading newspaper here) translated for you by Mrs. Mengelberg. It will give you some idea of the reception my Fourth has had here. *Much* warmer than the Third. Mengelberg has already put it in his next program and will repeat it several times after that. The last movement with the soprano solo made the greatest impression of all.

I'm wrestling now with the terribly exhausting rehearsal of the Second! The final is tonight.

I couldn't go on any real sight-seeing expedition up to now, because all my mornings and evenings were occupied. I went to Haarlem yesterday to look at Hals, but unfortunately the museum was only open till three. I'm hoping I may be able to cut a rehearsal tomorrow morning, and then I shall go to Zandvoort on the North Sea (you can get there in an hour by electric railway) and get out at Haarlem on the way and have better luck, I hope. Thank God, my head is turned for home. I set off early on Friday morning and shall be with you on Saturday at about 8.

Almschi—you really have been a lazy correspondent this time! I do take your state of health into account, but surely you could have written a postcard at least every day. Please, dearest Almschi, read the enclosed notice and then give it to Mama, who is a far better public for such matters and imbibes them with more understanding.

But whatever you think of them in general, you can't help being gladdened by the understanding and absence of prejudice in criticisms such as this. The other critics all adopt the same tone.

You never say a word of the children either. Putzi must have quite forgotten me and Guckerl won't even know me again.

A tender kiss to all three.

Your old

Gustl

Leipzig, November, 1904

My Almschili!

All the rehearsals are over and here I sit, quite shattered, enjoying a little peace with nothing but the performance in front of me. —And now, first of all: the orchestra, which yesterday was but a heap of ruins, a pile of unconnected noises, has now become an ordered structure. The stones took their places of their own accord at Arion's song, and I await today's performance with composure.

Their behavior has been charming, poor devils. Yesterday and today I pitched into them for four hours at a stretch, and instead of taking it in bad part they bade me an enthusiastic farewell at the end of it.

The work is arousing tremendous interest throughout the town; the leading critics came to both rehearsals and it is lucky I came here for the performance. Now for the details:

I gave a look round during the first rehearsal yesterday and caught sight of someone standing at the back like a worshipper. It was Mr. Nodnagel! At first I was enraged, and then touched. But what an eccentric! In the afternoon I went to Stägemann's. They were as cordial to me afterwards as before, asked after you and invited me to dinner. I had to decline as I was engaged to go to Hinrichsen. When I arrived (he had already telephoned to ask if he might come and fetch me), I found him at the piano with the piano edition for four hands of a Bruckner Symphony, playing one part with his hands and the second in his head. I sat down beside him and played it right through with him—secretly regarding it as my tribute of gratitude for his generosity, and some little amends for the expenses the poor fellow incurred owing to the failure of the Fifth.

Then we were joined by Straube, a distinguished musician and charming person, and a fanatical admirer of mine.

A publisher, Kahnt, has just been in to see me. He begged me with passion for my new songs and ballads. I shall send him the piano editions from Vienna and then he will make me an offer.

And now addio, my Almschl. Nikisch has asked me to lunch tomorrow (by telegram, as he's conducting in Berlin today) and afterwards I'm to play him my Fifth so as to initiate him into my intentions. In the evening I set off home; so early on the day after, Wednesday, I shall be with you! A thousand kisses from

Your

Curtl

My dear Mr. Mahler,

It is very disagreeable being banished to such a distance from you. I think of you every day and still feel the stimulus of our talks together. The greatest happiness of the children of earth lies in personality, but not only in their own. It may be that you can't help the greatness and goodness and the command of beauty, with which you are endowed, but all the same I thank you for the share I am permitted to have in them—a possession I can never lose. It means that long stages of my earthly pilgrimage are cheered and illumined as otherwise they could not be. I can think of no possible reason why I should not say so. Kindest regards from us both to your wife, and also to all whom we met on the evening we spent with you. For you—a shake of the hand and the expression of my lasting and devoted friendship—

Gerhart Hauptmann

Forgive the strange shape in which this will reach you. The lack of a passable envelope left me no choice.

Hotel de la Reine, Ospedaletti

28 February, 1904

My dear Mahler,

I can now regard myself as a convalescent. I have had a life of it, I can tell you, since the end of February, no life at all, in fact, although things might have been worse. I had a temperature almost without interruption and this condemned me to pass my days in a fret of vexation. It is a bitter pill to lie in bed, to give up all that makes life worth living—worst of all, in a country where life is seen in all its glory. The thought of all you are losing is hard to shut out. I became insufferable, impatient and exacting. I could face death, I believe, with philosophy. But I am no philosopher in the case of illness,—the one real affliction of mankind. That is the lesson I have learned from experience.

But now I am better and land is in sight. The doctors from Lugano gaily treated me for typhus and starved me on sops for six weary weeks. The seat of the malady was, in reality, the tip of my left lung and the proper treatment would have been super-alimentation, as I know now from the very able doctor who conducts this hospital. Following his directions, I eat as much as I can and drink a bottle of wine daily, not to mention beer, which I greatly enjoy, and lie all day long in the open air. The result is that the fever has entirely left me, I put on weight and feel my strength and my self-reliance returning. I cannot deny that even now I chafe at this passive-existence, for you, my dear, dear friend, know what it means to have your head full of nonsense. Often and often I have called you in to console me, or, rather, not you but all you have had to overcome.

My dear Mahler, it seems to me quite unnatural that we should stand on ceremony with each other. Now that the joy of life returns I imagine us meeting not long hence in the fulness of health and energy and as old friends. The misfortune of not having met in our youth must not stand in the way of our intimacy in the ripeness of age; for after all we follow the same path. I have a great desire to hear your music and to know you all through.

We cherish as a dream of the future to have you and your dear wife with us here, for a whole summer if possible. (Including, of course, your children.) I believe you would be comfortable and be able to work.

Am I asking too much?

Grethe sends her love.

All our best wishes to you all.

Ever, from the bottom of my heart,

Your

Gerhart Hauptmann

ARNOLD SCHÖNBERG TO GUSTAV MAHLER

12.xii.1904

My dear Director,

I must not speak as a musician to a musician if I am to give any idea of the incredible impression your symphony made on me: I can speak only as one human being to another. For I saw your very soul, naked, stark naked. It was revealed to me as a stretch of wild and secret country, with eerie chasms and abysses neighbored by sunlit, smiling meadows, haunts of idyllic repose. I felt it as an event of nature, which after scourging us with its terrors puts a rainbow in the sky. What does it matter that what I was told afterwards of your "program" did not seem to correspond altogether with what I had felt. Whether I am a good or a bad indicator of the feelings an experience arouses in me is not the point. Must I have a correct understanding of what I have lived and felt? And I believe I felt your symphony. I shared in the battling for illusion; I suffered the pangs of disillusionment; I saw the forces of evil and good wrestling with each other; I saw a man in torment struggling towards inward harmony; I divined a personality, a drama, and *truthfulness*, the most uncompromising truthfulness.

I had to let myself go. Forgive me. I cannot feel by halves. With me it is one thing or the other!

In all devotion
Arnold Schönberg

1905

Vienna, June

My Almscherl!

Lunch with Justi today. Arnold [Rosé] was back again from Graz and we discussed certain orchestra matters. He was very "winning." Thereafter I undressed and lay on the sofa to stew for a bit (the heat is simply murderous). Thereafter went out and drank a black coffee at the Imperial, in the course of which I fell asleep. The waiter woke me up. Pity—I was dreaming so pleasantly. But what about I've forgotten now. Now I'm in the office, inducing by degrees the appropriate state of mind for the *Feuersnot*, which this evening at 7 is being lavished on its one thousand enraptured listeners.

Maddening that the Shah does not come until the 15th. I might so well have got away on Sunday!

The little ones must be darlings now. It's a shame I can't be with them to hear Putzi marveling at everything and asking questions. Does she recognize her playground again? Has the railing been put up?

My dearest love and a hug, my Almscherl,

Gustav

Schluderbach, 1905

My Almschili!

After I had with desperate efforts avoided the restaurant car at Lienz and got a seat in one of the other coaches, I was made aware by a dull sensation that an attack of migraine was irresistibly approaching and by the time I reached Schluderbach it was upon me in all its fury. In vain I tried to arrest it by lying down: it drove me from the sofa out into the street. I raced round the lake (2½ hours) and returned here, where I spent the night, more or less recovered. Even on my walk, or run (through a forest of dwarf pines) I thought all the time: If only Almschi were here! You would love it. What a pity it is—for now, just now, there is not a holiday-maker to be seen—although I must admit the country people and soldiers (from Landro garrison) are indulging in Corpus Christi celebrations to such good effect that the whole place rocks. But go two paces from the inn and there is an end of all horror.

A thousand kisses,

Your

Gustl

Edlacherhof, 25 August, 1905

My dear!

Your very dear letter, addressed to the opera house, followed me here today. I'm very glad those visitors came so à propos. They might have been only a bore to me, whereas they distracted you from a rather fatiguing routine. But don't take any notice of what Rosthorn* says. If you could see me today and knew how well and rested I feel already and how exactly I know my physical strength, you would have no anxiety whatever. Your Rosthorns have not the dimmest notion of an entelechy such as mine. On the contrary, they cannot imagine the evil effects on me of *not* sticking to my work. And, as a matter of fact, there was in recent years much more cause for anxiety when I had those attacks of dizziness on going to bed—from which this year I was entirely free. So there you have the surest indication that it fatigued me a great deal less this year.

Although it never stopped raining, I went my five hours' walk again today. The food here is positively the best I ever came across in a country hotel. Unfortunately it is pouring again today. If it doesn't mean to stop I shall go back to Vienna tomorrow. But I give you my solemn promise that I shall only idle and walk—that is to say, I shall flee to the mountains again the very first fine day.

Is there no possibility, then, of your coming any earlier? I'm horribly desolate and utterly sick of solitude and hotel life.

A thousand greetings.

Your

Gustav

Berlin, 10.11.1905

My dearest heart!

I am sitting once more at the table from which you were bombarded day in, day out, four years ago; and I observe that my feelings have not changed since those days. My thoughts go to you with the same joy and love, and I rejoice now as then to tell you so. I am in a mad whirl today—seeing Ochs, Hülsen, Muck, Gerhart Hauptmann, Fernow, rehearsal for the concert—a talk with

* A distinguished Viennese physician.

Fried, etc., etc. I had quite a pleasant time with Strauss yesterday; but there is always with him that frigid, blasé feeling. However, he made me a present of his latest publication (Berlioz's *Treatise on Instrumentation* with comments of his own), which all the same will be of great interest to you and from which you will learn a great deal. I'll give it you for your library. He promised me further a score of *Salome*, which I likewise dedicate to you, so now you will be the object of the wildest envy on the part of all creative musicians.

But, as I said before, a little more warmth would be preferable to all this.

We are all going to Mrs. Wolff's tonight. Oh God, what motto shall I find to murmur there? But Fried is very docile and knows how to take a hint. (In any case, the occasion will tell me whether he has talent; yesterday he took it all too fast by half!) Now a cup of tea, and then Berliner, who had lunch with me too, is coming to take me to the concert. To Leipzig tomorrow at 8. The day after at 8 a.m. kisses and Putzi and Gucki, bath, breakfast, and then, with all speed, "off to work," for there's going to be a mad rush of it.

A thousand greetings, and also to Mama, dear Almschili.

Your

Gustav

COSIMA WAGNER TO GUSTAV MAHLER

Bayreuth, 8 June, 1905

My dear Director,

May I trespass on your kindness to ask you two questions?

The first relates to Fräulein von Mildenburg, whom you were once so good as to recommend to me for the part of Kundry. I hear very different, in fact contradictory, opinions expressed about the achievements of this gifted singer. Some praise her unreservedly, others say she is very unequal, and explain it by her poor health.

I should like to take your verdict as final, and if you will be so kind as to give it me you may rely on our silence as implicitly as I rely on you to regard this letter as confidential.

My second question is likewise of a confidential nature. It concerns my son's new opera *Bruder Lustig*, which Simons would like to perform at the Jubilee Theatre, as he did with *Kobold.*

My son told me that it might be troubling you to no purpose to send you his opera after the rejection of *Kobold*, but that at the same time it might seem discourteous not to ask whether the director of the Royal Opera House would like to consider his work, before he entered into negotiation with Simons.

I undertook to put this question and told him that there was nothing importunate in submitting his opera; for you had given sufficient proof of your good opinion of his work by the fine production of his *Bärenhäuter,* and although the season's program or other reasons had prevented you from accepting *Kobold,* you were certainly acquainted with the score and had presumably taken note of the performance, and were well aware of his merits as a playwright and composer. Therefore you would certainly tell me, without previous acquaintance with the score, whether you wished to see *Bruder Lustig* or not. May I request a reply by telegram? This will spare you the need to give your reasons and allow my son to communicate his decision to Simons without delay.

With my best thanks in advance for your replies to both my questions, I am,

Yours most sincerely,

C. Wagner

Bayreuth, 13 June, 1905

My dear Director,

My best thanks for your sympathetic and early reply to my questions. I will see whether the roles which Fräulein von Mildenburg undertakes can be understudied in such a way as to spare her excessive fatigue and to guard against all eventualities. In the first place it would be a question of Kundry. I have very pleasant memories of Fräulein von Mildenburg. I recollect the rehearsal of Isolde, which I went through very carefully with her (especially the first act), and was glad to hear from my son that this performance had been an important one.

Your opinion, dear Mr. Mahler, has decisive weight with me and I will see now whether we have success with the alternative casting.

I thank you also very cordially for your reply to my second question, for which perhaps I am even more indebted.

I did certainly assume that the achievements of my son as conductor, as dramatist and composer, and as stage-manager of the Bayreuth Festivals made it natural that his works, apart from the impression they made on any one person, should (as in the case of more than one opera house) be given to the public, which then was at liberty to give its verdict.

Your answer to this assumption of mine, shows me, dear Mr. Mahler, that you take no account of such circumstances in the case of a composer; you wish in the first place to gain a thorough knowledge of each work, so that if you accept it you can take its part, even against opposition, if necessary.

I find this not merely comprehensible but greatly to your credit. But the present case has an aspect of its own, and I crave your indulgence while I explain it to you.

After the performance of the *Bärenhäuter* in Vienna, and in consequence of it, you expressed to my son a wish to have his next opera (without having any knowledge of it). Unfortunately Siegfried was already committed to Munich; but in consideration of the honor you did him in the case of *Herzog Wildfang* he sent his *Kobold* to you in the first place. You kept it, dear Mr. Mahler, for a very considerable length of time, owing no doubt to the innumerable demands made upon you, and when you were asked for your decision you declined the work without giving any reasons for doing so. Thus a new situation came into being. It is difficult, I might say impossible, for my son to subject you, and himself, to the risk of another refusal, and you would not be the artist you are if you did not understand and esteem pride and sensibility in another artist. Now, however, we are gladdened by the good news that you look forward to his new work with great interest.

Will you not give rein to this feeling of yours and decide on the production without more ado, as you did for *Wildfang?* Even though *Kobold*, whether owing to its matter or form, its libretto or music, did not appeal to you and did not seem to you suitable for the Royal Opera House, you cannot have thought it unworthy of performance, for in that case you would not have been able to feel any interest in its successor. It is to this interest I appeal. I ask it to stir up the warm-hearted, trustful artist and to conquer the cautious and critical director. If it responds to my appeal, I ask again for a reply by telegram; but if the interest you feel is overborne, I shall take silence as a sufficient reply, reproaching myself, however, in advance, for having trespassed so long on your time, already so fully occupied. Whether I have the happiness to persuade you, dear Mr. Mahler, or whether you hold to your previous opinion, you may be sure that my son and I will accept your decision with sympathy, and that I remain with renewed warmth of esteem

Yours, etc.,

C. Wagner

1906

Amsterdam, March, 1906

. . . I played a few passages from my Eighth to Mengelberg and Diepenbrock yesterday. Funny, this work always makes the typical, strong appeal. It would be an odd thing if my most important work should be the most easily understood.

Amsterdam, 1906

My Almscherl!

Diary in brief!

Met at station by Mengelberg. As kind and hospitable as ever. Long talk and tired to bed. Little sleep though. Next morning at half-past nine, rehearsal. All brilliantly rehearsed in advance. Result magnificent. Afternoon, a drive, walks interspersed. Six o'clock, dinner. To bed at nine and slept beautifully until six. Today at nine, second rehearsal. Holland again delights me beyond measure. Consoling and characteristic above all is the note of cleanliness everywhere. The shining kitchen is only the symbol of all else. When you have had a meal here, you think with shuddering of the pigsties in less favored lands. Diepenbrock was already on the spot for the first rehearsal. There's a fine fellow for you. Not a moment passes but I wish you were here. I sleep in a large room with two beds side by side and, leading out of it (the door between has been removed), there is a small room with a cot. You see how thoughtfully it was all arranged for us. Mengelberg too is set on having the first performance of the Eighth, and Bodanzky and Hageman from Mannheim have also put in a word.

The orchestra is splendid and has taken to me hugely. It's a pleasure this time instead of hard work. They sent a deputation to me yesterday asking me to conduct the other items as well at one of the concerts (this was done at the first by Mengelberg). They said they wanted so much to learn Beethoven and Wagner from me. Isn't that charming? For it means that instead of two free mornings they have two rehearsals. *Tout comme chez nous!*

I embrace you many times, my dear. Do write!

Your

Gustav

Amsterdam, 1906

My dearest!

I am now installed here and have got through the first rehearsal also. *"Welch anderer Geist!"* The orchestra *splendidly rehearsed in advance* and a performance equal to any in Vienna. The chorus (in the *Klagende Lied*) very well rehearsed and trained. Mengelberg is a capital fellow! There's no one else I could entrust a work of mine to with entire confidence. The Symphony is already on the program for next week at The Hague, Rotterdam, Haarlem, Utrecht, and Arnhem, where Mengelberg is giving concerts with the orchestra from here. I am rehearsing the *Kindertotenlieder* today. I don't know the singer yet. Am curious.

I had a marked *succès* in Antwerp. Excellent notices. I got your letters here. Putzi's drawing is simply incredible! What an eye she has! I shall be at home early on *Monday!* Heavens! how glad I am! For today, my dear, all my love. Everyone here is indignant that you are not with me. The Mengelbergs would not hear of my going to the hotel. They are very warm-hearted and genuine people, and he is a man you can *rely* on. Diepenbrock was there too. I have true friends here.

Your

Gustl

Amsterdam, March, 1906

My dearest Almschili,

In spite of your "sharp" letter. Yesterday, then, the Symphony, a fine performance of the *Kindertotenlieder* except for the singer, who sang with no depth. This evening, final rehearsal of the *Klagende Lied;* tomorrow, performance; the day after, I leave. Thank God, I shall be with you all again on Monday. One feels quite desolate, although they are all so kind and spare themselves no pains. I have a stout following here in Amsterdam—the young people in particular are very enthusiastic. The audience *very attentive*, the press positively glowing.

And, most important of all, Mengelberg puts me constantly in his programs. Within the next fortnight, he is giving the Fifth again at The Hague, Rotterdam and Arnhem—and it is being repeated at two concerts here.

Meanwhile, there is something very tiresome going on in Vienna between Roller and the chorus. I fear it may have far-reaching consequences. I may easily be drawn in myself, out of sympathy with him.

You wretch, are you not ever going to write to me? Are you always on the spree until two in the morning? Servus!

Your

Gust

Essen, 22.5.1906

My dearest Almschi!

I am delighted by a young Russian (the well-known pianist and conductor, Gabrilowitsch) who has come here for my rehearsals and shares my table at the hotel. He tells me of my admirers among the young brigade in St. Petersburg. The rehearsals console me greatly. I hope I am not mistaken. So far I have taken them through the first three movements. I come to the last movement today. I was much interested by what you said about *Salome*. I told you so long ago. But now you under-value what is, after all, a very significant work and, as you rightly feel, a work of "virtuosity" in a bad sense. In that respect Wagner is quite another story. The longer you live and the more you learn, the more clearly you will feel the difference between the few who are *truly* great and the mere *virtuosi*. I am glad you see to the bottom of it so quickly. The coldness of Strauss's temperament, which is not a matter of his talent but of his nature as a man, does not escape you, and you are repelled by it. How is Putzerl? Don't ever forget to put in a word about her. All my love, my dear, and come on Friday. You are in for a treat.

Your old

Gustl

Salzburg, 1906

My Almschili!

In a ghastly turmoil! I am quite battered. I was met yesterday by Roller, Stoll and Hassinger, the last representing the Festival Committee (of maidens robed in white there was none). Took steps to get rid of all but Roller, who took me to the hotel and stayed on with me. Misurina* was on a visit to Burckhard. We went for a stroll in the town and fell in at once with Strauss, who joined us. I went and had supper with him in the hotel, while Roller went to the station to meet Schluderbach, I mean Misurina. Strauss left at eight-thirty to attend a Festival gathering; by this time Roller returned with Toblach, I mean to say, Schluderbach, and we spent a short time together. Whereafter, Tre Croci went to bed and Strauss came in elated from the party, accompanied by a journalist. We then discoursed for an hour about fees and royalties, etc., after which I went to bed. But not to sleep—the devil only knows why. Got up at six, breakfasted substantially, and now await the Munich concert-organizer. Rehearsal at ten. I shall then make my

---

* Alfred Roller's wife was called Milewa. Mahler was always calling her by other names, including names of places.

escape and see about throwing myself headlong from a height, or performing some other sensational feat. Then perhaps I shall have peace.

May the devil run off with this accursed tribe. Strauss has already composed a few scenes of *Elektra* (Hofmannsthal) He will not part with it for less than 10% a night and 100,000 marks down. (This, I confess, is only a supposition of mine.) As he made no further enquiry I told him nothing of the antiquated life I led in the summer. I don't think he would be greatly impressed to hear what old-fashioned rubbish I was busy on. Oh blessed, oh blessed a modern to be!

*   *   *

Write soon to your

Gustav

Salzburg, Summer, 1906

My dear Almschili!

Yesterday was distinguished by torrents of rain. I went to a concert in the morning (conducted by Rich. Strauss) in honor of Mozart. Bruckner's Ninth was performed (as, the day before, Beethoven's Fifth). Salzburg all agog with enthusiasm. It was an orgy. Anyway, a great quantity of lager was drunk afterwards. Then lunch with Strauss and Roller. Specht,* pale and somewhat uncertain, came in with the dessert. Strauss departed and I spent an hour over a quiet talk with Specht. Then donned a borrowed frock-coat and betook myself to the reception. After having been honored by a few words from his Highness, I retired weak with excitement, to the buffet, had a drink, ate a sandwich, and evaporated to the theater, where at six there began a most accomplished dress rehearsal of *Figaro* (with locked doors). Supped afterwards in the hotel with H., Dr. B., Roller and Specht. Specht took train joyfully for Vienna. Strauss (this is truth) keeps on insisting that I should write an opera. He says I have great talent for it. Tuesday evening—hurrah—I shall be with you. Oh, had I never left you! All my thoughts—

Your

Gustl

* Richard Specht, writer and critic.

Salzburg, 16.7.1906

My Almschili!

What a dear letter today. Your notation was perfectly right in feeling. I have only corrected a few details. (The harmonics are not quite "clean.") It is astonishing what a memory for music you have. I'm alone in the hotel, thank God. Roller is staying with Cortina next door. You would be astonished at Roller. He walks for hours with me. They are very nice to each other, but beyond that as unattached as if they were not married at all. We have all our meals together. Afterwards she goes up to her room and he attaches himself to me. Strauss too is now always with us and in general very charming, as he always is when alone with me. But his being will always remain alien to me. That way of thinking and feeling is worlds apart from mine. I wonder whether one of these days we shall meet on the same star. The rehearsal was excellent. I went straight down among the orchestra and saluted the soloists from below.

I went to *Don Juan* with Strauss yesterday (a box had been reserved for you and me). It was such an unspeakably bad performance that we left in outrage after the second scene. We supped quite alone in the hotel. Thank God, you could send such a good report of Gucki. A thousand greetings, my dear; it will not be long now.

Your

Gustl

P.S.—Once again—your musicianship really surprises me.

Telegram

Munich, 6 November

Arrived, all well—then to the hotel in right good will to have a bath and coffee swill. I sent you a poetic cable, as in Munich only able, for here art fills both house and stable. You can't help feeling almost Attic, whereat I do rejoice fanatic.

Gustav

ARNOLD SCHÖNBERG TO GUSTAV MAHLER

Vienna, 14.vi.1906

My dear Director,

I am not quite sure yet whether the engagement at the Opera refers to Zemlinsky,* or myself. However, that is a matter of indifference and was not really what I wanted to say at all. What I did want to say was how deeply impressed I was by the magnificence of the work I heard today. I cannot forbear telling you that such music could come from only one man in the world and that man is: Mahler. I have always held you very, very dear—only you have perhaps not known it—but today I know why.

I kiss your hands a thousand times.

Yours

Arnold Schönberg

Rottach-Egern No. 46 am Tegernsee
Upper Bavaria, 18 July, 1906

My dear Director,

I am just finishing my Chamber Symphony, and so have only today found time to answer your letter. Do not please take my delay amiss.

Your letter gave me extraordinary pleasure. Nothing could please me more than your saying that we had come nearer together. It gave me more pleasure and made me prouder than if you had praised a work of mine—although this takes nothing from the value I put on your opinion. To me, the most important thing between people is their personal attachment: without it, nothing else can have its full weight; and, however conscious I may be of the distance between us, I hope to be not altogether unworthy of your friendship.

And now for your friendly invitation. In my first feelings of joy at your letter I was ready to face the journey without thinking twice about it. But on further reflection I was forced to give up the idea. Anxiety on my wife's account—she is going to have a child early in September—would take all pleasure out of the project.

* Mahler had given Alex. von Zemlinsky an engagement at the Opera.

Moreover, there is the very great length of the journey to take into account—nearly fourteen hours. Anything might happen in that time before I could get back again.

And so, to my sorrow, I must give up all thought of it for this year. But I have another idea: you are conducting at the Salzburg Mozart Festival. That is only a few hours away and I could, at all events, come there. So, if you would let us know when you will be there and the dates of the performances, we could join you without fail for a few days. It would make me very happy if this plan were feasible. Your wife, I presume, will be there in any case? May I ask you to give her my heartiest greetings and to tell her how glad I am she has at last arrived at the knowledge that I am a "dear fellow." I have always maintained it, but unfortunately I am seldom believed!

I should be most grateful if you could let me know soon when the Salzburg Festival ends, so that I can plan accordingly. If we are not to meet before, I should very much like to send you my Chamber Symphony, and if, too, you have the time and the wish to look at it. Fortunately, it is not very long, and it is furnished with a piano-score for four hands (a very bad one, for I made it myself). I thank you again for your letter, and await your reply to my proposal of meeting at Salzburg.

Yours very sincerely and devotedly,
Arnold Schönberg

1907

Bristol Hotel, Berlin, January, 1907

My Almschili!

The first rehearsals are now over. The orchestra is not by any means first-rate—but competent and very attentive (making an exception of my favor, as I am told), but one notices the slovenliness of the local celebrities (*tout comme chez nous*). I hope for a tolerable performance.—Wolffs are markedly cool; quite pleasant for me—at least, they leave me in peace.—Fried sat open-mouthed from start to finish, and sucked me in hoof and hide, until at last he sat there incapable of movement, like a boa constrictor. Berliner joined us at night in the "restaurang" and Fried was quite profound. Finally he confessed that my absolute certainty of aim in all I did had opened his eyes as nothing else had ever done, and that he himself could do nothing (he was quick to add, though, that the rest could do even less!).

*   *   *

Your

Gustav

Hotel Bristol, Berlin, January, 1907

My dear, good Almschili,

I went to the Strauss's yesterday afternoon. *She* greeted me with: "Sh!—sh! Richard's asleep," and pulled me into her (very untidy) boudoir, where her old mother was sitting over coffee, and let loose a flood of nonsense about all the financial and sexual events of the last two years, rapidly interjecting questions about "a thousand and one" things without waiting for the answers. She would not hear of my going, told me Richard had had an exhausting rehearsal yesterday morning in Leipzig, had then returned to Berlin to conduct *Götterdämmerung* at night, and today, being reduced to pulp, had lain down to sleep in the afternoon, while she kept strictest watch. I was quite touched. Suddenly she leaped up: "But now to wake the brute." Before I could stop her, she dragged me by both hands into his room, and roused him with a stentorian shout: "Get up. Gustav's here." I was "Gustav" for an hour, and after that Director. Strauss got up with a patient smile, and the torrent of nonsense was resumed as a trio. Then we had tea and they took me back to the hotel in their automobile after it had been arranged that I should lunch with them on Sunday. There I found two front-row stalls for *Salome;* so I took Berliner with me.—The performance (orchestra and singers excellent—scenically utter tripe) and Stoll* again made an extraordinary impression on me. It is emphatically a work of genius, very powerful, and decidedly one of the most important works of our day. A Vulcan

---

* Mahler's stage-manager at the Vienna Opera House; but when his name was on the bill, Mahler himself directed the production.

lives and labors under a heap of slag, a subterranean fire—not merely a firework! It is exactly the same with Strauss's whole personality. That is why it is so difficult in his case to sift the chaff from the grain. But I have an immense respect for the whole phenomenon he presents, and it has been confirmed afresh. This is an immense pleasure to me, for it puts me entirely at one with him. Blech conducted excellently yesterday. Strauss conducts on Saturday and I am going again! Destinn was magnificent! John the Baptist (Berger) quite good. The rest moderate. Orchestra splendid. This evening Berliner and I are going to see Mrs. Wolff. I promise you, my dear, I shall not fall in love with her. She is not the girl you dreamed of. Anyway, I dreamed of you last night. Your hair was done as it was when you were a girl, and I thought you so charming! Almschili, do do your hair one day as you used in those days. I like it so much better than this modern Jewish fashion. Now, at twelve, I am going to rehearse with the singer. I fear I may have a shock. These last three days I have been sleeping until ten, and for an hour, too, in the afternoon. It suits me very well and probably these idle ways do me good. I kiss you, my dear heart! Have you nothing to say of the children? Many greetings to Mamerl too and tell her to be good. Karl too.

Your old
Gustl

I met Messchaert yesterday at the Opera. He was charming and very enthusiastic about my works.

Grand Hotel, Berlin, 13.1.07

My Luxi!

The last rehearsal is over now. I am very well satisfied. Wolffs have really done everything possible, quite contrary to their usual negligence. To lunch with Strauss afterwards. And besides that, a dinner-party for the Blechs. There was no one there when I arrived, but a moment later in came Mrs. Strauss, and began on a temperamental conversation, which fell steeply to this abysmal outburst: "My God, for a million—well no, that's not enough—five million! And then Richard can stop manufacturing music."

Almschili dear—I was interrupted by Hauptmann, whose dear

face did a little to lighten the terrible desolation brought on by that occasion with Strauss.—Hauptmann wants me to spend tomorrow evening with him at Leistikow's, having "sworn" he would bring me. As I cannot accept invitations, we agreed to have supper together in the hotel tomorrow without constraint. We talked of much else as well. I'll tell you all when I come. The detailed description of the dinner with the Strausses has got stuck in my throat. I will only say that "Ahna" filled me with a positive nausea, as also did his (Richard's) casual, absent-minded manner as he distributed the sunshine of his favor between me and Blech. The respectful and friendly consideration which I show him on such occasions awakes no echo, is not, probably, so much as noticed, is simply as though it had never been.—If I am to experience this sort of thing again, I feel I know neither myself nor the world about me. Are other men made of a different clay? It is enough to make one retreat to the wilderness, unsullied and alone, and never know another thing about the world.

I went yesterday to Reinhardt's Kammerspiel, an enchanting little theater in incredibly good taste, and quite unique, to see *Frühlingserwachen* by Wedekind. It is his Opus I and fifteen years old. Well—it took my breath away—immensely powerful and talented and full of poetry. What a shame it is when you think what must have become of him all these years. Among what sort of people has he fallen—and what has happened to him?

I wished every moment you were with me.

Today to *Salome* again, and I will have another try to see to the bottom of the problem of Strauss. My Almschili, I'll write you tomorrow after the public final rehearsal. For today, tenderest greetings, my heart, and thank you for writing so much and so sweetly.

Your

old Gustl

Grand Hotel, Berlin, 14.1.1907

My Almschl!

Salome, then, yesterday. The impression it made was stronger than ever and I am firmly convinced that it is one of the greatest masterpieces of our time. I cannot make out the drift of it, and can only surmise that it is the voice of the "earth-spirit" speaking from the heart of genius, a spirit which does not indeed make a dwelling-place for itself to suit human taste but in accordance with its own unfathomable needs. Perhaps in time I shall gain a clearer understanding of this "cocoon" it has spun for itself.

I met Strauss in the Opera House before the performance, and being alone he was his agreeable self again and insisted on our foregathering afterwards. So we met in a restaurant, he and his wife and mother-in-law and Berliner and I; and we had an exhaustive and most agreeable discussion. I thoroughly enjoyed it apart from the temperamental intermezzi contributed by the eternal feminine. However, she was in a good humor and on the "Gustav" footing with me.—This morning Hauptmann descended again; he's staying in this hotel. We're going to pay Leistikow a visit at six and afterwards at eight to *Friedensfest*.

In an hour's time, at twelve o'clock, there is the public rehearsal. My Third comes to me as a Haydn Symphony. So I dare say people will think me crazy. The whole affair interests me very little.

I had the enclosed letter from the Koenen. In my alarm I told Messchaert it was off for Vienna. For where should I be if I started accompanying every singer at their concerts?

A thousand greetings. How are the little ones?

> Your
>
> Gustl

Grand Hotel, Berlin, 15.1.1907

So, my Almschi, this is the last day in Berlin! Thank God! I am torn to shreds. The final rehearsal went off very well indeed yesterday. There was a tumult of clapping as soon as I appeared and enthusiastic applause after each movement as well as at the end. Wolff gave a dinner in celebration afterwards.—From there to Leistikow with Hauptmann for an hour—I still can't make out why he was so set on it. From there to *Friedensfest* at the Deutsches Theater. (Hauptmann insisted on my seeing it; otherwise I would much rather have stayed at home.) A horrible, realistic affair. If you can warm up to this sort of art, you may get something out of it. I certainly did my best to see the author's point of view and to do him justice. Hauptmann asked me to come up to his room next morning and discuss it. Reinhardt picked me up after the performance and took me to a beer-house and we talked it all over—the piano itself and the production. He's an extremely smart man of the theater, with whom it's a pleasure to talk shop.—Later on Wedekind joined us, at Reinhardt's invitation. I was in good form and let myself go for once. However, they were all very attentive and understanding. Perhaps it was of some help. Wedekind did not displease me. Today first thing, just after breakfast, Hauptmann came to the door. "Well, I've come for your verdict." So I gave it to him and we had a pleasant talk. After he had gone, in came his (charming) little boy with his English nurse. She said he would not be content until he had said good-morning to me. Wasn't that nice? I could tell from the son how the father felt towards me. 1000 greetings from

Your

Gustav

P.S.—Leistikow made no impression on me whatever.

Hotel Imperial, Frankfort, 15.1.1907

My Almschl,

The first rehearsal is over. The orchestra showed a willing spirit. Siloti from Petersburg has been commissioned, you must know, by the orchestra there to get me at all costs to conduct two concerts. His story is much the same as Gabrilowitsch's: they can't forget my rehearsals—they learned so much from them; and I must conduct a Haydn again for them and they would like, besides, the Ninth, some Wagner, and a Symphony of mine. As I am to have a thousand roubles for each concert, it is worth considering. The dates are the 21st and 28th of December! Perhaps you will come with me again? I feel I have been a year away from you already. (That is because you write me such dear letters and they have made me homesick for you.)

I don't myself know what to make of Strauss. How is one to explain his unequalness and jumbling together of bad and good? But all the same my opinion of *Salome* holds good. (You have to think of people like Titian, or the philosopher, Bacon.)

People in Vienna seem to have gone quite crazy. The newspapers here are continually inserting telegrams from them, saying that I have sent in my resignation—that I have piled up an enormous deficit, that I have become impossible, etc., etc.

Gucki is too sweet—

I kiss you many times, my dear—

Your

Gustav

Hotel Imperial, Frankfort, 16.1.07

My dearest!

A magnificent performance yesterday! The audience was appreciative and enthusiastic beyond all expectation.—Criticism fastened on the third movement again. In the morning, for example, I picked up the *Börsen Courier* at the station; it denies me in a few words all talent whatever. I cannot even orchestrate. It was unkind of Strauss not to be present. I found the enclosed card when I got home. Now that I look at it again it seems clear that Mrs. Pauline put her foot down! "You'll stop here and play your skat and then go to bed." Wolff, Fernow, Ochs and his wife, and Berliner joined me in the hotel after the concert. They arranged everything with the utmost care so as to spare me all worry. I was in the train at eight and arrived here at four.

I was met at the station by Rottenberg and a certain Siloti from Petersburg—who offered me an engagement there next year. Rottenberg has again been conducting rehearsals in advance and is the good old friend he always was.

Unfortunately I have to work my way through all the organizers of the Museum Concerts and have an invitation for every night. But I will see how much of it I can dodge. It seems that all the newspapers have reports from Vienna of my resignation. Does it mean that there are again those who desire my prolonged absence?

For today—a thousand greetings. Going early to bed. My dear, farewell—

Gustav

Hotel Imperial, Frankfort, 1907

My dear heart, your letter today overwhelms me with anxiety. You see, Almschili, one does not die of it—look at Mama with her heart—one goes full speed ahead and then suddenly comes the crash.

I beseech you, take proper care of yourself. Thank God, I shall be with you in three days and then I will look after you. Today's rehearsal was really good. My Symphony was excellent and the Schumann will be put right tomorrow (the violins, I confess, in the last, charming movement are more scratchious than gracious). There I have to hand it to the Philharmonic, but unfortunately they won't have any more to do with me.

I don't find the world very kind to me just now. I am a hunted stag, hounds in full cry. But, thank God, I am not one to sink by the wayside, and the hard knocks I have to put up with now from all sides (the Berlin critics are almost unanimously contemptuous) only stimulate me. I brush the mud from my clothes. *"Allen Gewalten zum Trotz sich erhalten."* How grand it is that we have 50,000 and a pension of 5000 a year to fall back on, and now we must set about saving with all speed. I send you a letter I had from Mengelberg. Loyalty like his does one good.—I have a good mind, anyway, to scratch Messchaert and Berlin. What is the good of being pelted with mud time after time? The curs obviously take me for a lamppost. The concert tomorrow, and then to Linz by night-train. There I shall already breathe our own air again and on Monday at 12.35 noon I arrive at West Station, where you will be waiting for me, and then home. I should like to see the little ones at table. They at least are works the critics cannot dismiss as miscarriages.

A thousand kisses, my heart, from your

Gustl

Berlin, 5.6.07

My darling Almschili!

I've been waiting for two hours to get a call through to you. I hope I succeed soon. Meanwhile, I write a word or two. I set off with a pretty fair migraine (I didn't want you to know)—Walter rushed to his flat for aspirin.—Very good night and quite recovered on arrival today. Bath (in my room), breakfast, and straight to Conried,* who is staying in the hotel. He was full of projects—all fire and fervor. First and foremost, wanted me on exactly the same footing as Caruso.—Then 8 months (180,000 kronen)—then 6. Finally we got to this: 3 months (15th of January to 15th of April) for which 75,000 kronen net, journey and all expenses paid (first-class hotel)! We have not yet come to an agreement about the length of the contract. He wants four years, I want one only.—As soon as I have spoken to you, I am going up to him again. I am to conduct Wagner and Mozart at the Opera and about 6 concerts (to include my C Minor with chorus).

Curse the thing—nothing for the last quarter of an hour but buzzing and scraping. I shall send you a telegram and give up all hope of speaking to you. I leave tomorrow evening and the day after I'll tell you all the details.

Thousand greetings from

Your

Gustav

kiss   kiss

4 years of 6 months at 125,000 kr.
making ½ million kronen
or an annual tour of 6-8 weeks
at 50,000 kronen
making 200,000 kronen in four years

kiss   kiss

Auf wiedersehen.

Vienna, 17.7.1907

Just to announce our safe arrival. I am going straight to the hotel to have a bath.—Tomorrow to Kovacs, and the day after, early on Friday, you will have a telegram. Be ready to set off at once wherever Kovacs orders.†

Don't forget, Almschili, to pack the Oberon things. They are in

---

* Heinrich Conried, then manager of the Metropolitan Opera, New York.
† This was the first news since the death of our child and the subsequent examination of Mahler by the doctor—after which he traveled straight to Vienna to consult Professor Kovacs. He confirmed the first diagnosis.

the bookcase in my room in the lower shelves. Don't forget any of them. Please, both of you, don't lift a finger over the packing!

Devotedly

Your

Gustav

Vienna, July, 1907

My dearest Almscherl!

Now a brief report: we got here at six. I straight to the hotel, where a bath, and then ate some ham in a café. There I came across Karpath, who says he had it on the best authority that Prince Liechtenstein said: "We shall not let Mahler go; we shall not accept his resignation." Well—*vederemo.*

I feel very well—if Blumenthal had not said anything, I should have gone on in the same old way—and certainly not have gone to bed before twelve last night. So you see, my dear, everything has its good side.—I shall avoid all fatigue from now on, and if I am to stay on here I shall put myself entirely in Kovacs' hands (make a practice of going up to the Semmering with you, etc.)— I think of you both continually, my dears, and hope we shall be together again tomorrow or the day after. I will telegraph this evening the moment I leave Kovacs. I imagine you will both have to pass through Vienna, and that you, Almscherl, will consult Kovacs too. I will arrange it all with him.

*   *   *

A thousand greetings, my dearest,

Your

Gustav

Last Months of Official Activities at the Vienna Opera

Mid-August, 1907

My Almschili,

Slept beautifully again last night; sending you some "documents," amongst which you will find W.'s* love-letter of chief interest.—He seems to have acquired the conviction from the *Neue*

* Weingartner.

Mahler when Director of the Vienna Opera

Freie Presse that there might be circumstances in which I could help or injure him. We are having superb weather here and I hope you are too, for then you can get some real pleasure from your stay.—When do you come? I have not seen anybody yet. Only Przist and Wondra, who are behaving beautifully. I am welcomed respectfully and cordially by all at the Opera House. So, all told, things are going better than we expected.

No letter from you today so far. I hope it may still come.

Devotedly your

Gustav

Vienna, 30.9.1907

My dearest Almscherl,

In the first place, I am in despair. All the shops are shut and even if they weren't I shouldn't know what to buy you for your birthday. So I can only hope that my love and good wishes for tomorrow will be accepted instead of a costly birthday present. And what else really is there to give when one has given oneself?—When you are here and we take one of our happy strolls along the Kärntnerstrasse, we'll find something nice for you. How's that? I look forward to it eagerly.—And now for an account of my doings. I shall have to rack my brains. Yesterday, then, after writing the card with my hand bandaged with lint by Roller, we walked by the road I have so often walked with my Almscherl, over the Hohe Warte to the electric railway and so by train to the theater, where I quickly convinced myself that all the uproar about bad acoustics* was only a silly newspaper scare (spread abroad, as I have reason to believe, and kept going, principally by Schalk). Pollak came in during the performance and begged me to spend the night with him. But I appeased his agitated heart and took him into the box with me, where he sat with me in judgment and agreed that there was nothing amiss with the sound. After the first act I went onto the stage, pitched into Schalk and Wondra,† and then turned upon some of the bystanders, after which Pollak and I retired to the Imperial, where I had a beef-steak and some very appetizing plum tarts. I was in the train by 9 and up at the Kahlenberg by 10.30.

* Mahler had had the orchestra covered in.
† Art-adviser at the Opera.

Straight to my apartments, which consist of two very dirty rooms with broken furniture covered in plush. An unbelievably beautiful view from the window of Vienna, pricked out with lights and framed by the lovely dark woods of the Wienerwald. Being tired to death I undressed without coming into contact with the furniture and slept without a break until half-past seven. Out of bed and to breakfast (dressed, of course) amidst a mob of Viennese, and so on foot by Wildgrube and Hohe Warte to the electric and so to the theater, where a Sunday's calm! At half-past eleven to the *Intendant*—most affectionately welcomed, everything arranged, and to lunch with Pollak.

Tonight the *Meistersinger* with a guest-conductor. Up again after Act One to the Kahlenberg very happily; it was a splendid idea of Mama's.

I must append to my account of yesterday that I was not alone with Moser [Kolo] for lunch; besides Hoffmann, there were three others there, with none of whom I was acquainted, which, needless to say, I did not find comforting.

The latest is my discovery on signing for my salary today that from now on I have 15 florins instead of 5 to pay in stamps. I receive my salary tomorrow morning and will send it to you at once; I hope for a line from you by that time, already much desired.— You will not, I hope, be astonished to hear that I miss you at every turn and think of you unceasingly.

If only I had a letter from you, if only a little one, in my hand at this moment! My dear heart, it is a terrible nuisance not being able to write to you from the Opera—for it is hard to find a moment on the way there and back. Don't forget that I sometimes do the journey from the Kahlenberg to town twice a day. A thousand greetings and kisses, my darling Luxi, and let me hear from you.

> Your
>
> Gustav

30.9.07

Dearest,

The heat here begins to be rather oppressive. I had myself inoculated yesterday. By Dr. Hamperl, who examined me too at the same time.—He found a *slight* valvular defect, which is entirely compensated, and he makes nothing of the whole affair. He tells me I can certainly carry on with my work just as I did before and in general live a normal life, apart from avoiding over-fatigue. It is funny that in substance he said just what Blumenthal said, but his whole way of saying it was somehow reassuring. Also I find I have no fear of conducting now. I am seeing Montenuovo tomorrow for the first time.—Zemlinsky has been to see me too; you will be surprised how fat in the face he is now. Marriage appears to suit him.—I should really be very glad to go up to the Schneeberg! Don't you think a little high air would be good for you too? Perhaps Roller will come too, if you come.

A thousand,

Your Gustav

Petersburg, 24.10.1907

My Almschi!

So I go on my way—I wish I could say on my way back.

I must add to my account of the journey that I had a two hours' wait in Warsaw and thought with emotion of our similar experience there. A morose waiter in greasy "tails" and dirty shirt gave me tea—to my great discomfort. I could not persuade myself to take anything else from the fly-ridden buffet (the Varsovites make a specialty of blue-bottles at this season). But I took out my papers and amused myself for an hour. Then I walked up and down in search of our old Jew. I did not find him, but to make up for it there were any number of young ones. (I was not tempted to bring you one as a memento.) Nevertheless, I had my reward. There is something very odd about seeing such strange types of humanity. You want to ask each one, who he is, what he does, and what he wishes and hopes for. Young and old were indistinguishable. There was a party of women which interested me very much, three generations, two old, one middle-aged (very sympathetic) and three flappers, in three sizes like organ-pipes; the eldest of the three was accompanied by a tall young man. All were Slav in type. They moved about from one part of the station to another, always forming a circle whenever they came to a stop, but did not get into the train. What on earth were they doing in the station?

After that, a twenty-four hour journey. By day I collated my Fifth Symphony, and by night slept splendidly.

*   *   *

Always, always

Your

Gustav

Helsingfors, 2.11.1907

My Almschili!

Yesterday was my first day in Helsingfors. Unfortunately there is a thaw here and I have had to discard my fine fur coat. I went to a People's Concert in the evening—and so got to know my orchestra at the same time. It is amazingly good and well trained, which speaks well for the Director of Music here—Kajanus, who has of course a great reputation in the musical world.—He paid me a visit in the afternoon and kept me company. An extremely sympathetic, serious, and modest man.

At the concert in the evening—I was having a drink of beer— Axel Galén suddenly sat down beside me, his wife with him. And after the concert Kajanus and his wife and a pianist from Brussels joined us. Galén was in tremendous form and I took to him greatly. Nevertheless, I left them at eleven and went to bed, which surprised them all very much, as they keep it up here until all hours, and indeed until morning. On Saturday, the day after the concert, Galén is going to take me for an excursion in his motor-boat. Then in the evening I return to St. Petersburg.

I heard some pieces of Sibelius at the concert too—the Finnish national composer, who makes a great stir not only here but throughout the world of music. In one of them, the most hackneyed clichés were served up, with harmonizations in the "Nordic" style, as a national dish. *"Pui Kaiki!"**

This is always the way with these national geniuses. It is the same in Russia and Sweden, not to mention Italy—all those harlots and their *souteneurs*. Axel puts the matter in a different light with his dozen brandies before dinner and his motor-boat; there you

---

* This was the nearest Gucki could get to *"Pfui Teufel."*

have the genuine article if you want vitality and race. No news from you so far.

All my thoughts, my dear Almschili,

Gustav

Helsingfors, 2..11.1907

Dearest,

Concert yesterday. People came from all over Finland. Sibelius paid me a call in the morning. I found him extremely sympathetic, as all Finns are. Galén too joined us after the concert. Now I am waiting for him to come and take me out to the Skerries in his motor-boat. Unfortunately, it's raining, which I fear will damp the pleasure a little. But wait a moment—what's this? The sun came out just as I wrote those very words. So perhaps it will be quite enjoyable after all.

The parenthesis in your letter, saying the time had come to leave the Semmering, did not please me at all. But—Almschi! Is that really any reason? You ought to have stayed on up there if it was doing you good. We can raise the 100 florins somehow. Surely you know by now what a precious thing health is.

I set off for Petersburg tonight. Thank God, the time draws to an end. I am getting very tired of it all by now, although I'm in the best of hands both here and in Petersburg. I went to the Opera here yesterday. *Onegin*. They had everything at their disposal, but the use they made of it was crude and often dilettantish—it is always the way, and will be soon even in Vienna! As you will see in due course.

Am really curious to know whether I shall have anything but telegrams from you in the course of the week. A thousand.

Gustav

Petersburg, 7.11.1907

My dear Almschili!

I've been ringing for the waiter for the past hour to come and bring me some notepaper. So I must write on this telegraph form —and so, of course, in telegraphic style.

I have been revising the orchestral parts since yesterday morn-

ing after arrival from Finland—just done, after much tribulation.
Middle finger of my right hand has a large hole in it. The day with
Galén was very pleasant. He and a very famous architect, whose
name has escaped me, busied themselves about me like two ants.
They wrapped me in rugs and fed me on Finnish sandwiches until
I was quite ill. I shivered like a greyhound (but so did they). After
a three hours' run through the Skerries with ever-changing views,
we arrived at the end of our voyage, where we were met by carriages
and horses and driven very merrily to a charming house—quite
à la Hoffmann—more of a castle really, and most hospitably welcomed.

The architect lives there with a friend (his name has not escaped
me; it is Gesellius) winter and summer. It is on a lake and looks
over the sea from the upper windows. The rooms are charming, à
la Hohe Warte translated into Finnish. They are both architects,
equally delightful and equally young, and they both married wives
as young as themselves and lived a very happy life together (they
were friends as boys); but about a year ago, when they had been
married for a year, they came to the conclusion that life without
variety was "mere existence." What was to be done? Well—they
exchanged wives and have been living for the last year as merrily
as ever, building new houses and populating their own. There's
a pretty story for you.—When it got dusk, we sat in the twilight
in front of the open fire, where huge logs blazed and glowed as
though in a smithy. Galén who had kept his eyes fixed on me
throughout the trip in the most singular way (as if he'd spotted a
hare), suddenly set up an easel and began on my portrait. Lit up
only by the fire, quite à la Rembrandt. After he had been painting
away for half an hour I got restless, and we went for a walk in
the wood. I was thankful to have made my escape and took care
not to remind him of the portrait. An hour passed: I had to go,
and was just bidding them all farewell when my host brought the
easel along and there, to the wonder of all, was my portrait—
completely finished. Very fine as a painting and also very like. You
would be astonished! What a fellow he is. To look at too—you
should see him at the wheel—usually very upright, his eyes like
burning coals, fixed on the distance—taut and erect—like a Viking.
I should think women must be tremendously taken with him! They

were all of them so kind to me, too, I was quite touched; and yet
in spite of their warm welcome they were never for one moment
officious. I even lay down in the next room for a nap on the sofa,
without a word said, and there was not a sound to disturb me.

*   *   *

A thousand greetings from

Your

Gustav

GUSTAV MAHLER TO THE INTENDANT, PRINCE MONTENUOVO

THE DIRECTOR OF THE ROYAL AND IMPERIAL OPERA HOUSE

Your Highness,

Forgive me troubling you with a letter in reference to our conversation of yesterday. My future relations with the Royal Opera
House were clearly defined, but it did not occur to me (or, rather,
I forgot) to raise the question of my personal interests; that is to
say, what view your Highness takes of my future in the financial
sense. As a decision on this point has become a matter of immediate
concern, allow me to place before your Highness what I regard
as desirable in view of the alteration in my circumstances.

1. As regards my pension:

I am entitled to retire on a pension of 5500 florins at the end of
my tenth year of service (on May 1st of this year).—Until recently,
I might well have reckoned on claiming the higher pension of
7000 florins to which a further three years' service would have
entitled me.

My way of living has been planned on this basis—for I am not
by any means past my work, nor has your Highness ever hinted
that my retirement was other than premature—and also I have
entered into commitments, which I must in any case meet, such
as insurance policies for the benefit of my wife and children and
the building of a house in the country. It would weigh very hardly
on me for the rest of my life, if through unforeseen circumstances
and, as I may well say, no fault of my own I were to be deprived
of advantages on which I had every reason to count; and I there-

fore request that I may be granted the pension of 7000 florins assured to me by decree after thirteen years of service.

2. In order to wind up my present household and way of life with a quiet mind (I am forced to leave Vienna, at any rate for some years, for reasons I need not go into) I request the payment of 10,000 florins in final compensation; and would point out, in furtherance of this request, that the first half-year of my appointment from May the 1st to November the 1st, 1897, I received only 2500 florins, although I had the full responsibilities as Director, and also as conductor of the orchestra. The reason given for this at the time was that my predecessor, Jahn, was to enjoy his full remuneration during that period (and even up to the beginning of the following year). What I ask is, therefore, more or less the same as was granted at that time to my predecessor.

3. The assurance in the event of my death for my wife and two children of the pension for widows and orphans, as laid down by royal statute. (Your Highness was kind enough to draw my attention to this point).

In expressing frankly and in full what I should desire in the event of my departure, I rely on the kindness your Highness has always shown me and which at our last meeting your Highness was good enough to express. It is not for me to champion my own cause by alluding to the manner in which I have carried out my duties during ten, one might well say, war-years.

I ask your Highness's forgiveness for the liberty I take and with the expression of my gratitude beg to remain your Highness's obedient servant,

Mahler

PRINCE MONTENUOVO TO GUSTAV MAHLER

DEPUTY INTENDANT PRINCE MONTENUOVO

Semmering, 10.8.1907

Dear Director,

I did not until yesterday receive the definite and official intimation (accompanied by his own written reply) that Weingartner consented to take up the appointment on the 1st of January, 1908.

I make haste to inform you of this, as I have been keenly aware of the suspense in which you have been kept. My only consolation is that your freedom comes within the appointed time, for you told me yourself in Vienna that difficulties on account of your American engagement would not arise until *after* the 1st of January. I have arranged everything satisfactorily with W. He will come to Vienna at the beginning of September. I am glad to be able to tell you also that your three requests have been put before his Majesty and that, after handing over your office on 1.1.1908, you will be granted

I. a pension of k.14,000 instead of the pension to which you are entitled under your contract,

II. a sum of k.20,000 in full compensation, and lastly

III. your wife after your death will be entitled to the pension of the widow of a Privy Councillor (although you did not rank as such) in accordance with the Statute of Court Pensions.

It gives me great pleasure to have been successful in settling all this in accordance with your wishes.

Please treat W.'s appointment as strictly confidential for the time being. I do not wish the matter to be made public until I consider that the moment has come.

Conried need now delay no longer making your engagement public. Please inform him of this.

Cordial greetings,
Montenuovo

FELIX WEINGARTNER TO GUSTAV MAHLER

Bad Kreuth, 22.8.1907

My dear Mr. Mahler,

What so lately appeared incredible has now come true: I am really to be your successor in Vienna. There is much I might say, but may I confine myself to the expression of one brief wish?

I learn from the newspapers that you are going to reside in Vienna. My wish and hope, then, are that the friendly relations which have existed between us, but seem to have lapsed for several years, may revive, and thereafter continue without interruption.

I look forward with warmth to seeing you again in Vienna, and hope it may be soon. Until then I remain, with my best wishes,

Ever most sincerely yours,

Felix Weingartner

DIARY OF MRS. BERTHA ZUCKERKANDL

When we said good-by to Mahler for the last time, he said: "After all, I take my home with me, my Alma and my child. And it is only now, when I am released from the crushing burden of work, that I know what will henceforth be my dearest task. Alma has sacrificed ten years of her youth to me. No one can ever know with what absolute selflessness she has subordinated her life to me and my work. It is with a light heart I go on my way with her."

1908

Hotel Blauer Stern, Prague, September, 1908
Friday, 8 o'clock in the morning

Only a few words in great haste today, my dear Almschi. Your dear little note and the cards written in the train gave me enormous pleasure. Unfortunately, this wonderful entering-into-possession-of-oneself is undone the moment one returns to the noise and confusion of everyday life. The only thing then is to *think oneself back* into that blissful state, and to make it a practice at every opportunity to look back at that other world and to draw one breath of that other air.—I have now done at last with the special rehearsals and there is the first full rehearsal at 10 in the morning. The hotel and the town are shockingly noisy. I have even had to take the room next door in case of being roused up four or five times a night by a snoring neighbor (he leaves today at last). A thousand greetings, my Almscherl. If only you were here!

Your

Gustav

Hotel Blauer Stern, Prague
10 September, 1908

My dearest Almscherl!

Motto: How blessed, how blessed

a barber

waiter

tenor

rentier

member of the committee of the Universal German Music
Society

to be.—

"Who hath brought me into this land?"

I have, needless to say, no wits left for writing the anyhow-articu-
late, anywhere-written, anywhen-sent-off letter. I have to revise
parts and meditate on how to make a kettledrum out of a fish-kettle,
a trumpet out of a rusty watering-can, a concert-hall out of a wine
shop. I have extracted only one bit of consolation out of all this
turmoil.—One of the trumpets asked Bodanzky in despair: "I'd
just like to know what's beautiful about blowing away at a trumpet
stopped up to high C." This gave me an insight at once into the
lot of man, who likewise cannot understand why he must endure
being stopped to the piercing agony of his own existence, cannot
see what it's for, and how his screech is to be attuned to the great
harmony of the universal symphony of all creation.

Bodanzky answered the unhappy man very logically: "Wait a
bit! You can't expect to understand it yet." (I have, you see, been
rehearsing the wind on its own—as in this vale of tears, where the
consolation of the violins and double-basses, which form the
groundwork and anchor of all the other instruments, are as yet
denied us.) "When all the rest come in, you'll soon see what you're
there for."—

So let us patiently make the best of the turmoil.

Keussler is here too. A splendid fellow. I am going to have a
vegetarian supper with him after the rehearsal on Saturday evening.

Servus, old Almschl, you too must make the best of the high
stop. One day, after all, the sourdine will fall off!

Your

Gustav

Hotel Blauer Stern, Prague, 22 September

My Almscherl!

I was very glad to have your dear little letter today. Yesterday was very pleasing. The orchestra very good and willing.—I am constantly attended by a staff of young (very charming) people—not to mention Bodanzky, or Klemperer, who did the splendid piano edition of the Second for two hands.

I am eager to know what after all we are going to make of the summer. I leave it entirely in your hands. Today we have the second rehearsal.

The conductor of the Czech orchestra here, Dr. J. Zemanek, who had a rousing success with my Fourth this year, pleases me personally very much. From what Bodanzky and others tell me of the performance it must have been grand. A thousand kisses, my Almschi, and here's to our speedy reunion!

Your

Gustav

Amsterdam, 1908

Dearest Almscherl!

I am feeling very anxious. Your silence means, in any case, that your liver is not in good order. And now all this packing will be the last straw.* Almschi, please, let it go as it likes. What does it matter whether a few crocks are broken or not?—And if the worst comes to the worst, don't come before the 11th. The few extra days might lighten your labors greatly.—Here all goes very well indeed. Mengelberg wants the VIII unconditionally. The conditions in any case would be perfect in so far as I should have a well-trained chorus and orchestra, rehearsed as he only can, at my unrestricted disposal. *Vederemo!* Bodanzky and Hegeman, Bock and Fried have announced themselves by telegram. The Clemenceaus will be here by Sunday. So it does not look altogether like peace and seclusion. The orchestra is magnificent—balm after the experience in New York. Kreisler is giving concerts here at the moment and haunts my rehearsals.—I like him extremely both as a man and an artist.

---

* On giving up the flat in Auenbruggergasse all our effects had to be packed and stored with the furniture.

The Mengelbergs are as warm-hearted as ever and hospitable as only the Dutch can be. Diepenbrock is a delight to me. He has great depth and truth.—If only I had some news of you, to keep me from worrying so much.

The last rehearsal today.—Probably, however, I shall conduct the whole program at the 3rd concert (Wagner, *Faust Overture, Siegfried Idyll, Meistersinger Overture*—and then my VII).

A thousand greetings, my dear, to you all.

Your
Gustav

GUSTAV MAHLER TO DIRECTOR DIPPEL*

Dear Director,

Allow me, in the first place, to reply to two points in your kind letter.

1. *Nozze di Figaro* on the 19th of December is not possible. I shall certainly keep my promise to be at the disposal of the theater for rehearsals before the commencement of my engagement, in so far as this is practicable. I must, however, presumably devote the whole time that I reserve for this purpose, namely from the 30th of November to the 17th of December, to the piano rehearsals. As neither I, nor the personnel as an ensemble, will be continuously available, the number of rehearsals we can reckon on will, besides, be a limited one; and I shall have to rest content if rehearsal with piano, which with a whole cast is extremely difficult and tedious, can be got through before the commencement of my engagement. But then on top of that there would be the producer's rehearsals and the orchestra rehearsals, to which I must give quite as much time and care as Conried let me give last year to *Don Giovanni.*

2. It is inconceivable to me that a new production of *Tristan* should be put on without my being consulted in any way, and I cannot give my consent. Further, I expressly stated when the contract was being discussed, *as you yourself can witness,* that I wished

---

* In answer to a long letter in which Andreas Dippel made various proposals to Mahler, and in particular that Toscanini should conduct some performances of *Tristan* at the Metropolitan with the Milan *mise en scène* before Mahler's arrival.

to keep in my hands for the ensuing season those works which I had already rehearsed and conducted in New York. I was given every assurance that this should be so, and it was only at your request and desire that I abstained from having it put in writing in the contract. If recently—out of consideration for the wishes of my colleague—I gave a free hand to the new Director, it was with the express exception of *Tristan*.—I took very special pains with *Tristan* last season and can well maintain that the form in which this work now appears in New York is my spiritual property. If Toscanini, for whom, though unknown to me, I have the greatest respect, and whom I consider it an honor to be able to salute as a colleague, were now to take over *Tristan* before my arrival, the work would obviously be given an entirely new character, and it would be quite out of the question for me to resume my performances in the course of the season. I must therefore urgently request that it shall be reserved for my direction and not be put in the repertoire until after the 17th of December.

I hasten to inform you by return of post of my attitude to this question and will reply to the rest of your letter in the course of a few days.

With all good wishes,

Yours very sincerely,

Mahler

HANS PFITZNER TO GUSTAV MAHLER

23 St. Urban, Strassburg, 18 Aug., 1908

Dear and honored friend!

As I may call you after your letter, which was a quite unexpected pleasure. I would have replied at once, but that I could not say at once all that went through my head. I cannot any the more do so now, but I cannot bear to leave you any longer without an answer of some sort. I hope soon to make a better answer by word of mouth than I can on paper and so beg you to have patience. Lest you should be led by this to think I have something very definite in mind, I must explain that I am cursed with what for me is a disastrous candor, which goes to incredible lengths in my relations with a person like yourself; and now after your letter I feel, as I never to the same extent felt before, the need to be completely honest with you, even at the risk of putting a distance between us just when you have begun to draw nearer. And naturally you have the right to keep your intimacy for, or to accept the intimacy of, only those who unreservedly admire you as a composer. I have never yet been able to go into this thoroughly with you and it is not a question which can be disposed of by a yes or a no. All I mean is that supposing, after a thorough study of one of your works, I was unable to arrive at that attitude to your compositions which you seem to feel is essential to a really close personal intercourse, you must allow me on my side not to deceive you by taking shelter in evasions.

All that, of course, is self-evident, and you must please put it down to my clumsiness if I seem to labor the point; and do not take me up wrongly—I have so often got into hot water that I am always afraid lest any word I say outside the merest commonplaces may be made a rod to beat me with. But there is certainly no risk of that with you!

I have offered Rosé the first performance in public of a new piano quintet of mine, which I hope in due course to play with him myself. Please give my warmest regards to your dear wife, to whom I shall write soon. My heartiest greetings to you and my thanks for your friendship, which is an unqualified happiness to me.

Hans Pfitzner

1909

Toblach, June, 1909

My Almscherl!

That was a very dear letter from you today (and the second in one day, too). To gain a spiritual center—that's the thing. From there, everything has another aspect. And it throws a light on your inner self that you should have turned to Goethe. It shows that you reach up to the light, inwardly as well as outwardly.—

Your interpretation of the final stanza is good; better, I am sure, than those offered by the learned commentators (whom, I confess, I have never read, but I know that this passage has kept them busy for the last hundred years). It is a peculiarity of the interpretation of works of art that the rational element in them (that is, what is soluble by reason) is almost never their true reality, but only a veil which hides their form. But in as far as a soul needs a body —which there is no disputing—an artist is bound to derive the means of creation from the rational world. Whenever he himself is not clear, or rather has not achieved wholeness within himself, the rational overcomes what is spontaneously artistic, and makes an undue claim on the attention. Now *Faust* is in fact a mixture of all this, and as its composition occupied the whole of a long life the stones of which it is built do not match, and have often been left simply as undressed stone. Hence, one has to approach the poem in various ways and from different sides.—But the chief thing is still the artistic conception, which no mere words can ever explain. Its truth shows a different face to each one of us—and a different one to each of us at different ages; just as Beethoven's symphonies are new and different at every hearing and never the same to one person as to another. If I am to try to tell you what my reason at its present stage has to say to these final verses—well, I'll try, but I don't know whether I shall succeed. I take those four lines, then, in the closest connection with the preceding ones— as a direct continuation, in one sense, of the lines they follow, and in another sense, as the peak of the whole tremendous pyramid, a world presented and fashioned step by step, in one situation and development after another. All point, at first dimly and then from scene to scene (particularly in the Second Part, where the poet's own powers have matured to match his task) with growing mastery, to this supreme moment, which though beyond expression, scarcely even to be surmised, touches the very heart of feeling.

It is all an allegory to convey something which, whatever form it is given, can never be adequately expressed. Only the transitory lends itself to description; but what we feel, surmise but will never reach (or know here as an actual happening), the in-transitory behind all appearance, is indescribable. That which draws us by its mystic force, what every created thing, perhaps even the very stones, feels with absolute certainty as the center of its being, what Goethe here—again employing an image—

calls the eternal feminine—that is to say, the resting-place, the goal, in opposition to the striving and struggling towards the goal (the eternal masculine)—you are quite right in calling the force of love. There are infinite representations and names for it. (You have only to think of how a child, an animal, or persons of a lower or higher development live their lives.) Goethe himself reveals it stage by stage, on and on, in image after image, more and more clearly as he draws nearer the end: in Faust's impassioned search for Helen, in the Walpurgis night, in the still inchoate Homunculus, through the manifold entelechies of lower and higher degree; he presents and expresses it with a growing clearness and certainty right on to the *mater gloriosa*—the personification of the eternal feminine!

And so in immediate relation to the final scene Goethe in person addresses his listeners. He says:

"All that is transitory (what I have presented to you here these two evenings) is nothing but images, inadequate, naturally, in their earthly manifestation; but there, freed from the body of earthly inadequacy, they will be actual, and we shall then need no paraphrase, no similitudes or images for them; there is done what here is in vain described, for it is indescribable. And what is it? Again I can only reply in imagery and say: The eternal feminine has drawn us on—we have arrived—we are at rest—we possess what on earth we could only strive and struggle for. Christ calls this 'eternal blessedness,' and I cannot do better than employ this beautiful and sufficient mythology—the most complete conception to which at this epoch of humanity it is possible to attain."

I hope I have expressed myself clearly. There is always the danger of an exuberance of words in such infinitely delicate and, as I said above, unrational matters. That is why all commentary is so disgusting. No more for today.

A thousand greetings from

Your Gustav

Toblach, 24 June, 1909, Monday

My dearest Almschi,

. . . But the house and the whole place are too delicious—except for the noise, which is a ceaseless torment. The farm people

either whisper so that the windows rattle or go on tiptoe so that the house rocks. The two merry scions of the house twitter all day long: Bibi, Bibi (this is their Esperanto and means. everything).
The dog reminds me too that I am but "a man among men," and barks all day from peep of dawn and right on until its masters are sweetly dreaming. I wake every quarter of an hour, to rue the snore however gentle.—The devil take it—what a beautiful world it would be if one had two yokes of land fenced about, and were all alone in the middle.

Every time I come back from a walk I think that you and Guckerl must be coming to meet me. It is good, very good, to be alone all day; but in the afternoon, from tea-time onwards, I miss you dreadfully.

A thousand greetings, my Almschili,

Your

Gustav

Toblach, 27 June, 1909

My Almscherl!

Your letter yesterday did not come until the afternoon (I go for the second post myself) and I was very anxious by that time.

Your moods (induced this time by a dream) are very understandable to me, for I myself go through the same thing a thousand times over; this may surprise you, but it may at the same time be a consolation and even make it easier to understand yourself. Man—and probably all forms of life—are unceasingly productive. This occurs inevitably at all stages as a consequence of life itself. When the energy of production fails, then the entelechy dies; that is, it must acquire a new body. At the stage where men of a higher development are found, production (which is natural to the majority in the form of reproduction) is accompanied by an act of self-realization; and hence its creativeness is heightened on the one hand, and on the other is manifested as a challenge to the moral being. This then is where we find the source of all the restlessness of such men. In between the brief moments in the life of the man of genius when these challenges are answered, there are the long barren stretches of existence which wring the soul with unanswerable longings. And it is just this ceaseless struggle and its torments that give the life of these few its character.—Now perhaps you will guess, or know, what I think of the "works" of this person or that. They are, properly speaking, the ephemeral and mortal part of him; but what a man makes of himself—what he becomes through the untiring effort to live and to be, is permanent. This is the meaning, my dear Almschi, of all that has happened to you, of all that has been laid on you as a necessity of the growth of the soul and the forging of the personality. And you still have a long life before you. Persist in exerting this inner force (as indeed you do), claim as your very own your utmost of beauty and power. (More than this none of us can do—and only the elect in any case) "spread yourself abroad," excrcise yourself in beauty, in goodness, grow unceasingly (that is the true productiveness), and be assured of what I always preach: what we leave behind us is only the husk, the shell. The *Meistersinger*, the Ninth, *Faust*—all of them are only the discarded husk! No more, properly speaking, than our bodies are! I don't of course mean that artistic creation is superfluous. It is a necessity of man for growth and *joy*, which again is a question of health and creative energy.—But what actual need is there of notes? How often I see you in that joyful mood I know so well, when you have "opened out."

I still haven't ventured down into the hut. It is always such an upheaval to move in that I can't face it.

A thousand greetings, my Almschi.

Gustav

Tell me more of Gucki soon.

With friends at Göding, 1909

My Almschili!

I wrote yesterday. But hear from my talk on the telephone that you have not had the letter yet. I hope you have had it by now. I have spent an anxious day in spite of all. I feel marvelous here! To be able to sit working by the open window, and breathing the air, the trees and flowers all the time—this is a delight I have never known till now. I see now how perverse my life in summer has always been. On the other hand, I have avoided the truly murderous, infernal noise, which never ceases here day or night. But a place like this I must have. Karl says he won't rest until he has found it for us. All told, staying here suits me remarkably well I feel myself getting better every minute. It's no good—human nature must have sun and warmth—I shudder now when I think of my various workshops; although I have spent the happiest hours of my life in them, it has probably been at the price of my health.

Your

Gustav

ENGELBERT HUMPERDINCK TO GUSTAV MAHLER

Whitsuntide, 30, May, 1909

CONFIDENTIAL

Honored Master!

Your brother-in-law has kindly given me your present address, and I hasten to lay the following before you.

You have doubtless already learned from the newspapers of the proposal to establish a second opera house in Berlin in response to a long-felt need of the capital of the empire. With this object a committee was formed a few months ago to organize the undertaking, and with it is associated a company which has raised the capital required. The purchase of a large site on the Friedrich-strasse is in contemplation, and here a building is to be erected as far as possible after the pattern of Bayreuth; negotiations have been initiated which will enable Wagner's works to be performed even before the expiry of the embargo. The building, which will be begun in October, ought to be so far advanced in $1\frac{1}{2}$ years that the opening could take place in the spring of 1911.

We still, however, lack what is more important than all else: the future director of our Richard Wagner Theater, who must be not only a man of proved attainments and firm will, but above all a great artist and, in short, combine all those qualities which are summed up in the name: Mahler, a guarantee in itself of an artistic program unsurpassable in its range and excellence. And as the bearer of this name is at the present time within reach, I venture, my dear Master, to ask whether you would be disposed to answer our call and to take this great work in hand. The position of general director which we have in mind would naturally in your case be furnished with the most far-reaching powers—similar to those you had at your command in Vienna. I can therefore well believe that the task of giving life to a new and unique enterprise would perhaps have a charm for you.

I scarcely need say how delighted I should be personally to know that you were at the head of it. As soon as we hear that you are not in principle disinclined to consider the proposal, our managing-director, Mr. Delmar, will get into touch with you personally and in due course travel to Vienna, in order to arrange all business matters with you. Meanwhile I await an early and, I hope, a favorable reply and remain, with the assurance of my lasting esteem, yours most sincerely,

E. Humperdinck

I may of course rely on your kind discretion for the time being.

ARNOLD SCHÖNBERG TO GUSTAV MAHLER

29.12.1909

My dear Director,

So many things got in the way that I was quite unable to find time to write to you immediately after the Seventh. In earlier days I should have been in haste to say something at once while the feelings it aroused were still warm and at the full. Perhaps I feared lest the impression might fade. And in fact, I must confess, it did not on previous occasions last long. But this time (and that is the main point) I knew I might wait as long as I liked: the impressions made on me by the Seventh, and before that, by the Third, are permanent. I am now really and entirely yours. I know that for a certainty. For I had less the feeling than previously of that sensational intensity which excites and lashes one on, which in a word moves the listener in such a way as to make him lose his balance without giving him anything in its place. On the contrary, I had the impression of perfect repose based on artistic harmony; of something that set me in motion without simply upsetting my center of gravity and leaving me to my fate; that drew me calmly and pleasingly into its orbit—as though by that force of attraction which guides the planets in their courses, which leaves them to go their own way, influencing them, certainly, but in a manner so measured and preordained that there are never any sudden jolts.

This may sound a little bombastic perhaps. Nevertheless, it seems to me to express one thing which I supremely felt: I have put you with the classical composers. But as one who to me is still a *pioneer*. I mean, there is surely a difference in being spared all extraneous excitement, being at rest and in tranquility, in the state in which beauty is enjoyed. And before it used to be quite otherwise with me; I know this for certain, even if I cannot now express the difference clearly. There used to be, as it were, moments of artistic conflict; personal feelings; extraneous matter; details of artistry; problems of orchestration. Of all that there was this time not a trace.

I had not much time to look through the score beforehand, and was only slightly acquainted with it. My request for the permission of the Concert Club to attend the final rehearsal received no reply, although there were critics present.

And so I had this strong and perfectly clear impression from what was almost a first hearing and without any previous study of the work.

I cannot say whether the performance was good or not. On the whole I believe it was not bad, in so far as Löwe clearly took the trouble to reproduce with accuracy the directions in the score. Further than this I cannot say he went; I often thought I detected that this or that ought to have gone otherwise—but I mean, it was not bad for Löwe, and it is hard to see why he should understand this work in particular when he has been conducting for so many years without understanding any work whatever.

Which movement did I like the best? Each one! I can make no distinction. Perhaps I was somewhat hesitant at the beginning of the first movement. But in any case only for a short time. And from then onwards I grew warmer and warmer. From one minute to the next I felt better and better. And there was not a moment's relapse. I was in tune to the very end. And it was all so transparently clear to me. In short, at a first hearing I felt so many subtleties of form, and yet could follow a main line throughout. It gave me extraordinary pleasure. I simply cannot understand why I was so unresponsive before.

Alma Mahler

I should very much like to hear how you are and what you are doing over there. I did not of course believe the story of the opera *Theseus*, and at once imagined to myself the joke to which it was to be traced. Of course everyone in Vienna took it in good faith. Nobody thought to himself: "What does that mean—*Theseus?*" All I know of him myself is his temple. He occupies no other niche in my consciousness, since I have long ago shed whatever I gathered from history lessons. How came it that he of all people should be your vehicle, your means of expression? Nobody hit on the clue: Weingartner—Orestes; Strauss—Elektra: therefore: Mahler—Theseus. Greek too. It was left for me to see that it was a parodistical reply of yours to some egregious interrogator, asking: "But how is it, Director, that you have never yet written anything for the operatic stage, when you are . . ." I should be very proud if my guess turned out to be correct.

Of myself I can only report that there is little to be said. I have signed an agreement with the Universal Edition in terms very favorable—to the Universal Edition.

The Ansorge Club is devoting an evening to me on the 14th of January: the *Gurrelieder*, with piano, a song-cycle after Stefan George, three new piano pieces. My monodrama is to be performed in Mannheim.

And in Paris my second quartet. If it ever comes off?!? Perhaps one day you will send me a picture postcard with a small (very small) picture and plenty of room for the text. With cordial greetings—

Arnold Schönberg

1910

From Vienna to Tobelbad, June, 1910

My dearest Almschili!

When I told you the last morning at Tobelbad how nice you looked, it was the expression of a spontaneous delight as I saw you coming to meet me and looking so sweet and charming. But you know me by this time. In art as in life I am at the mercy of spontaneity. If I had to compose, not a note would come. Four years ago, on the first day of the holidays, I went up to the hut at Maiernigg with the firm resolution of idling the holiday away (I needed to so much that year) and recruiting my strength. On the threshold of my old workshop the *Spiritus Creator* took hold of me and shook me and drove me on for the next eight weeks until my greatest work was done.—One summer before that I made up my mind to finish the Seventh, both Andantes of which were there on my table. I plagued myself for two weeks until I sank into gloom, as you well remember; then I tore off to the Dolomites. There I was led the same dance, and at last gave it up and returned home, convinced that the whole summer was lost. You were not at Krumpendorf to meet me, because I had not let you know the time of my arrival. I got into the boat to be rowed across. At the first stroke of the oars the theme (or rather the rhythm and character) of the introduction to the first movement came into my head —and in four weeks the first, third and fifth movements were done. Do you remember? You see, my love, you know enough of me and my ways not to be wounded by me. And particularly when you can see for yourself that I live only for you and Gucki, and that nothing can ever come between you and my love. Everything else is so insipid—a bad wood-cut next to a Titian. Only get really well, my Luxerl, so that you can be at my side and we can enjoy life together again as good comrades. Living and loving are as the flowers of a tree which grows higher of itself, or often spreads abroad; flowers, or fruit that falls in winter—you have only to wait for the spring in the full assurance that they will bud again.

Greetings, my Almscherl,

Your

Gustav

Munich, June

My Almschi!

It worries me today to have no letter from you after your so sad one of yesterday. Are you hiding something? For I feel there must be something to be read between the lines.

Full rehearsal today—part 2. There, too, God (Mahler) saw that it was good.

The soloists arrive tomorrow; Sunday, God willing, I shall be at Toblach, unless you perhaps decide that I shall come straight to Tobelbad. In which case, please telegraph.—But if you agree, please give the necessary orders at once so that I shall find all I need at Toblach.—If necessary, send me the keys required. I want to be able to get at the books there, and clothes too in the long run. Also tell them to get in fresh, good butter, on which I chiefly live. I've already arranged for everything else, from Vienna. I've still a lot to get through here this week. People are collecting in herds: Rosé with his quartet, R. Strauss with the Philharmonic, critics from every nation, etc., etc. Lord, what visitations threaten me! But I will put a good face on the awful business. But one thing I will do from today on: have my meals in my room. I must have rest and seclusion to get me through these exertions. You are always in my thoughts, my Almscherl; write every day, do, if only a p.c.

Your

Gustav

Munich, June

I send you my love, Almscherl, between two rehearsals (this is a trying day). Today was the first with orchestra and singers. It was staggering—the effect their quite inadequate numbers made. The orchestra literally raved at the end of the rehearsal.

Imagine it, Fried and Klemperer came to meet me as I entered the hall. That was pretty smart of them. On the other hand, on returning to the hotel I find Arnold's card. (He could surely have found out where the rehearsal was taking place.) Now I am going to have my meal in my room, as usual, and have asked Fried to join me. We start up again at six o'clock and tomorrow morning the children join in. God willing, I leave on Sunday morning for Toblach, where I shall arrive at about four.—I promise faithfully not to touch a note there, but to do nothing but eat, walk and above all *sleep*, a thing impossible to think of in Munich for the mere hooting of cars.

The publisher (Herztka) is here too and as happy as a snow-king. But it does really sound overwhelming. . . .

                              Greetings, my Almschili

                                                  Your

                                                        Gustav

                                                  Munich, June

My Almscherl,

You have hit on the salient point in Plato sure enough. In the discourses of Socrates, Plato gives his own philosophy, which, as the misunderstood "Platonic love," has influenced thought right down the centuries to the present day. The essence of it is really Goethe's idea that all love is generative, creative, and that there is a physical and spiritual generation which is the emanation of this "Eros." You have it in the last scene of *Faust,* presented symbolically. What strikes one first in the *Symposium* is its imaginative force and the dramatic fire of the "story." When I read it as a boy, I remember being delighted most of all by the sudden irruption of Alcibiades, crowned with vine-leaves and pulsing with young blood—and then, in delightful contrast as a dying echo of it all, by the way Socrates, the only one of the company who has not fallen into a drunken sleep, gets up thoughtfully and goes out onto the market-place to philosophize. It is only when youth is past that one arrives at a pleasure in the various themes, and finally at the discovery that it all draws to a head, by cunningly contrived gradations, in the wonderful discussion between Diotima and Socrates, which gives the core of Plato's thought, his whole outlook on the world. In all Plato's writings Socrates is the cask into which he pours his wine. What a man must Socrates have been to have left such a pupil with such an imperishable memory and love! The comparison between him and Christ is an obvious one and has arisen spontaneously in all ages.—The contrasts are due to their respective times and circumstances. There, you have the light of the highest culture, young men, and a "reporter" of the highest intellectual attainments; here, the darkness of a childish and ingenuous age, and children as the vessels for the most wonderful practical wisdom, which is the product of normal personality, of a direct and intensive contemplation and grasp of facts. In each case, Eros as Creator of the world! No more for today, my dear, except my love,—and do write!

Your

Gustav

Innsbruck, 25.8. 1910

In Lichten Fernen noch ein traumhaft Glänzen
ein grauer Schleier deckt der Bilder Saal;
das Auge thränt noch nach entschwund'nen Lenzen—
das Herz verstummt schon in Erinn'rungsqual.

"Höllische Unruhe fast—und Schmerz"
Gesegnet des Weges treue Gesellen.
Umgürtet die Seele mit dreifachem Erz,
schliesst auf des Leides Lind'rungsquellen!

Auch mir gab Gott zu sagen, was ich leide—
O Wonne, dass ich nicht für ewig scheide.
Ein Herz blieb mein—und schlägt mir heimathwärts
"O himmlische Unruh—Lieb—und fast kein Schmerz!"

Beloved! I wanted to send this as a telegram but I see that it would be ridiculous and so I am sending it by special delivery.

My own, my Beloved,

Your Gustav

In a railway carriage on the homeward journey.

27 August, 1910

Nachtschatten sind verweht an einem mächt'gen Wort,
Verstummt der Qualen nie ermattet Wühlen.
Zusammen flosz zu einem einzigen Akkord
Mein zagend Denken und mein brausend Fühlen.

Ich liebe Dich!—ist meine stärke, die ich preis
Die Lebensmelodie, die ich in Schmerz errungen,
O liebe mich!—ist meine Weisheit, die ich weisz,
Der Grundton, auf dem jene mir erklungen.

Ich liebe Dich—ward meines Lebens Sinn.
Wie selig will ich Welt und Traum verschlafen,
O liebe mich!—Du meines Sturms Gewinn!
Heil mir— ich ~~m...b de. WcL—ich bin~~ im Hafen!

27 August, 1910
On my bedside-table in the morning, Toblach

My darling,
      my lyre,
   Come and exorcize the spirits of darkness, they claw hold of me today, they throw me to the ground. Don't leave me, my staff, come soon * so that I can rise up. I lie there and wait and ask in the silence of my heart whether I can still be saved or whether I am damned.

17 August 1910
On my bed-side table
in the morning, Toblach

Du süsse Hand, die mich gebunden!
O holdes Bund, das ich gefunden!
Mit Wollust fühl' ich mich gefangen
und ew'ge Sklaverei ist mein Verlangen!

O wonniger Tod in schmerzensvollen Stunden!
O Leben—spriesse auf aus meinen Wunden!

17 August, 1910

Meiner Holden!

Immer Gegenwärtigen!
Die Zeit ist da, die Feder ist zur Hand—
Doch die Gedanken wollen nicht verweilen.
Auf die fünf Linien blick ich unverwandt—
Es flimmern von den Augen mir die Zeilen—
denn noch bin ich geblendet von dem Licht,
das mir gestrahlt von Aphroditens Angesicht!

Und was mein Herz auch singt und dringt—
es schweifen alle Sinne in die Runde!

* I always went to his hut at midday to bring him in to lunch.

O Sehnen, dass mich ewig an die Stelle zwingt,
Wo mir das Leben ward aus süssestem der Munde!

Zusammenfassen will ich alle Schauer meiner Lust,
der Gotteswonne Ewigkeit an ihrer Brust
zu einer Melodie, die wie der Sonnenbogen
den Himmel ihrer Holdheit kühn durchzogen—

in tiefste Tiefen tauchend ihrer Schöne,
dann flammend niedersinkt zum Hochzeitsbett!
O fände doch bei Dir, wie eh'mals meine Töne,
Mein Liebessehnen Heimatsruh und Stätt'!

On my writing-table in the evening

Holdeste! Liebste!
Mein Saitenspiel!
Und mein Sturmlied!

Du Herrliche! O könnt ich Töne finden—
Mein stammelnd Seufzen Dir in Worte künden!
Mein Athem ist—mein Wesen nicht mehr meins!
Nicht ich mehr, ich bin von mir selbst geschieden
nicht eher kann mich Himmelsruh befrieden,
als bis ich trunken Deines süssen Weins!

Der Lenz hat mich und Dich zu sich bezwungen,
Ich gab mich gleich, nicht hab ich erst gerungen.
  Ich starb—wie gern—und süsz küsst er mich wach!
Die Töne brausen—wüthen mir in Herzen—
die heissen Worte flammen—Hochzeitskerzen—
  es strömt mein Wesen Dir in's Brautgemach!

Munich, 1910

But Almschilitzilitzilitzili!

How did you read the "ominous" telegram then? Didn't you see at once it was a joke? I couldn't mean such absurd bombast to be taken seriously! You ought to have cut that inflated balloon adrift at once! But now for yesterday—I must tell you that the feverish feeling I had on arrival at the hotel increased yesterday morning (while I was writing to you) so noticeably that I lay down at once on my bed in alarm and had a doctor sent for (all because of next week). He examined me and found white fur on the right side (septic) with acute inflammation of the whole throat.—It gave me a horrible fright and I insisted at once on being wrapped up and sweated. (He would not paint the throat but gave me a wonderful antiseptic, which would be splendid for you too—a half lozenge every half hour, a drug that has only been available in Germany since a year ago.) First of all, I had to put the whole hotel in a turmoil to get the necessary blankets, etc. Meanwhile I had Gutmann in and appointed him bath-man. I lay motionless for three hours sweating profusely. Gutmann had to wipe my face and eyes with a towel every now and then. Oh, how I fretted for a sign of life from my saint! But nothing came—and at last your telegram of "bewilderment," which plunged me in despair at having innocently given my Almschili a bad moment.—The second came only in the afternoon, but even then I was none the wiser as to how my dear one was.

Gutmann was called away on business, and so I spent the afternoon most wretchedly, alone with my very melancholy thoughts. The doctor returned in the evening and found a slight improvement. The night passed quietly—today I awoke with my temperature normal and a good appetite. The doctor came, found me a great deal better and gave his consent to the rehearsal.—My Almscherl, you need not be anxious, I shall behave like an angel and be perfectly well when you come. But—no sign from you— the suspense is awful—it simply is not a life when I don't see your sweet eyes and hear your dear voice.—And you simply don't need me, or you would have had to write to me. After all, a message written out by some telegraph miss isn't the same as your own living hand.

It was a joy when I woke early today (4.30) and the very first thing I saw was the gleam of your dear little ring—I kissed it, and it was my joy and consolation, as it has been all through these lonely days. You know, it wouldn't give me any pleasure if you had given it me—but to wear now and then what you have worn on your finger means such a lot to me! Almschili, have you got over the disaster in the station yet?

Gutmann comes for me at 10, I want to hear the final rehearsal of the Ninth. Perhaps I may not go to the concert at night but go to bed at nine. Rehearsals start tomorrow. If only I had

some news of you! All the love of my heart, you dear one. I hang
on the hope of a dear word from my beloved.

Your
Gustav

Look at the enclosed! Isn't it kind of them to make the new
street for us?

My beloved!

Here I sit once more! The afternoon rehearsal is over—final
scene—every note addressed to you! I was so madly excited, just
as though I were sitting by your bed again, as it used to be in those
old, delightful days, "telling you all about it!"—Oh, how lovely
it is to love! And only now do I know what it is! Pain has lost its
power and death its thorn. Tristan speaks truth; I am immortal,
for how could Tristan's love die? Now I am spending a quiet
evening again—I am almost well again now. I ate with appetite
and mean to be in perfect health when my treasure comes.

*   *   *

Your letter of today was so dear, and for the first time for eight
weeks—in my whole life, for that matter—I feel the blissful
happiness love gives to one who, loving with all his soul, knows
he is loved in return. After all, my dream has come true: "I lost
the world, but found my harbor!" But, Almschi, you must tell it
me over and over again—for by tomorrow I know I shall no
longer believe it! For it is a happiness that knows no rest. Now,
good night, my darling, my sweet—perhaps you laugh today at
your schoolboy—telegraph when you come!

My beloved,
your Gustav

FERRUCCIO BUSONI TO GUSTAV MAHLER

28 May, 1910

Dear Master and Friend,

I do not know at the moment what chance there is of our meeting again in America—fresh engagements prevent me from re-

turning to New York. But I cannot let you go without taking any farewell, and it is in my heart to tell you that I honor and love you equally as a man and a musician, that I feel we have been brought nearer together by these weeks in America (thanks to our common sufferings); that I have gained much thereby; that I thank you for the masterly performance of *Turandot*, for the pleasure it gave me, and for the repetition of it you plan in Rome.

Please take this ingenuous outburst with the same simplicity of feeling as prompts me to confide it to you.

To be in your company has a purifying influence and rejuvenates all who enter it. For this reason, I speak here almost as a child.

I should wish to include your wife in the bond of sympathy I venture to claim, and I beg her to keep a friendly feeling for me.

I myself am her devoted servant and was enriched by the brief opportunity of making her acquaintance.

I envy you the 1st of May in Rome. Time and place alike summon up the Old World of Europe at its most beautiful. But I do not grudge you the joy of it; indeed I wish you all the joys life can offer. May these wishes accompany you on your voyage and beyond, as also the affection with which I sign myself,

Yours very sincerely,

Ferruccio Busoni

THOMAS MANN TO GUSTAV MAHLER

Bad-Tölz, September, 1910

My dear Sir,

I was incapable of saying, that evening in the hotel, how deeply indebted to you I was for the impressions of the 12th of September. It is an imperative necessity to make at least some small acknowledgement, and so I beg your acceptance of the book—my latest—which I send you herewith.

It is certainly a very poor return for what I received—a mere feather's weight in the hand of the man who, as I believe, expresses the art of our time in its profoundest and most sacred form.

It is but a trifle.

Perhaps it may afford you tolerable entertainment for an idle hour or two.

Yours sincerely,

Thomas Mann

ARNOLD SCHÖNBERG TO GUSTAV MAHLER

113 Hauptstrasse, Hietzinger, xiii

5.7.1910

My dear Director,

Your fiftieth birthday gives me an excuse for telling you, what I should like to tell you many times over, how highly I honor you. And also how often I am bound to remember, and to be pained by the remembrance, that in earlier days I used to vex you so often by my contradictoriness. I feel I was wrong to obtrude my own opinions, instead of listening to what you had to say and to what is more important than opinions, namely, the resonance of a great personality. If the overtones of my own opinions could not harmonize, always at least, with what was the substance of your utterances (I know, since I am the younger, that I have the right to differ, if only from immaturity, and to learn by experience instead of taking things on trust), I ought at least to have bowed down unconditionally to the reality which emanates from greatness, that nameless quality I felt very clearly in your presence and which for me is the power of genius. Of the presence and influence of this power, my feeling can never be unaware.

Nevertheless, I contradicted you—why, I do not know. Perhaps it was blindness, perhaps self-will. Or perhaps it was love, for I had a tremendous veneration for you all the time. It was a sort of girlish passion: love vexed by hate.

I have for long wanted to write you this letter, or one that would, if possible, express better what I mean; for it has long been on my mind. I find it a matter for shame not to have understood you from the first; but to have gone on to vexing you fills me with remorse.

I have only one excuse: I was not young enough; I had begun to be occupied too much with my own development. Perhaps you may find it in you to give weight to this.

And perhaps too you will set down to my credit the attitude I now have towards you and your work; how highly I honor you in every way.

And now my wish for your fiftieth birthday is that you may soon return to our hated and beloved Vienna; and that you may feel inclined to conduct here and yet not do so, because such riff-raff certainly don't deserve it; or that you may feel no inclination and yet do it for our joy, because perhaps we do deserve it. In any case, that you may be with us again. And that you, who have so much cause for bitterness, may receive honor and lay it as a plaster to the wounds which blindness (this more than malevolence) has inflicted. I know if you were in Vienna now, you would be so warmly wrapped in honor that you might forget all your earlier and fully justified resentments.

I hope and most eagerly desire that it will soon be so, and I should be happy if I could in any way help to bring it about.

With warmest esteem and devotion,

Yours,

Arnold Schönberg

After Gustav Mahler's death I found these memoranda for the Tenth Symphony:

3D MOVEMENT (PURGATORIO)

Page 4: *Death! Transfiguration!*
Page 3: *COMPASSION!*
       O God! O God, why hast thou forsaken me?

4TH MOVEMENT

Title page: (Scherzo, 1st Phrase) crossed through.
Underneath: *The Devil leads me in a dance*

    Madness seizes me, Accursed!
    Demolish me that I may forget my being!
    that I may cease to exist, that I may . . .

End of Movement: (Completely muffled drum) *None but you knows what it signifies!*

    Ah! Ah! Ah! Fare thee well my lyre!
    Farewell, Farewell, Farewell Ah well—Ah Ah

5. FINALE

Page 10: *To live for thee! To die for thee! Almschi!*

And once more, at the end of the finished part of the Tenth Symphony:
    To live for thee!
        To die for thee!
            Almschi!

The word Almschi corresponds to the melody as in the first instance.